Principles of Biology

Principles

Neal D. Buffaloe

Professor of Biology
Arkansas State Teachers College

# of Biology

Prentice-Hall, Inc.

Englewood Cliffs, N. J.,

Prentice-Hall Biological Science Series

William D. McElroy and Carl P. Swanson, *Editors*

Principles of Biology
Neal D. Buffaloe

Second printing . . . . . August, 1962

Design and Drawings by Felix Cooper

Library of Congress Catalog Card No.: 62-14191

Printed in the United States of America

70605—C

To
HAROLD C. BOLD
Master Teacher

Preface

Within the past few years, a definite tendency has developed toward the writing of lengthy textbooks for use in elementary college biology. The rationale behind this development is obvious and certainly valid: Knowledge has expanded, and so many topics are fundamental to an understanding of modern biology that it takes a large book to cover them all.

Notwithstanding, the exhaustive text fails to satisfy every teacher of biology, especially for use in certain types of introductory courses. For example, many colleges offer a one-semester course in connection with a program of general education, and teachers often experience difficulty in adapting such a course to a book so packed with information that there must of necessity be a great deal of picking and choosing. The student frequently feels overwhelmed by sheer weight, and the greatest strength of many a fine and lengthy text, its thoroughness, becomes its greatest weakness in a brief course. Furthermore, even in the year course (and much more so in the semester course), the teacher usually faces a dilemma. Either he sticks to the text and thus has no time to introduce valuable library work, or else he is obliged to skip portions, thus destroying the continuity of words and ideas that the author has labored so carefully to construct. Quite often, the teacher falls victim to the worst features of both methods, and trims the book down to his own needs, omitting the library work as well.

This book constitutes a mild revolt against what appears to be an almost frantic race for volume and abundant description. It is believed that it will serve best as a nucleus around which the resourceful teacher may synthesize the cytoplasm of a successful course, whether for a semester or for a year. Thus, if the teacher chooses to pursue any topic further, or to assign library work in the suggested or other references, he has only to do so. Used wisely, the materials should be adequate for a semester's work. While the book is written specifically for a one-semester course, it might easily be adapted to a year course by the teacher who is willing to give his students a good bit of freedom in the library (an almost forgotten method of teaching) or who might care to supplement this basic plan with selections from the excellent FOUNDATIONS OF MODERN BIOLOGY series by Prentice-Hall. The author has found it highly successful to offer a one-semester course for all students of the college, including his beginning or potential majors, followed in the case of this latter group by a semester each of classical botany and zoology. This three-semester plan of basic biology has many advantages in preparing the student for more advanced work. Regardless of the academic interest of the student, however, the author is of the conviction that a principles approach, aimed at fundamental life processes and related to other fields than biology, is far more valuable to the college freshman than is a course which is largely devoted to the memorization of descriptive and perhaps isolated information.

Certain features of the book deserve some explanation. The subject of evolution has deliberately been placed near the end of the book, rather than being made an integral part of the entire book. This has its disadvantages, but in terms of the background understanding of most college freshmen, it is believed to be a realistic approach. To a far greater extent than is justified, we assume a background that the student simply does not have, and he is usually not prepared to accept evolution as a scientific(?) pronouncement from his book or his teacher before he is given any valid reasons for doing so. Many teachers may feel that the final chapter, entitled "Biology, Evolution and Human Affairs," is somewhat out of place in a textbook of biology, and yet, of what value is our discipline to a liberal education if we cannot relate it to the whole of human experience? This material constitutes an attempt in a direction that we have mostly chosen to avoid, and it is hoped that it is to at least a small degree a successful attempt.

The questions at the ends of chapters are not intended to provide the teacher with testing material, although he may find it expedient to select from them in order to ensure that his students are getting the most from the book. They are designed primarily to help the student review the material, and they can be a valuable teaching aid if they are used judiciously. References to additional reading are confined to works which the student at this level might be expected to understand. They are only representative, for the most part, and the teacher may wish to make substitutions.

Many persons, including a number of students, helped in the preparation of this book. The author acknowledges with gratitude the suggestions that he has received. He wishes especially to thank Professors Thomas J. Burgess, Richard A. Collins, Marjorie C. Malin, Jewel E. Moore, Joseph E. Smith, Clark Stevens and Francis R. Trainor, all of whom read the original manuscript in its entirety, and Professors Kenneth R. Piety, Glenn F. Powers and Jacob Sacks, each of whom read and criticized certain portions. Professor Allen F. Robinette and Mr. Lucian Farrar are due special thanks for their suggestions and help in regard to the preparation of illustrations. The staff of Prentice-Hall have been most helpful, and with their assistance, the preparation of the text has been a pleasure. Finally, the author is deeply indebted to the person to whom this book is dedicated for his constant encouragement, his suggestions and his criticisms, and for a personal and professional relationship that has been most inspiring.

In the final analysis, of course, the author assumes responsibility for the plan and content of this volume. It is hoped that it may prove to be a contribution to the teaching of biology.

NEAL D. BUFFALOE

Conway, Arkansas

Contents

CHAPTER 8 **Responsiveness**   *249*

CHAPTER 9 **Adaptation**   *277*

CHAPTER 10 **Biology, Evolution and
Human Affairs**   *315*

Glossary   *330*

Index   *351*

Principles of Biology

CHAPTER 1

Science and Biology

It is an extremely fascinating pastime to gain the reactions of different people to the term "biology." A simple and interesting game of word association may be played in this vein by asking college freshmen to express the first idea that crosses their minds upon hearing this term. Answers are frequently as follows:

"It reminds me of a man with a butterfly net."
"I think of a frog."
"A greenhouse."
"Bugs and worms."
"Biology is the study of the human body."

Thus it becomes a challenge to the teacher of a beginning group to present the principles of biology in such a way that the student leaves the course with a far more intelligent and meaningful idea of this area of human interest than he previously had entertained. As a result the student himself, in the course of his studies, usually experiences a change in attitude from possible disdain to respect and finally to a full appreciation for and interest in a field that can be identified as one of the more dynamic intellectual disciplines.

SCIENCE AND THE SCIENTIFIC METHOD

By way of introduction to the field of biology, it seems logical to direct some attention toward its relation to other sciences. Although the word from which "science" is derived (L. *scientia*, knowledge) was once used in regard to knowledge of any sort, present-day meaning restricts it to knowledge which originates through observation and experimentation, as contrasted to that which comes to us through tradition or sheer reason. Whereas the social sciences depend upon all these knowledge sources, the **natural sciences** (those dealing with phenomena of our material universe) rely exclusively upon the **scientific method,** that is, observation and experimentation with their logical accompaniments, for new knowledge. In popular usage, the word "science" most commonly means natural science.

The natural sciences fall logically into two categories. The **physical sciences** such as physics, chemistry, and geology deal with those phenomena which are non-living. The **life sciences** may all be included in one large area, **biology** (Gr. *bios*, life + *logos*, discourse), which is the science of living organisms. Each of these sciences mentioned includes, of course, many lesser branches or subdivisions.

It becomes necessary here to clarify further what is meant by the scientific method. Perhaps an example of the way in which a scientist approaches a problem will serve in this connection. Let us suppose that our hypothetical scientist owns a plot of ground which consistently yields a poor corn crop. He focuses his attention on this problem and begins to search for possible reasons why this should be so. His train of thought might run something like this: "Perhaps there is not sufficient rainfall on this ground. No, this could not be the answer because another plot just across the road from mine consistently yields a good crop. Perhaps it is not cultivated as thoroughly as it should be. This could be the cause, although I believe that it is plowed as much as the plot across the road. Maybe there is a deficiency of nitrogen in the soil. At least, this would be a starting point."

Notice that our investigator has considered three possibilities regarding the problem. He has rejected one completely, and of the other two, one seems more likely than the other. Thus, he has selected a tentative explanation, which may be called an **hypothesis** and which is of value at this point only as a means of approaching the problem. His next step is clear. In order to test his hypothesis, he must administer nitrogen to the soil. He may encounter additional problems at this point in regard to the quantity of nitrogen needed, but in time he will either prove or disprove his hypothesis. If he disproves it, he will be obliged to formulate a new hypothesis and start all over. However, let us suppose that he adds nitrogen and does make a better crop. Is he justified in considering the problem solved? Actually, he has only strengthened his hypothesis. However, if he continues to produce good crops by the addition of nitrogen, his hypothesis becomes more than just a suspicion. *It has gained predictive value* because he knows now what to expect when he administers nitrogen. This is true because he has verified the strength of his hypothesis through repetition of the experiment. At this point, the generalization becomes a **theory.**

Perhaps most people would be content to let the problem rest here because, for all practical purposes, it seems to be solved. As a matter of fact, all that has been proved thus far is that the addition of nitrogen has appeared to increase crop yield in this one particular instance. It cannot be stated with certainty that there was a nitrogen deficiency, and it is at this point that the importance of **control** experiments is made clear. By a control, the scientist means an experiment to compare what would have happened had the variable factor (in this case, addition of nitrogen) *not* been put into the main experiment. In order that the hypothesis of nitrogen deficiency may be subjected to a critical test, therefore, the investigator should reserve a part of his field for *no nitrogen treatment.* Then, (assuming that all other variables are ruled out) a difference in yield between the experimental and control plots is sufficient ground for saying that there was a nitrogen deficiency in this particular field.

Let us note carefully that the investigator is able to broaden his theory at this point. His former one, limited in use to his own field, may now be enlarged to include other fields as well. It might be stated something like this: "When the yield of a corn crop is below expectation, and other common factors associated with crop failure have been ruled out, the addition of nitrogen will increase yield." Perhaps he is not interested in following through on this theory, but if he does, it is certain that it will, in turn, give rise to other theories.

> **This is one of the basic features of the scientific method, namely, that one theory leads to other theories, which sometimes replace it or render it obsolete. This, then, is the major activity of science—the formulation and use of theories.**

Most people, perhaps, labor under the impression that the major activity of science is the discovery of facts, which leads us to discuss another characteristic of scientific investigation. **Strictly speaking, there is no such thing as a scientific "fact" or "truth."** Fact and truth are terms which are meaningful only in a historical or possibly a philosophical sense.[1] To illustrate, suppose a person makes this statement: "I

---

[1] Of course, we sometimes use these terms in a purely literary sense, as in the expressions "It is true that . . . ," "As a matter of fact . . . ," and so on.

spent last evening with my grandmother, who lives in Thornburg." If this is true, it is only true historically. No amount of experimentation or present observation can decide the issue one way or the other. Now consider this statement: "If a person swallows a gram of potassium cyanide, it will kill him." Probably, this is as "true" as scientific statement can become, but it cannot be called a fact until it is historically proven. Even then, it would be true of only one person at a time! This distinction may seem tedious, but it is the only framework within which the scientist can operate. It is for this reason that he speaks of "data" rather than "facts," and he uses the terms "principle" and "law" to replace the word "truth." The statement given above in regard to cyanide certainly ranks as a principle, which means that it is so universally reliable in predictability as to be almost absolutely dependable. If a scientific generalization is such that no exceptions to it are known to have occurred, nor are any expected, then it may be termed a law. This is especially true if it has a broad application in scientific work. For example, the law of gravity holds that objects which are heavier than air, when released in our atmosphere, travel in the direction of the earth's center. No exceptions to this statement have ever been observed, nor do we anticipate any as long as present physical forces control our planet. Furthermore, it is used very frequently as a base of reference for various theories and principles. It is thus called a law rather than a principle. Actually, the scientist seldom stops to quibble over the exact distinctions between theories, principles, and laws, and he may use these words rather interchangeably. It is commonly understood, nevertheless, that a principle is something of a "graduated" theory and that a law is still more definite or useful in its application.

What, then, is science? One of the great scientists and educators of our century, James Bryant Conant, has defined it as "an interconnected series of concepts and conceptual schemes that have developed as a result of experimentation and observation and are fruitful of further experimentation and observations."[2] This definition is a very workable one, and it serves to eliminate many activities which are often termed scientific. Witness, for example, the application of the words "science" and "scientific" to commercial products whose sponsors hope to catch the public imagination with a magic word but whose endeavors are fruitful of no further experimentation and observations except in the realm of advertising! Actually, there is nothing mysterious or even necessarily difficult about the activities to which we refer as the "scientific method." Although the more complex problems of science require prepared minds for their successful pursuit, almost any person could follow the observational and ex-

[2] *Science and Common Sense.* New Haven: Yale University Press, 1951.

perimental procedures which were outlined above in regard to the hypothetical corn crop. As applied to natural phenomena, therefore, the scientific method differs little from "common sense" thinking, except that it becomes more exact and critical in its observations, its experiments, its controls, and its deductions.

In actual practice, the working scientist is usually caught up in a maze of difficult questions which involve hypothesis, theory, principle, law, observation, and experimentation all at one time. An almost unlimited number of examples might be cited to show this, either from the history of science or from present-day endeavor. Since scientific method and procedure are timeless, however, and because the passage of time gives us certain advantages of analysis, we shall cite an example from the past.

Virtually everyone today, whether he is familiar with biology or not, accepts the principle of **biogenesis,** which holds that life comes from life. In other words, it is commonly understood that new organisms, whether relatively simple or quite complex, spring from parents. It may be surprising to many that as late as the middle of the nineteenth century a controversy was raging among biologists as to whether some living forms arise directly from non-living matter. It had been successfully shown before this time that animals and plants large enough to be seen with the eye did indeed arise only from parents as far as could be determined, but on the microscopic level, the issue was far from settled. As a generalization, therefore, biogenesis was merely a theory which was held by one school of biologists.

One of the foremost proponents of the theory of biogenesis was a French biologist, Louis Pasteur (1822–1895), who sought to prove it beyond question. Those who opposed this view held that life developed whenever oxygen came into contact with suitable nutrient materials, and they sought to demonstrate this by heating such materials in order to kill organisms already present (which, as it turned out, they failed to do) and then allowing oxygen to reach them. By about the year 1860, Pasteur had already satisfied himself by experimentation that nutrient materials, upon coming in contact with air, would indeed show within hours the presence of teeming millions of microscopic organisms. His hypothesis was that a number of these were present in the material to begin with, and that heating was not carried on sufficiently long to kill all of them. When enough heat was employed to kill all microorganisms present, he reasoned, the nutrient material should remain free of them unless some were introduced (possibly being carried on dust particles of the air) and allowed to grow.

In order to test this hypothesis, Pasteur devised a most ingenious and simple experiment, which he described as follows:

I place into a glass flask one of the following liquids, all extremely alterable upon contact with ordinary air; water of brewers' yeast, water of brewer's yeast with sugar added, urine, sugar beet juice, pepper water; I then draw out the neck of the flask in such a way as to give it various curvatures. I then bring the liquid to a boil for several minutes until steam issues freely through the open narrow end of the neck, without any other precautions. I then allow the flask to cool. It is a remarkable thing, likely to astonish everybody used to the delicacy of experiments relating to so-called "spontaneous" generation, that the liquid in such a flask will remain indefinitely unchanged. It may be handled without fear, it may be transported from one place to another, it may be submitted to all the temperature variations of the seasons, and the liquid does not undergo the least alteration. . . .

It would seem that the ordinary air, entering with force during the first moments, ought to enter the flask in an entirely crude state. This is true, but it meets a liquid still at a temperature approaching the boiling point. The entrance of air then occurs more slowly, and when the liquid is sufficiently cooled so as not to rob the germs of their vitality, the entrance of the air is sufficiently slow so that it leaves in the humid curves of the neck all the dust capable of acting on the infusions and there bringing about organized formations. At least, I do not see any other possible explanation for these curious results. For, if after one or several months in the incubator, the neck of the flask is removed by a stroke of the file, without otherwise touching the flask, after 24, 36, or 48 hours, the molds and the infusoria will begin to show themselves exactly as in the open, or as if the flask had been inoculated with dust from the air.[3]

Although this experiment appears to be quite simple at first inspection, it is really an involved one from the standpoint of scientific procedure. In performing it, Pasteur was obliged to depend upon many theories, principles, and laws which had been set forth either by himself in previous experiments or by investigators who preceded him. Notice that in the first sentence he declares that the liquids he uses are "all extremely alterable upon contact with ordinary air." This generalization takes into consideration his previous work with such liquids, the role of oxygen in biochemical activities, and (although not specifically stated) the role of microorganisms in such alterations as he has in mind. In performing the experiment, he utilizes previous knowledge regarding the effect of heat upon experimental materials and upon microorganisms. Even his technical manipulation of the glass necks of his flasks depends upon a physical principle. Almost every sentence of his account (and the entire report is much longer than this excerpt) implies the utilization of previously developed theories and principles. Finally, his own conclusion from the experiment is declared to be a new principle, namely, that life comes only from life, even on the microscopic level.

In order to demonstrate that theories and principles are open to

[3] From *Annales de Chemie et de Physique*, Vol. 64, 1862. Selected from the abridged translation by M. L. Gabriel which appears in *Great Experiments in Biology* (see reference at end of chapter).

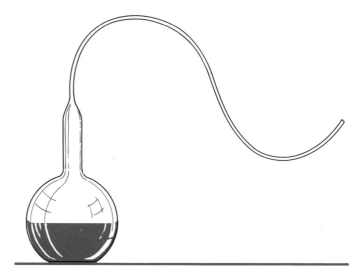

1   The type of flask used by Pasteur in his studies on spontaneous generation. Because of the curvature of the neck, dust particles carrying bacteria could not enter the flask, but air could.

further examination when new evidence appears, let us shift the scene to the present day. Although the biogenetic principle still serves as a working basis for biologists, we no longer feel as certain as we once did that it is universally applicable, or at least that it has always been absolutely maintained. For reasons that will be set forth in a later chapter, we believe that we have a suitable explanation for the origin of life on this planet (and after all, life had to originate at some point for biogenesis ever to begin). Once we have admitted the necessity for the spontaneous generation of life one time, we cannot logically deny the possibility of its occurrence many times. However, our past experience with organisms indicates that we get along better if we stay within the framework of the biogenetic principle, which leads us to another aspect of scientific theory. **A good theory** (or principle, if you please) **is one which accounts for more data and is more reliable in predictability than any available alternate theory.** It is *not* one that is the last word in its pronouncements. Science can only pursue truth—it cannot state it.

Thus it is that theories, principles, and even laws give way to others, forming what Conant calls an interconnected series of concepts and conceptual schemes. In this way, science goes on seeking but, in a sense, never finding. It is content to build scaffolding upon which to stand while it builds a new level on its edifice, then letting the new level itself serve as the scaffolding for a still higher one. Sometimes it has to tear down a portion of what it has built and start over according to newer specifications. Also, it must be content to realize that its building will never be finished, for this is the very essence of science and the scientific method.

THE FIELDS OF BIOLOGY

Since a great many sciences are subsumed under the term "biology," it is important that the student be familiar with at least the most outstanding of these. By way of being orderly, let us view the biological sciences from two different standpoints. The first might be termed a **natural** standpoint from which fields may be defined according to the appearance of organisms in nature. It is generally recognized that two great groups of living things exist; with a few exceptions, every organism is considered to be either a **plant** or an **animal.** The study of plants, from whatever standpoint, is called **botany** (Gr. *botane*, plant), and the study of animals is called **zoology** (Gr. *zoon*, animal + *logos*, discourse). Within these two subdivisions of biology, there are still smaller fields devoted to the study of particular groups of plants or animals. Thus, the study of mosses is called **bryology** (Gr. *bryon*, moss); the study of fungi is **mycology** (Gr. *mycos*, mold); the study of bacteria is **bacteriology;** that of fishes, **ichthyology** (Gr. *ichthyos*, fish); that of reptiles, **herpetology** (Gr. *herpein*, to creep); and so on.

From an entirely different viewpoint, fields of biology have developed according to the interests of investigators in various biological aspects of organisms. We might call this a **differential** standpoint. The fields of biology which have arisen as a result of such interests may be grouped together according to whether they are **morphologically** oriented (being concerned with **structure**) or **physiologically** oriented (having to do with **function**). Some of the more important morphological fields are **anatomy** (Gr. *anatomia*, to cut up) which is the study of structure as determined by dissection; **histology** (Gr. *histos*, tissue), the study of tissues (microscopic anatomy); **taxonomy** (Gr. *taxon*, arrangement), the science of classification; and **paleontology** (Gr. *palaios*, ancient), the study of fossil organisms. Virtually any physiological study of organisms is simply termed **physiology** (Gr. *phusis*, function). Certain fields are actually both morphological and physiological in point of view. Some of these are **cytology** (Gr. *cytos*, cell), the study of cells; **embryology** (Gr. *embryon*, to swell), the study of development; **genetics** (Gr. *genesis*, to be born), the study of heredity; and **ecology** (Gr. *oikos*, house), the study of the relations of organisms to each other and to their environments.

Now it should not be supposed that a biologist selects some field of interest and then proceeds to isolate himself from the knowledge and techniques of other fields. For example, an ecologist is obliged to know a good bit about taxonomy, and some of his work might very well involve still other fields such as anatomy and genetics. Also, fields which are purely morphological in approach may sometimes employ physiological techniques, and vice versa. An anatomist, for instance, might be interested in the over-all structure of some animal or animal group. In order to learn the significance of an organ or part of a given animal, he might very well be driven to study its development and perhaps even the physiological activities of the part in question. In spite of a certain amount of overlapping, however, the modern biologist is obliged to specialize in one branch or another of his science. This is because biological knowledge is now so vast that no individual can hope to keep abreast of all developments. Of course, there are certain fundamental principles which unify the several fields of biology, and we shall attempt to learn some of the more important of these as we proceed through the following chapters.

VALUES TO BE DERIVED FROM THE STUDY OF BIOLOGY

Perhaps no field of intellectual pursuit is in less need of justification than biology. Its practical contributions to civilization alone have made most people aware of its importance. Nevertheless, it is perfectly in order for the college student to ask, "Why study biology?", a question which must be answered satisfactorily before he can feel that his time is being used wisely. In view of this, the following are submitted for consideration.

A KNOWLEDGE OF BIOLOGY ENSURES A HIGHER STANDARD OF LIVING. An understanding of even a few of the principles which govern living organisms enables a person to take a rational attitude toward disease and health and to participate intelligently in programs designed in our society to promote better health standards. For example, some people are still hostile toward the practice of vaccination for the prevention of certain diseases, even to the point that their own children may suffer from such an attitude. By and large, such attitudes are the result of ignorance or prejudice. To cite another example, certain diseases such as cancer are imperfectly understood, and research workers are sometimes driven to investigations which seem far removed from the problem. The person who is familiar with biological principles is in a much better position to understand the need for basic research in such difficult areas and to work toward its promotion and support.

MANY PROBLEMS OF OUR PRESENT CIVILIZATION ARE ESSENTIALLY BIO-LOGICAL IN NATURE AND THEREFORE DEPEND UPON A KNOWLEDGE OF THIS FIELD FOR THEIR SATISFACTORY UNDERSTANDING. We are living in a fast-moving age. Our advances in all the sciences have been and will continue to be such that there are grave implications for the human race. We have been warned, for example, that increased exposure to ionizing radiations which arise from nuclear explosions may have serious genetic effects upon human beings. What are these effects, and how serious are they? As long as an individual is ignorant of the biological basis for genetic stability and change, he is ill-equipped to grasp the significance of such warnings. Certainly, he is in a poor position to discuss such matters or to vote on them. Other issues such as the expansion of human populations, conservation of natural resources, and the increase of food production involve problems that are essentially biological ones, and the informed person can no longer afford to be ignorant of the fundamental principles of biology.

THE STUDY OF BIOLOGY MAKES POSSIBLE THE DEVELOPMENT OF A PROFESSIONAL OR AMATEUR INTEREST IN CERTAIN AREAS. Although not everyone desires to become a physician, an agriculturist, or a research scientist, a sound background in biology is essential to such professions. Quite frequently, a student becomes oriented in the direction of some such field after having been introduced to the principles of biology. Furthermore, a great many persons discover an interest or hobby in some phase of the field that becomes personally rewarding.

THE STUDY OF BIOLOGY ENABLES ONE TO ATTAIN TO A HIGHER DEGREE OF INTELLECTUAL FREEDOM. The primary function of a college education should be that of providing a student with certain intellectual tools for critical thinking. It is believed that an acquaintance with the scientific method and repeated demonstrations of its practical value cannot help but enable a person to become more responsible and mature in regard to problems which he will meet and which he will need to solve. A gain in knowledge itself will enable him to distinguish reality from superstition in regard to a great many issues that he will encounter in his society. It is to be hoped that some of the examples of the great search for truth, which is the underlying philosophy of every science, will so impress him that this attitude will predominate in all areas of his thinking. It might be said that humanity divides itself into two great groups: there are advantage-seekers, and there are truth-seekers. Real intellectual freedom demands allegiance to the latter group, and it is believed that the study of biology, among other fields of knowledge, can encourage such an attitude.

THE PRINCIPLES OF BIOLOGY DEMONSTRATE A DEFINITE ORDERLINESS IN OUR UNIVERSE. Regardless of what one finally comes to regard as the logical consequences of such orderliness, biology and the other natural sciences are concerned with the formulation of theories, principles, and laws which describe this orderliness in the simplest terms possible. It behooves an educated person at least to be aware of this aspect of his environment, and whatever personal philosophy he comes to formulate, it will be far more meaningful when related to something more definite than mere emotional feeling.

Certainly, there are many advantages to be gained from a study of biology which are not listed above, but perhaps these will be sufficient for the time being. The student will probably find that other values will occur to him during his course of study.

Regardless of whether or not the student sees any immediate value to be gained from biology or any other intellectual discipline, he should seek to demonstrate a wholesome attitude toward all areas of learning. A great biologist of the nineteenth century, Thomas Henry Huxley, once stated that "an educated man is one who has learned to appreciate all beauty, whether in nature or in art, and to respect others as himself." The field of biology can lead the dedicated student to much beauty, and it can also teach him respect.

QUESTIONS

1. What is a control experiment? Although Pasteur had no stated control experiment in that portion of his work which is presented in this chapter, what really constituted his control?

2. If you were asked in a psychology class to react by word association to the term "biology," how would you respond?

3. Distinguish between the terms hypothesis, theory, principle, and law.

4. Outline the fields of biology which were presented in this chapter under the proper headings, and define each field.

5. To what extent do you agree that humanity can be divided into groups of "advantage-seekers" and "truth-seekers?" Do you think that such a division is an oversimplification?

6. Do you agree that the primary function of a college education is that of providing a student with intellectual tools for critical thinking? What other values are to be expected in a college education?

7. Evaluate the definition of an educated man by Thomas Henry Huxley (see the last paragraph in the text of this chapter). According to this, could a person be educated who had never attended a formal school or college?

8. Think of a simple biological problem to which you do not presently know the answer. In terms of the scientific method, how would you attack this problem?

9. Your teacher is probably a specialist in one of the fields of biology discussed in this chapter. Ask him to spend a few minutes talking about his major interest in biology.

10. Suppose that while a person is driving, his car stops. He proposes one hypothesis after another until he finds the cause. In terms of Conant's definition, is this science? What is the difference in science and technology?

REFERENCES

CONANT, J. B. *Science and Common Sense.* New Haven: Yale University Press, 1951. A great scientist and educator, who is quoted in this chapter, takes a close look at science and its methods.

DE KRUIF, PAUL. *Microbe Hunters.* New York: Harcourt, Brace and Co., Inc., 1926. Although this highly readable book is devoted to the efforts of various men who helped to establish the science of bacteriology, it is of interest to the student at this point because it exemplifies the approach of the scientist to the pursuit of research.

GABRIEL, M. L. and **S. FOGEL** (editors). *Great Experiments in Biology.* Englewood Cliffs, N.J.: Prentice-Hall, Inc., 1955. Certain experiments which are now considered classics are reviewed in this work. It will be well worth the student's time to read at least a few of the inclusions.

WEISS, PAUL. "The Challenge of Biology," *Science 118* (1953), pp. 33–34. An outstanding biologist sets forth in brief form the attitudes and goals which are characteristic of present-day biologists.

CHAPTER 2

The Nature of Matter

In the preceding chapter, the sciences were distinguished from one another to a certain extent. It should be pointed out in addition that the approach of a science to its particular materials may be **descriptive** (based largely upon observation), or it may be **experimental.** In the past, physics and chemistry have tended to be almost wholly experimental sciences, whereas biology has been chiefly descriptive. For example, if a biologist were to survey a given area of land in order to determine the kinds of trees present, this would be a purely descriptive study. Recent years have seen a radical change, however, in the approach of all areas of biology to the accumulation of data. Although there is still much of a descriptive nature to be accomplished, biology has come to employ many of the concepts and principles of physics and chemistry in its experimental pursuits. This is particularly true of the biological sciences which are chiefly physiological in nature. For this reason, it is necessary that the present-day student of biology be familiar with certain fundamental principles of physics and chemistry, without which many concepts introduced later in this text will prove to be meaningless.

SOME ELEMENTARY PRINCIPLES OF PHYSICAL SCIENCE

Matter and Energy

The term **matter** is used to describe anything which occupies space and possesses weight. Thus, any definite object or substance within our material universe which can be apprehended by means of our senses or by instruments comes under this definition, whether living or non-living. The term **substance** is used to describe matter which is uniform throughout, such as sugar, copper, water, and so on. From the negative standpoint, materials such as milk, dirt, air, and wood are *not* substances, because each is composed of several different kinds of matter.

Matter may exist as a **solid,** a **liquid,** or a **gas.** It is possible to convert most substances from one of these states to either of the others by the addition or subtraction of heat. Water, for instance, can be made to take the form of ice (a solid) or steam (a gas) by this means. Such a change does not alter the fundamental composition of water; it only alters its **physical state.** Hence, such a change is called a **physical change.** However, if water were subjected to some process by which it could be made to combine with some other substance or to separate into its component parts (hydrogen and oxygen), such alteration of fundamental composition would be termed a **chemical change.**

Chemists and physicists, using a variety of substances, have investigated chemical changes exhaustively and have concluded that matter consists of certain fundamental particles called **atoms.** For purposes of present definition, an atom may be considered the smallest unit of matter which can enter into chemical changes. Just how large is an atom? Exact methods of computation indicate an almost unbelievable degree of smallness. It has been estimated that 100,000,000 atoms arranged in a row would measure only an inch. Compared with the number of possible substances which exist, there are relatively few kinds of atoms. To be exact, physical scientists recognize the existence of only ninety-two naturally occurring kinds, although others have been produced artificially which have not been encountered in nature.

Let us suppose that we were able to obtain a substance made up of only one kind of atom. This would be an **elementary substance,** or as it is generally termed, an **element,** there being possible only ninety-two such substances in nature. Hence, an element is a substance composed of similar atoms. All these elements have been given names, some of which existed long before the particulate nature of the elements they represent was known. For purposes of brevity there are symbols which represent each name. For example, the symbol of the element phosphorus is P, that of calcium Ca, that of copper Cu (L. *cuprum*), that of iron Fe

(L. *ferrum*), and so on. A complete list of the elements can be found in any introductory textbook of chemistry.

Much evidence has accumulated which indicates that atoms themselves are not compact or solid units but that they are composed of a relatively compact **nucleus,**[1] made up of particles which exhibit positive electrical charges called **protons** and particles exhibiting no charges at all called **neutrons.** This nucleus is encircled by negatively charged particles called **electrons,** which are in constant orbital motion about the nucleus.[2] Variations in the relative numbers of these particles making up individual atoms account for the differences in the elements which they comprise.

Our simplified concept of the atom, therefore, is that of a miniature solar system in which the nucleus is analogous to the sun and the electrons represent planets (Fig. 2). Thus an atom consists more of space than of anything else. Actually, it is impossible to illustrate by means of a diagram just how much space really exists in an atom. To draw an analogy, suppose that an atom were expanded in size until it measured a mile in diameter. The nucleus would then be about twice the size of a baseball, and the electrons would be smaller than golf balls.

Energy is defined as the capacity to do work, a concept that is admittedly difficult to grasp since we are accustomed to defining most terms according to purely material ideas. It simplifies the problem somewhat to think of energy in terms of *activity* rather than in terms of *structure.* The most common forms of energy are heat (**thermal** energy), electricity, light (**radiant** energy), mechanical energy, and chemical energy. Any of these forms may be converted to another, but energy cannot be either created or destroyed, a principle which has been termed the **law of conservation of energy.** Changes in matter are accompanied by changes in energy. Energy may be stored (**potential** energy) or expended (**kinetic** energy). Matter and energy relationships within living systems will be considered in a later chapter.

---

[1] This term has an entirely different usage in biology, being employed to describe a part of the living cell. It is derived from a Latin word meaning "kernel" and is used a great deal in our language to describe a central object or even an idea. These separate applications of the term should not be confused.

[2] This concept, which was proposed by Niels Bohr in 1913, has been generally accepted by physical scientists as a satisfactory elementary representation of atomic structure. Certain aspects of it, however, may not be valid. Whether neutrons, electrons, and protons are actually "particles" is a point of some debate. Furthermore, many other types of "particles" than those mentioned here are recognized, and there are explanations of atomic structure which are technically more satisfactory than the Bohr theory. However, for purposes of simplification, this classical representation will serve better at this point, it is felt, than will any other.

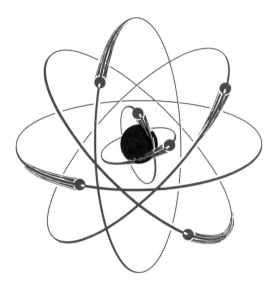

2 Theoretical structure of the carbon atom, whose six electrons occupy two separate "shells" around the nucleus. Both the electrons and the nucleus are greatly enlarged in terms of their actual sizes in relation to space within the atom.

The Interaction of Atoms

All atoms are ordinarily electrically neutral because the number of protons in the nucleus equals the number of electrons surrounding it. There are conditions, however, under which electrons may be removed from or added to an atom, thus giving it a net negative or positive charge as the case may be. An atom which exhibits either a positive or a negative charge due to such an imbalance between protons and electrons is called an **ion.**

In order to understand the conditions which make possible the combination of atoms and the transfer of electrons to and from atoms, it is necessary to recognize that electrons do not revolve about the nucleus in a haphazard fashion. Rather, there are orbits, or "shells," each of which is restricted in the number of electrons it can contain. The simplest atom, that of hydrogen, is characterized by the presence of only one proton in the nucleus and one electron in orbit (Fig. 3a). The helium atom possesses two protons in the nucleus and two electrons occupying the same shell (Fig. 3b).

Experimental evidence indicates that the first shell surrounding the nucleus of an atom never contains more than two electrons. In the atom of lithium, for example, which possesses three protons in the nucleus and three electrons in orbit, two of these three electrons orbit in the first shell and the third in a second shell outside. This second shell, unlike the first, may contain as many as eight electrons. When more than ten electrons are present in the atom, therefore, a third shell is established outside the other two. This third shell may contain as many as eighteen electrons, the fourth shell thirty-two, and so on according to the following formula:

$$\text{maximum number of electrons} = 2 \times n^2,$$

n being the number of the shell counting from the nucleus.

However, regardless of the possible number of electrons within a given shell according to this formula, the number of electrons in the outermost orbit of an atom ordinarily does not exceed eight.

Some atoms show a definite tendency to interact with other atoms to form substances that may be completely unlike the elements of which they are composed. If the ninety-two different kinds of atoms be considered the alphabet of matter, then these combination products are the words. Furthermore, as is the case governing the possible association of alphabetical letters in the formation of words, there are certain combinations of atoms which are possible, and there are some which are not possible. This tendency for or against combination depends upon the arrangement of electrons in the outermost orbits of the atoms involved.

To illustrate, the atom of hydrogen exhibits an outer orbit with one electron. To be completely "filled" or "satisfied," this orbit requires two electrons. Thus hydrogen tends to be attracted to any atom that can furnish an electron to its outer orbit. The atom of carbon, with a total of six electrons, has four of these in its outer orbit, and this orbit requires

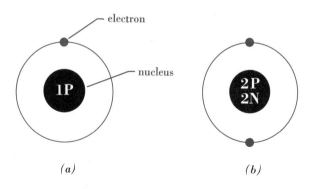

(a)   *(b)*

3   Two-dimensional representation of hydrogen atom, at a, and helium atom, at b. The nucleus of the hydrogen atom contains one proton and no neutrons; that of the helium atom contains two protons and two neutrons.

eight to be completely filled. Let us suppose that four hydrogen atoms
"lend" their electrons to the outer orbit of a carbon atom, meanwhile
"borrowing" an electron each from carbon. In this way, the hydrogen
atoms become closely associated with the carbon atom in a sort of cooperative enterprise whereby all atoms satisfy their outer orbits (Fig. 4).

Such a structure composed of atoms which share electrons, with
the result that all orbits have been satisfied, is called a **molecule.** The
molecule described above is one of **methane,** and its formula is CH_4.[3]
The bonds uniting the carbon atom and the hydrogen atoms are called
covalent bonds, and many such molecules taken together comprise a
covalent compound. By way of comparison, molecules sustain the same
relationship to covalent compounds as atoms do to elements. A covalent
compound, therefore, is a substance composed of similar molecules.

In another type of atomic interaction, electrons actually leave
the incomplete outer orbit and transfer to the unsatisfied orbits of other
atoms. The atom of sodium, for example, exhibits eleven electrons, two
of which occupy the first shell, eight of which occupy the second shell,
with the remaining electron residing in the third shell. The chlorine atom,
with seventeen electrons, seven of which occupy the third shell, will readily
accept this lone electron of the sodium atom. In other words, such atoms
with more than four electrons in the outermost shell tend to satisfy the

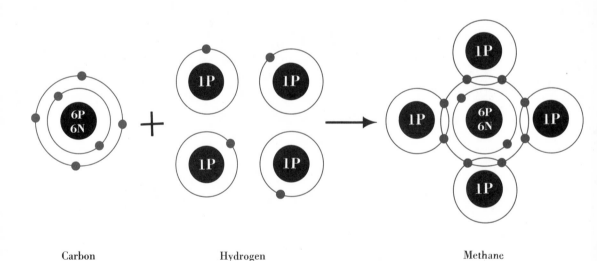

Carbon   Hydrogen   Methane

4 Formation of a molecule of methane by the combination of one carbon atom and four
hydrogen atoms.

[3] In chemical notation of this type, the "4" refers only to the symbol it follows. In this case, therefore, the formula tells us that the molecule of methane
is composed of one carbon atom and four hydrogen atoms.

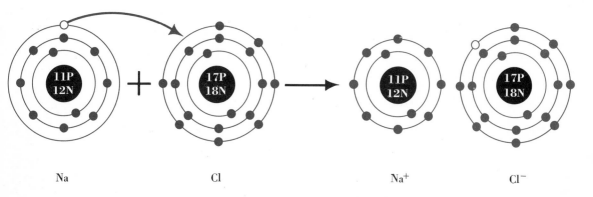

5 Electron transfer from sodium (Na) to chlorine (Cl), resulting in sodium and chloride ions.

completeness of this shell, whereas those with less than four tend to give them up, presenting a satisfied shell to the outside. When such an electron transfer from sodium to chlorine is accomplished, the substance **sodium chloride** is formed (Fig. 5).

Such a compound as sodium chloride is actually composed of two types of ions, since the sodium atom has lost an electron to chlorine, which alters the net charge of each. In this relationship, the sodium ion bears a net charge of $+1$ (since there are now eleven protons and only ten electrons in the atom), and the chloride ion bears a net charge of -1 (there being seventeen protons and eighteen electrons in the atom). In contrast to covalent compounds, where electron loss and gain are not responsible for the combination of atoms to form molecules, a substance such as sodium chloride, which comes about as a result of electron transfer, is called an **electrovalent compound.**

Because atoms which interact by electron transfer actually form *ions* rather than *molecules,* we do not speak of molecules of such substances as sodium chloride. It must be recognized that electrovalent compounds are fundamentally different from covalent compounds in this respect. We are obliged to define a compound, therefore, as a substance which is composed of similar molecules or interactive ions.

Water plus any substance which dissociates into individual ions or molecules within it so that these become uniformly distributed is termed an **aqueous solution.** There are many types of solutions known to chemists, but since water is universally the **solvent** found in living organisms, we shall restrict ourselves to this concept of a solution.

It frequently becomes necessary to deal with a combination of two or more substances which are associated together, each of which retains its own properties. We call such a group of substances a **mixture.** A mixture may be made up of several substances in solution, or of substances some of which are in solution, but it need not be associated with the term solution at all.

Acids, Bases, and Salts

Whenever a substance ionizes or reacts in such a way as to produce hydrogen (H^+) ions, it is termed an **acid.** Similarly, a substance which ionizes or reacts in such a way as to produce hydroxyl (OH^-)[4] ions is termed a **base.** Any substance which yields ions other than hydrogen or hydroxyl ions is termed a **salt.** Salts may be formed by the reaction of an acid and a base, as the following example will illustrate.

$$H^+Cl^- \quad + \quad Na^+OH^- \quad \rightarrow \quad Na^+Cl^- \quad + H_2O$$

hydrochloric acid   sodium hydroxide   sodium chloride   water

In this case, hydrogen and hydroxyl ions join to form water, and sodium chloride remains dissociated as sodium and chloride ions. Thus sodium chloride is a salt because in its dissociation neither ion is hydrogen nor hydroxyl.

Organic and Inorganic Compounds

For many years, it was supposed that living organisms were characterized by the presence of compounds which were fundamentally different from those found in non-living matter. Many such compounds were known to exist which were associated only with living organisms, and these were called **organic** compounds, all others being designated **inorganic** compounds.

Although it is still a good rule of thumb in biology to associate organic compounds with organisms and their chemical activities, the original distinction is no longer a valid one in chemistry. To qualify according to present-day general usage, a compound need only be characterized by having one or more carbon atoms in its molecules to be considered organic, with the exception that one group of carbon compounds, the carbonates, are classed as inorganic. Thus many organic compounds are known which are never associated with living organisms at all. In fact, thousands of such compounds which do not occur naturally have been produced synthetically in the laboratory. Furthermore, many inorganic compounds are quite closely associated with living systems, as will be made apparent in later chapters.

Nevertheless, organic compounds, other than those which are produced synthetically in the laboratory, are the products of living matter. Thus, the original distinction is valid to a degree. It should be pointed out that carbon is something of a fundamental element of living matter. It exhibits certain unusual abilities to undergo changes associated with

---

[4] Such combinations of atoms which remain together and function as a unit are called **radicals.**

the storage and release of energy and hence serves as an important energy carrier of the living world.

MOLECULAR GEOMETRY AND CHEMICAL ACTIVITY

Although it is usually necessary to diagram molecules according to a two-dimensional pattern, it should be understood that they are really three-dimensional. For teaching purposes, this can be illustrated for any given molecule by means of models (Fig. 6).

It has been known for some time that molecular geometry is very definitely related to chemical activity. The simplest examples of this relationship are those in which the degree of space, or distance, between portions of molecules control the degree to which they can react. For instance, the molecules of two compounds called **maleic acid** and **fumaric acid** are identical in the number and proportion of atoms they possess (formula: $C_4H_4O_4$), but the different geometric arrangement of atoms in each type of molecule lends entirely different properties to each of these compounds. Structurally, they may be represented two-dimensionally as follows:

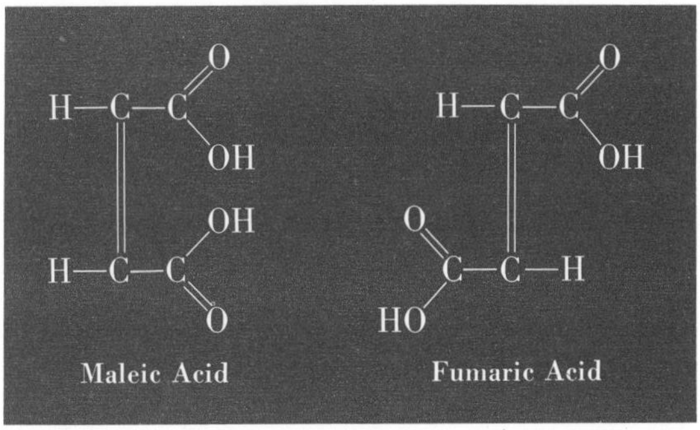

Maleic Acid   Fumaric Acid

By heating maleic acid, it can be made to form **maleic anhydride** and water as is shown below.

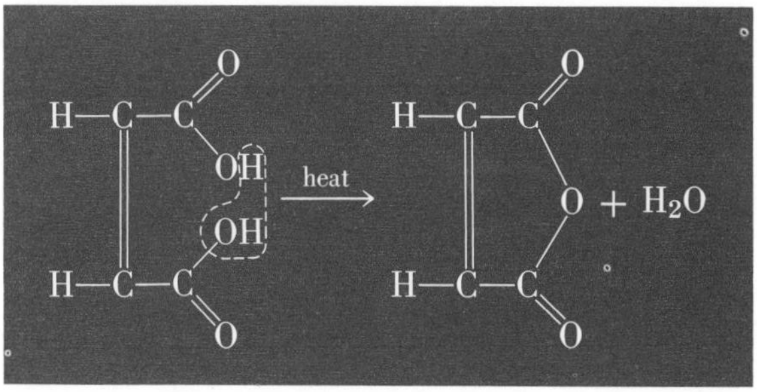

However, fumaric acid cannot be made to form an anhydride and water, and this is explained by assuming that OH groups are too far

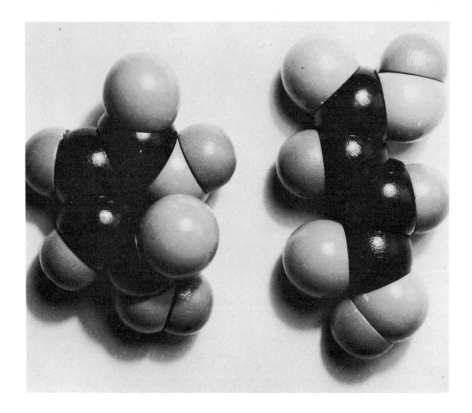

6 Models of maleic acid (left) and fumaric acid (right). By the use of such models, a three-dimensional concept of molecules can be gained.

apart on the molecule for a change in bonding to occur and for the groups to combine and form water. Such compounds as maleic and fumaric acids, whose molecules are represented by the same formula but which differ from each other in molecular structure, are called **isomeric compounds** or **isomers.** A great many instances of isomerism are known to chemistry.

The relationship between molecular structure and function is most pronounced in those compounds which are associated with living organisms. For present purposes, we shall exemplify this by introducing the concept of **enzyme-substrate** reactions. Enzymes are rather complex organic compounds which are vital to living systems inasmuch as they make reactions possible that would otherwise occur too slowly to be of much consequence. A substrate is any substance which is altered by enzymatic action. One of the most fundamental characteristics of enzymes is their **specificity,** or ability to bring about a reaction with one or only a few substrates. To draw an analogy, a given enzyme is like a key which is specific for only one lock or type of lock. By means of special techniques, biochemists have learned that only a small portion of a given enzyme molecule represents the specific area, just as many keys might be shaped similarly except for the "notched" area. When lock and key (substrate and enzyme) come into intimate contact, the substrate is altered in a highly specific manner, as is shown conceptually in Fig. 7. In some cases, the reaction yields two products, as illustrated in this figure, and in others the product is merely altered. In still other reactions, two or more substrate molecules are combined, yielding a more complex product.

There are many chemical reactions which occur within living organisms that are best explained according to the concept of geometric configuration of molecules. We shall consider some of these in later chapters.

CONCLUSION

It is hoped that this brief presentation of fundamental principles will make possible a more complete understanding of subsequent topics. Certainly other useful concepts of physics and chemistry might be introduced, and other relevant principles will be developed as the need arises. However, we are now equipped with words and concepts which are necessary for an understanding of many biological principles and for the proper relation of the physical sciences to biology.

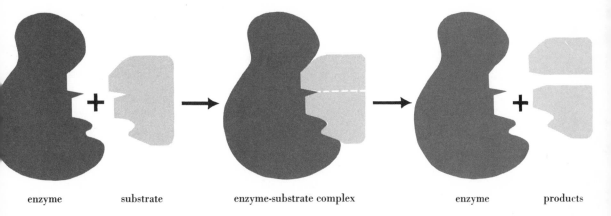

enzyme   substrate   enzyme-substrate complex   enzyme   products

7 Diagrammatic representation of an enzyme-substrate reaction. According to this concept, the enzyme is geometrically specific for this particular substrate, and the substrate molecule is split into two product molecules. The enzyme remains unchanged at the end, and may serve over and over in such reactions.

QUESTIONS

Multiple Choice

1. The number of elements known to occur naturally is (a) eight, (b) sixty-four, (c) ninety-two, (d) $2 \times n^2$, (e) infinite.

2. Which of the following is defined as the smallest unit of matter that can enter into chemical changes? (a) electron, (b) proton, (c) ion, (d) isomer, (e) atom.

3. An atom of the element bromine has thirty-five electrons. All "shells" are filled except the outermost one. How many electrons occupy this outermost shell? (a) one, (b) two, (c) five, (d) seven, (e) thirteen.

4. The central portion of an atom is called the (a) nucleus, (b) proton, (c) neutron, (d) orbit, (e) element.

5. An atom which exhibits either a positive or a negative charge is called (a) a molecule, (b) a compound, (c) an ion, (d) an element, (e) an electron.

6. The law of conservation of energy holds that (a) whenever matter is converted to energy, some energy will be lost as heat; (b) inorganic compounds cannot be broken down to produce energy; (c) matter may exist as a solid, a liquid, or a gas; (d) energy cannot be either created or destroyed; (e) energy is conserved by being stored in molecules of organic compounds.

7. An atom bears somewhat the same relationship to an element as a molecule does to (a) a substance, (b) an inorganic compound, (c) a covalent compound, (d) an electrovalent compound, (e) a mixture.

8. Whenever a substance ionizes or reacts in such a way as to produce hydrogen ions, it is termed (a) an acid, (b) a base, (c) a salt, (d) a molecule, (e) a compound.

9. Two molecules whose formulas are the same but which differ from each other geometrically are called (a) enzymes, (b) substrates, (c) ions, (d) isomers, (e) acids.

10. Ask a chemistry student or teacher which of the following (there are more than one) could *not* combine with sodium, and why: (a) lithium, (b) iodine, (c) magnesium, (d) neon, (e) oxygen.

Questions for Consideration and Discussion

1. How satisfactory is the Bohr theory of atomic structure to physical scientists? Perhaps your teacher will ask a chemist or a physicist to prepare a statement answering this question which can be read to the class.

2. Distinguish properly between covalent and electrovalent compounds.

3. Distinguish properly between organic and inorganic compounds.

4. What is an aqueous solution? Why is this type of solution particularly interesting to the biologist?

5. Why were maleic and fumaric acids introduced in this chapter? What is shown by their respective responses to heat?

6. Define energy. Do you feel that your definition is completely satisfactory and understandable to you?

7. In what way is carbon a rather unique element?

8. Is the combination of sodium and chlorine to form sodium chloride a chemical or a physical change? Justify your answer.

9. Would the term "nucleus" probably bring to mind the same idea to a biologist as it would to a physicist? Explain.

10. Why is it necessary that the present-day student of biology understand something of physics and chemistry?

REFERENCES

ASHFORD, T. A. *From Atoms To Stars.* New York: Holt, Rinehart and Winston, Inc., 1960. This textbook on physical science is written for the student who has no previous knowledge of the subject and should be of help in regard to the principles set forth in this chapter. Chapters 11 and 12, entitled "Atoms As Miniature Solar Systems" and "Planetary Electrons and Chemistry," respectively, are especially important in this connection.

GAMOW, G. *Mr. Tompkins Explores the Atom.* New York: The Macmillan Company, 1944. This entertaining little book features a trip to the world of atomic structure, where electrons are personified. It is a deeper and more revealing volume than superficial inspection might indicate.

————. *Matter, Earth and Sky.* Englewood Cliffs, N.J.: Prentice-Hall, Inc., 1958. The author of the work cited above deals with the fundamental principles of physical science at greater length in this textbook. His chapter entitled "The Chemistry of Life" is of particular interest to the student of biology.

SISLER, H. H., C. A. VAN DER WERF, and **A. W. DAVIDSON.** *College Chemistry—A Systematic Approach.* New York: The Macmillan Company, 1961. This book is one of several excellent texts which are currently being published. For the student who wishes to delve more deeply into the principles of chemistry, it should serve admirably.

The Organization
of Living Matter

All matter is composed of atoms and molecules, but a great difference in degree of complexity exists between non-living matter and that which is so organized as to exhibit the phenomenon called life. Chemical analysis of a rock, for example, reveals the presence of compounds that are comparatively simple in make-up. In contrast, careful analysis of living matter always reveals the presence of compounds which are extremely complex in molecular composition, together with those which are relatively simple. It becomes our present task to gain at least a degree of understanding in regard to the nature and organization of this living matter.

THE NATURE OF LIFE

It is a matter of some concern to the biologist that he cannot define in precise terms that which he studies and tries to understand. The term "life" is extremely difficult to define in exact terms because it is something of an abstraction. We find it necessary, in dealing with other abstractions, to define them in terms of their characteristics. The word "beauty" is such a term. Beauty is known by any number of concrete and easily defineable characteristics, but it is not subject to definition according to material concepts. Even such a down-to-earth term as "fire" comes under this classification. We know it by its characteristics. It is hot, it burns, it destroys, it is the *result* of materially defineable phenomena, but it escapes exact definition itself.

Thus it is with the term "life." We recognize the difference between a living organism and a non-living object, or even between living and dead organisms. However, we must realize that what we call "life" is the *result* of a certain organization and activity of chemical substances. When this organization and activity are irreversibly destroyed, life is destroyed. Thus, the term "life" is best considered an abstraction or a literary term, not a scientific one.

Nevertheless, we can go far toward understanding life by studying its characteristics. We know by observation and experimentation that living matter is capable of carrying on elaborate chemical activities (metabolism); it grows, it reproduces itself, it exhibits responsiveness to stimuli, and it adapts itself to environmental circumstances. These five characteristics are considered to be of sufficient importance that in this text a chapter is devoted to each of them.

THE CELL AND ITS STRUCTURE

There seems to have arisen no special need for a term to describe non-living matter. Living matter, however, is called **protoplasm** (Gr. *protos*, first + *plasma*, form). It is typically a more or less viscous, translucent kind of material that is a complex mixture of many substances, although there are variations in its physical and chemical composition. It may contain material which is itself neither living nor a necessary accompaniment of life, such as fat or starch particles. Whenever the term protoplasm is used, however, it refers to a given unit or quantity of matter in which the characteristics of life are manifested.

Protoplasm is typically maintained in units called **cells** which constitute the structural building blocks of organisms. Some organisms consist of only one complete unit of protoplasm, and hence are said to be **unicellular.** However, the great majority of organisms are **multicellular.**

Cells vary greatly in both size and shape, and it thus is somewhat meaningless to speak of a "typical" cell. Those which are shown in Fig. 8 are representative of non-specialized plant and animal cells, however, and their respective sizes may be considered somewhat typical. Many types of cells are smaller than these, and many are larger.

Regardless of superficial differences, most cells have certain features in common. The protoplasm which composes a cell is divided into a **nucleus** and **cytoplasm,** the former being incompletely separated from the latter by a **nuclear membrane.** The cytoplasm, in turn, is

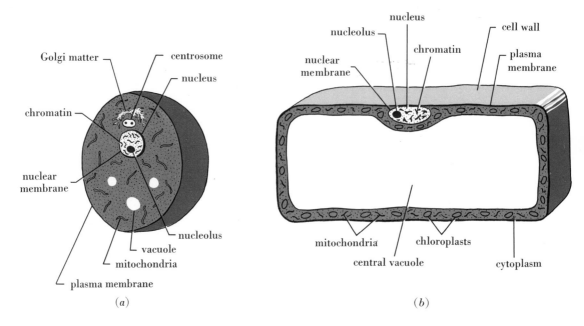

Golgi matter — centrosome — nucleus — chromatin — nuclear membrane — nucleolus — vacuole — mitochondria — plasma membrane

(a)

nucleus — nucleolus — nuclear membrane — chromatin — cell wall — plasma membrane — mitochondria — chloroplasts — central vacuole — cytoplasm

(b)

8 Representative cells in sectional view, magnified about 2,000 times. a, animal cell. b, plant cell.

limited at its outer boundary by a **plasma membrane.** It must be pointed out that in a very few types of cells this definite nucleus-cytoplasm relationship does not exist, or in some cases does not persist, but such a relationship within the cell should be considered typical. The nucleus contains within its membrane a material called **nucleoplasm,** in which one or more **nucleoli** and a mass of **chromatin** may be observed. Scattered about in the cytoplasm are numerous **mitochondria,** which may exist in a variety of shapes in different types of cells. Extremely small bodies called **microsomes** are also present in the cytoplasm. The mitochondria and microsomes are closely associated with a complex network called the **endoplasmic reticulum,** which forms a sort of "skeleton" for the cell. Hence, these inclusions are not scattered throughout the cytoplasm in a haphazard fashion; there is a definite organization involving all parts of the cell. An irregular network of material called the **Golgi matter** may readily be demonstrated in animal cells; although this material is more difficult to detect in plant cells, it is typical of them also. From one to several **vacuoles** are frequently exhibited, these being areas within the cytoplasm which are filled with a watery, non-protoplasmic fluid. Various granules and other poorly-defined objects are frequently visible in the cytoplasm.

In addition to features which are shared in common, typical plant cells may be distinguished from those of animals by several characteristics. One difference exists in regard to the outer limits of each type of cell. In plants, a rigid **cell wall**, composed chiefly of cellulose, typically surrounds the cell and delimits it as a unit from others. This wall is non-living and is not strictly a part of the cell, having been formed by the cytoplasm during its inception and growth. The plasma membrane lies just within this wall. Most animal cells, in contrast, are simply limited by their plasma membranes, although some possess a flexible, non-living

9 A portion of rat liver cell, thin section, as photographed by means of the electron microscope. Note internal structure of mitochondria. A portion of the endoplasmic reticulum is shown; note attached microsomes, which appear as small dots. Several structures may be seen in this view of the cell that are not indentified in the text. Magnification: about 50,000 (Courtesy Dr. K. R. Porter).

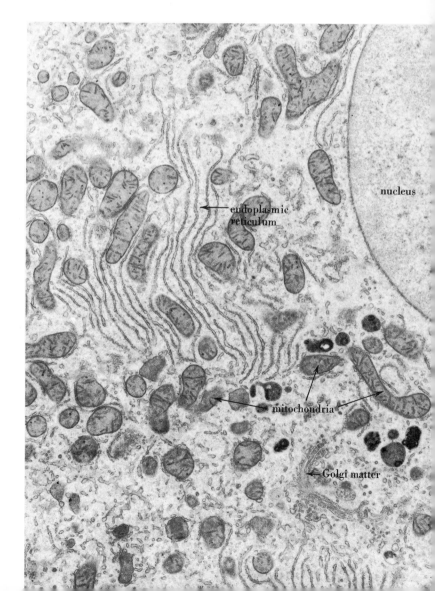

pellicle which corresponds to the plant cell wall.[1] Associated closely with the nucleus in most animal cells but not typical of most plant cells is the **centrosome,** a somewhat clear area in which a pair of granules, the **centrioles,** can usually be seen when the cell is stained appropriately. The centrioles are closely associated with the process of cell division. Plant cells may exhibit various types of **plastids,** the most common type being the **chloroplast** of green plants. Finally, plant and animal cells differ in that the vacuoles which are formed in the latter are less conspicuous than those of mature plant cells and show no tendency to coalesce in the formation of one large central vacuole (Fig. 8).

It should be remembered that there are many variations of these generalizations regarding plant and animal cells and that no one type of cell may be regarded as "typical." Furthermore, many of the structures mentioned require special staining or microscopical techniques in order to be demonstrated, and it should not be expected that they could all be seen at one time within any one cell.

THE NATURE OF PROTOPLASM

Having examined the gross structure of the cell, let us take a still closer look at protoplasm. By means of special chemical techniques, much has been learned about the nature and organization of this material. Such knowledge has shed considerable light on certain fundamental life processes. Furthermore, many important problems which are the concern of modern biology involve the physics and chemistry of protoplasm.

Elements Present in Protoplasm

From the chemical standpoint, it might logically be supposed that protoplasm should contain rare or unusual elements which are completely absent from non-living matter. This is not the case. The most abundant elements found in protoplasm are also among the most abundant in the non-living world. These are as follows:

Calcium	Nitrogen
Carbon	Oxygen
Chlorine	Phosphorus
Hydrogen	Potassium
Iron	Potassium
Magnesium	Sulfur

---

[1] Since there is some confusion as to whether or not one includes the cell wall or pellicle when he speaks of a cell, the term **protoplast** is widely used to describe the entire unit lying within any such non-living structure. Some biologists use the terms protoplast and cell synonymously.

In addition, the elements boron, copper, fluorine, manganese, and silicon are always present in extremely small quantities. Certain others such as aluminum, cobalt, and zinc may be present, depending upon the particular plant or animal protoplasmic system involved. Of the twelve elements listed above, carbon, hydrogen, nitrogen, oxygen, and phosphorus are found in far greater abundance in protoplasm than are any others.

Compounds Present in Protoplasm

The elements of protoplasm may exist as independent ions in some cases, or they may be organized into compounds, some of which are extremely complex in fundamental molecular structure. In the main, these are of three types, as follows.

WATER. About seventy-five to eighty-five per cent of protoplasm is made up of water. This high proportion of water to other substances seems to be necessary for the solution of ions and molecules, for the suspension of molecular aggregates, and for participation in certain chemical reactions that occur within cells.

INORGANIC SALTS. Certain inorganic salts, such as sodium chloride and calcium carbonate, are always present in protoplasm. Salts exist as ions in solution and play an important part in metabolism. For example, certain chemical reactions within cells occur only if specific elements are present in the vicinity of the reactive molecules. Furthermore, some of these elements (iron, copper, and magnesium are examples) are important raw materials for the synthesis of key molecules within the cell. Even though the elements which make up inorganic salts are present within protoplasm in minute amounts as compared with the types of compounds listed below, and with water, they are indispensable to the normal activities of the cell.

ORGANIC COMPOUNDS. Many organic compounds are found in protoplasm. Molecules of these compounds serve a variety of functions; certain types serve as storehouses of energy, while others help to form structures that are physically necessary to the efficient functioning of the protoplasmic system of which they are a part. The most important organic compounds may be classified as follows.

Fuel compounds. These function in the storage and release of energy, and are of three types.

1. Carbohydrates. Molecules of carbohydrates (Fig. 10) are composed of carbon chains, with every carbon atom except those on one end characteristically maintaining bonds with a hydrogen atom and a hydroxyl group. Although there are carbohydrates whose molecules con-

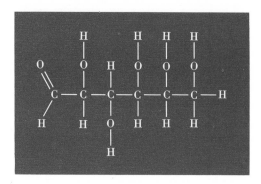

10 The structure of glucose, a monosaccharide carbohydrate.

tain three, four, or five carbons, the most common simple carbohydrates are those whose molecules have six carbon atoms. There are several isomers of this six-carbon group, all of which have the formula $C_6H_{12}O_6$. Besides **glucose,** shown in Fig. 10, **galactose** and **fructose** are among the more common isomers. Those carbohydrates exhibiting six or fewer carbon atoms in their molecules are called the **monosaccharides,** or **simple sugars.** These may link together in the formation of more complex units. A common **disaccharide,** for example, is **sucrose,** or common table sugar (formula $C_{12}H_{22}O_{11}$), which is composed of a glucose unit and a fructose unit. There are also many other disaccharides. **Trisaccharide** sugars are fairly common. In addition, there are **polysaccharides,** such as **starch** and **glycogen,** which are composed entirely of linked glucose units. These two polysaccharides are important storage products in plants and animals, respectively. Another important polysaccharide is **cellulose** which makes up a large part of the typical plant cell wall. The formula for polysaccharides is usually expressed as $(C_6H_{10}O_5)_n$, where n can be any number.

2. Fats. Like carbohydrates, fats are composed of molecules containing carbon, hydrogen, and oxygen. However, the arrangement and relative proportions of these elements lend to the fats an altogether different set of characteristics than those of carbohydrates. They are quite insoluble in water, for example, and are much richer in potential energy, gram for gram, than are either carbohydrates or proteins. Most fats are composed of two fractions, **glycerol** and **fatty acids** (Fig. 11). In some fats, this pattern is altered to include the elements phosphorus and nitrogen. These "higher" fats, in particular, are structurally important to the cell in that they make up a large portion of such membranes as the plasma membrane and those which enclose mitochondria. The "simple" fats, in contrast, are chiefly important as a readily available energy source and as a storage material.

3. Proteins. Like carbohydrates and fats, proteins always have carbon, hydrogen, and oxygen in their molecules. In addition, however, the protein molecule always possesses nitrogen, and other elements may also be present. Molecules of protein are very long and complex and are made up of linked units called **amino acids.** An amino acid is a type of compound in which the molecules always exhibit the following pattern:

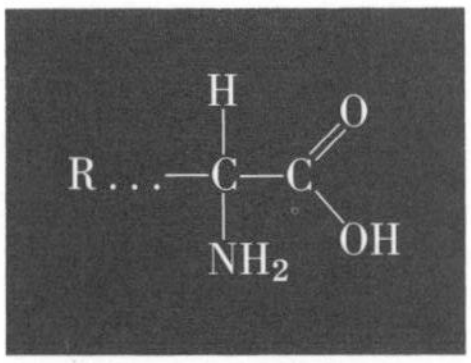

The "R" in this molecular configuration stands for "radical" and means that several different kinds, numbers, and arrangements of atoms may link to this common grouping. As a matter of fact, some twenty-five different arrangements represented here by "R" are known; hence, there are some twenty-five different amino acids. These may be considered the "letters" of a protein word-system because their number and arrangement determines the nature of a given protein molecule. When one considers that thousands of these may be linked to form a single large molecule, it becomes obvious that the number of different possible kinds

11 A representative fat molecule and its breakdown to glycerol and three fatty acid molecules in the process of hydrolysis. In this process, the bonds are broken, with H and OH portions of water being attached as indicated. The dotted lines signify that several carbon atoms, each flanked by two hydrogen atoms, may form chains of considerable length.

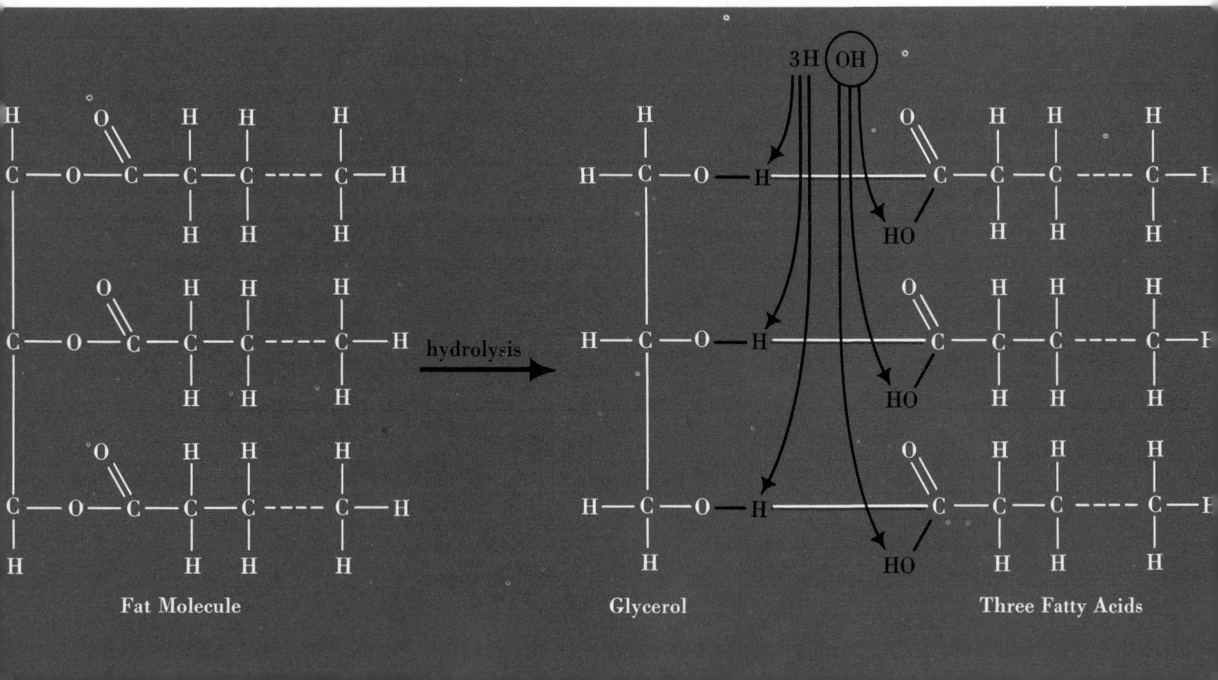

Fat Molecule　　　　　　　　　Glycerol　　　　　　　　Three Fatty Acids

of protein molecules is almost infinite. In the molecule, the amino acids are linked in such a way that the COOH group of one is attached to the NH₂ group of another. This can be illustrated by showing how two given amino acids are joined together. Suppose we take the simplest amino acid, **glycine,** and the next simplest, **alanine,** and subject them to the biochemical process of **dehydration:**

As a result of a large number of such reactions taking place in the synthesis of protein, which is itself an intracellular process, long molecules are built up (Fig. 12). When two given amino acids are separated from one another, the opposite type of reaction to that illustrated above, called **hydrolysis,** occurs. As might be predicted, these reactions occur in the formation and breakdown of fats and carbohydrates also.

Enzymes. These compounds, which were introduced in the preceding chapter (see page 22), are protoplasmic "spark-plugs," making possible chemical reactions in their environments which would not occur to any appreciable degree without them. By correct chemical definition, an enzyme is an organic catalyst, and a catalyst is a substance which alters the rate of a specific chemical reaction but which remains unchanged at the conclusion of the reaction. Chemically, enzymes are proteins, but their molecules are specialized for a catalytic function rather than an energy-yielding one. We have already observed that protein molecules may be extremely long (this is particularly true of enzymes), and these long molecular chains become folded according to specific patterns. Apparently, the specificity of enzymes is due not only to the sequence of amino acids at the "specific" site of a given molecule but also to the geometry of a certain folding pattern. As a general rule, enzymes work very rapidly, catalyzing one reaction after another. By exact methods of measurement, it has been found that some enzyme molecules are capable of catalyzing as many as 50,000 reactions within a second's time! This accounts for the fact that, as is generally true of catalysts, a very small amount of enzyme may catalyze a large amount of substrate. This is possible because a given enzyme molecule can be used over and over again by the cell, until it ultimately "wears out" and is replaced. There is a high degree of enzymatic localization within the cell according to type;

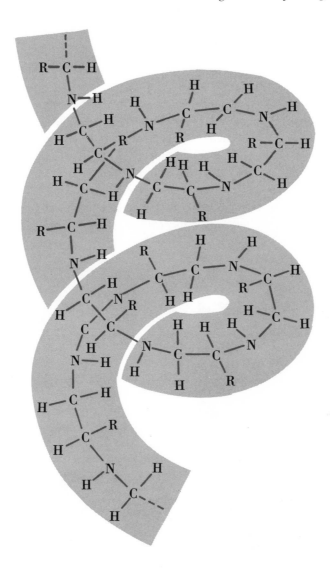

12 A portion of a protein molecule, drawn according to one concept of structure. Amino acids are linked together by the nitrogen (N) of one and a carbon (C) of another. R represents any "radical," or continuing chemical group, of the amino acid. A long protein molecule apparently is folded upon itself in some fashion such as that shown here.

certain types are found only in the mitochondria, others only within microsomes, and so on.

Nucleic acids. Just as polysaccharides are composed of monosaccharide units and proteins of amino acids, the nucleic acids, whose molecules are extremely complex, are made up of units called **nucleotides.** A nucleotide itself is composed of a five-carbon **sugar,** a **base,** and a **phosphate group** (Fig. 13). The sugar involved may be either **ribose** or **deoxyribose;** hence, we recognize two different kinds of nucleotides: **ribonucleotides** and **deoxyribonucleotides.** In a nucleic acid molecule, all the nucleotides are of one type or the other; thus, two fundamental types of nucleic acids exist, **ribonucleic acid (RNA)** and **deoxyribonucleic acid (DNA).** There are four different ribonucleotides and four different deoxyribonucleotides, due to differences in the bases involved. As these are linked together in the formation of RNA or DNA molecules, respectively, the different arrangements which become possible are virtually infinite. It appears that it is the specific arrangement of the nucleotides to form nucleic acids within the protoplasm of a given organism that determines its characteristics. In other words, proto-

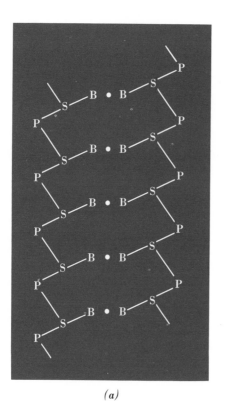

(a)

(b)

13 A portion of a DNA molecule, according to one interpretation a, the bases, B, of nucleotides are attached in the manner indicated, forming a double chain. b, the double chain assumes the shape of a spiral. The ribbons represent the sugar (S)-phosphate (P) portions of linked nucleotides, and the bars represent the attached bases of opposing nucleotides. This theoretical structure of the DNA molecule (which may stretch out in this pattern for an indefinite distance) was first proposed by J. D. Watson and F. H. C. Crick, and is known as the **Watson-Crick model** of DNA.

plasmic systems vary from organism to organism chiefly because the nucleic acids of one are not exactly like those of any other. In the cell, DNA is restricted to the nucleus where it makes up a large part of the chromatin mass. RNA is found both in the nucleus (concentrated in the nucleolus) and the cytoplasm (localized chiefly in the microsomes and mitochondria).

Nucleic acids join with proteins to form **nucleoproteins,** which are the largest molecules known to chemistry. One very striking feature of nucleoproteins is their ability to reproduce themselves. **Apparently, no other type of molecule is capable of this.** A given nucleoprotein molecule seems to serve as a model, or template, to which units necessary for the construction of a new molecule exactly like it are attracted under certain conditions. As we shall see later, this feature of nucleoproteins has extremely important ramifications in the over-all biology of organisms. Suffice it to say here that this ability for self-duplication renders nucleoproteins the most unique structural components of a unique material, protoplasm.

Vitamins. As compared with proteins and nucleic acids, the vitamins are characterized by simple molecular structure. Furthermore, there are relatively few different vitamins. These substances, which are commonly known by their letter designations, have achieved prominence during the past few decades because of their importance in the diet of human beings. Very small amounts of vitamins are sufficient to prevent **deficiency diseases** such as **scurvy** (resulting from a lack of vitamin C) and **rickets** (caused by a deficiency of vitamin D). More recently, the roles played by vitamins in the cell have become better known. One of the major activities of vitamins is that of serving as raw materials from which a special class of compounds, the **co-enzymes,** are made. As their group name indicates, co-enzymes (like the various ions which were mentioned earlier) make it possible for certain enzymes to carry out their specific functions. For example, one of the better-known co-enzymes found in cells is called **co-enzyme A,** often abbreviated **Co-A,** and its formation in the cell depends upon the presence of **pantothenic acid,** one of the B vitamins. This vitamin is necessary because it forms a part of the Co-A molecule that cannot be furnished by any other substance. Hence, the human and other higher animal diseases which are associated with vitamin deficiency are the reflection of cellular abnormalities resulting from an impairment of normal protoplasmic machinery.

It should be kept in mind that this outline is quite artificial and may lend a false impression that molecules and ions are nicely catalogued in the cell into tight little functional compartments. Actually, the presentation given above is merely one way to organize these various materials for learning purposes. Furthermore, those listed here are only the types of substances that we are calling "most important" for the present time. There are others, as we shall see.

The Physical Relationship of Protoplasmic Inclusions

From the foregoing discussion, it might be inferred that the most outstanding feature of protoplasm is its chemical make-up. Although it is true that some highly unique materials such as enzymes and nucleic acids go far toward making this a valid assumption, there is another side to the story. The compounds and elements of protoplasm might be mixed together in the exact proportions found in a given unit of protoplasm, but the resulting material would not be alive. Even after a previously living unit of protoplasm has died, it is no longer protoplasm by correct definition. The ingredients still are all present, but the proper organization is lacking. The one factor that renders such a chemical mixture living, therefore, is the physical relationship which the various components bear to each other. This relationship goes beyond the mere localization of structural *parts* of the cell; it involves molecular and energetic associations that are both intimate and delicate.

Let us draw an analogy. Suppose a master watchmaker invents a clock whose parts are so intricately arranged that only he knows the secret of its operation. Suppose further that he dies, and the clock is given to a novice. Upon observing the clock and its parts, this second person might well conclude that the clock operates successfully because it is composed of certain wheels and gears. In a sense, of course, this is true. It could hardly operate without them. However, many things are composed of wheels and gears that do not keep time, and in the final analysis, it is the physical relationship which these parts bear to each other that makes the instrument a clock. If the novice essays to take it apart, he will have wheels and gears, but he will not have a clock and never will again unless he can learn the secret of the original relationships. There is yet another point to be made from this analogy. When the master craftsman originally made the clock, he put a great deal of his "genius" into it. Does this mean that there is some mysterious influence, undefineable in physical and chemical terms, still floating around inside the clock? Not at all. His genius is measurable only by its results, and we understand that the word is a literary one.

Only within recent decades have biologists as a group come to view the living cell from this "clock," or mechanistic, approach.[2] In fact, the concept is extended to the whole organism, whose body may be com-

---

[2] It should not be inferred from this analogy that the biologist who takes this view of the living cell is obliged to postulate a creator to correspond to the master craftsman. He may or he may not, depending upon his own personal philosophy. Should he believe that a supreme being originally set the balance of protoplasm, however, this would not make him any less a mechanist *in terms of present-day biological processes.* This problem is dealt with more fully in Chapter 10, and the student may wish to read these passages at this point.

posed of billions of cells. However, it is on the cytological level that this approach has proved to be most fruitful. The mechanistic point of view is a "conceptual scheme" within whose framework we have found it possible to launch other conceptual schemes, thus fulfilling the highest requirements of science.

Because the machinery of the cell is quite intricate, there are formidable barriers which stand in the way of understanding it very well, to say nothing of the immense task of putting it together synthetically. Hence, most biologists are not overly optimistic that either the goals of complete understanding or the artificial production of living protoplasm are near accomplishment, although great strides have been made toward both. **Thus far, life seems to come only from previous life in an unbroken chain, at least under conditions which prevail at present on earth.**

We can, however, come to some understanding in regard to a few of the physical principles governing the organization of protoplasm, although many which are known require for their understanding a knowledge of concepts and principles that are beyond the scope of this text. Some of those which are profitable to us will be introduced in later chapters.

Let us note at this point that the cell is the smallest and least complex unit of matter which can unquestionably be called living.[3] This means that, within limits of specialization, it can carry on all the basic activities which characterize organisms. In other words, the activities to which we refer as metabolism, growth, reproduction, responsiveness, and adaptation are, in the final analysis, carried on by protoplasm. Protoplasm is the material of which cells are composed; hence, these characteristics of life are really characteristics of the cell as a unit. It should be kept in mind as one considers these fundamental activities that a cell is a highly organized entity whose material substance is so ordered as to warrant its being considered "living." *In its own right,* therefore, and not simply by virtue of its association with other such units in a complex organism, the cell holds this unique distinction.

---

[3] Viruses, some of which are causative agents of diseases in various plants and animals, are extremely small units of matter which manifest certain characteristics associated with protoplasm. Typically, they consist of nucleoprotein coated with protein (Fig. 14). Although they reproduce themselves, they do not carry on the complex chemical activities associated with protoplasm, and many biologists do not consider them to be living in the strict sense of the word. In fact, they can reproduce only within living cells, and in this respect they behave somewhat as "free" or "wild" nucleoproteins. Certainly they are complex, on the molecular level, and perhaps they should be considered an exception to the strict distinction that is usually drawn between living and nonliving units of matter. In the final analysis, of course, the problem is largely one of definition.

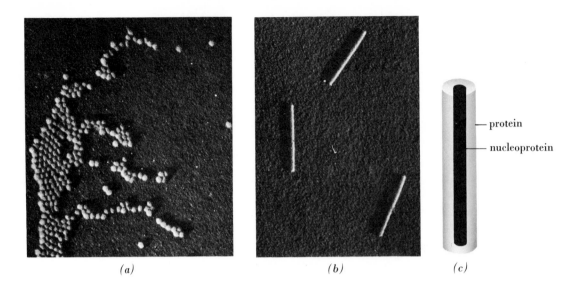

(a)   *(b)*   protein

nucleoprotein

(c)

14 Some representative viruses. a, electron photomicrograph of tomato bushy stunt virus, magnified 57,000 times. b, electron photomicrograph of tobacco mosaic virus, magnified 65,500 times. c, diagram of a virus showing typical structure. A core of nucleoprotein is surrounded by an "overcoat" of protein. Electron photomicrographs courtesy of Dr. R. C. Williams.

CONCLUSION

Perhaps this discussion will have produced an awareness that biologists place great emphasis on the study of cells and protoplasm. Since the phenomena which are associated with life occur only in connection with them, it is obvious that only through such studies can they be discovered and understood. Although a multicellular organism is more than a mere sum of its parts, nevertheless its parts, or cells, must be understood to some extent before appreciable progress can be made in understanding the whole organism. For this reason, and because certain human diseases such as cancer are dependent upon cellular abnormalities, cell studies enjoy high prestige in modern biological research. It is to be hoped that such studies will result not only in improved standards for mankind, but that they will also provide answers to many of life's most interesting and puzzling questions. On the basis of past achievements along these lines, there is every reason for optimism.

QUESTIONS

Multiple Choice

1. Which of the following are found almost exclusively in animal cells? (a) nuclei, (b) nucleoli, (c) plastids, (d) mitochondria, (e) centrioles.

2. Which of the above are found exclusively in plant cells?

3. The question, "What is life?" (a) is not really capable of being answered scientifically, so most scientists do not attempt to answer it; (b) has been studied exhaustively by biologists who have only partially answered it; (c) has been answered to the satisfaction of most biologists; (d) should be easy to answer, since it is a simple matter to distinguish between living, non-living, and dead things; (e) should not concern biologists, since it is rather a philosophical question.

4. Protoplasm is actually (a) a substance, (b) a mixture, (c) a compound, (d) a solution.

5. Which of the following could one expect to find in the *least* quantity in a given cell? (a) hydrogen, (b) oxygen, (c) phosphorus, (d) potassium, (e) nitrogen.

6. Which of the elements above is always present in protein, but never in simple fats or carbohydrates?

7. Which of the following is capable of self-reproduction? (a) an enzyme molecule, (b) a protein molecule, (c) a carbohydrate molecule, (d) a water molecule, (e) a nucleoprotein molecule.

8. Which of the molecular types listed above serves to alter the rate of certain chemical reactions in the cell?

9. In which of the following is DNA concentrated? (a) cell wall, (b) nucleolus, (c) chromatin, (d) plasma membrane, (e) microsome.

10. Which of the following is the smallest and least complex unit of matter which can unquestionably be called living? (a) cell, (b) nucleus, (c) nucleoprotein molecule, (d) mitochondrion, (e) virus.

True-false

1. As a general rule, enzymes work very slowly.

2. A nucleotide is composed of three fractions: a sugar, a base, and a phosphate group.

3. In a nucleic acid molecule, ribonucleotides and deoxyribonucleotides may be linked to each other at random throughout the molecule.

4. Since viruses are capable of reproduction, they are universally regarded by biologists as being living organisms.

5. Biologists first synthesized living protoplasm about the year 1940.

6. Most fats are composed of two fractions, glycerol and fatty acids.

7. As compared with the molecules of other organic compounds, those of the nucleoproteins are rather short and simple.

8. Many vitamins are necessary to the cell in the synthesis of co-enzymes.

9. Mitochondria and microsomes are closely associated with the endoplasmic reticulum in the cytoplasm.

10. To be truly living, an organism must consist of more than one cell.

Questions for Consideration and Discussion

1. Define the following: enzyme, co-enzyme, substrate, carbohydrate, fat, protein, amino acid, vitamin, hydrolysis, dehydration.

2. List the characteristics of living matter as they are presented in this chapter and explain what each means.

3. Distinguish properly between DNA and RNA. What are the units called which make up nucleic acid molecules? How many different kinds are there in RNA molecules and in DNA molecules?

4. What did the author attempt to show by his analogy regarding a clock and its parts?

5. List the characteristics presented in this chapter which animal and plant cells share, and list those which are characteristic only of one or the other.

6. A cytologist was given a large grant of money by a foundation in order that he might study division rates in the cells of a certain worm. Persons who donated this money to the foundation were interested in promoting cancer research. Do you think that this grant may have been justified?

7. Distinguish between the terms protoplasm, protoplast, and cytoplasm.

8. Ask your teacher for an example of a cell in which the definite nucleus-cytoplasm relationship does not exist. Find out also if there are cells that lose their nuclei as they mature.

9. From the standpoint of the student, why do you suppose that a knowledge of elementary cytology is necessary to an understanding of the structure and function of complex, multicellular organisms?

10. Do you suppose that all the structures known to characterize a plant or an animal cell could be seen at one time within any given cell? Explain your answer.

REFERENCES

BUTLER, J. A. V. *Inside the Living Cell.* New York: Basic Books, Inc., 1959. This small book is written in such a manner that the person of limited background can understand it. The author considers a number of cellular problems that are highly important to biology as a whole.

GERARD, R. W. *Unresting Cells.* New York: Harper & Brothers, Publishers, 1940. This highly readable book is a classic in biology, and will serve the student well as a general treatment on cells.

MC ELROY, W. D. *Cellular Physiology and Biochemistry.* Englewood Cliffs, N.J.: Prentice-Hall, Inc., 1961. This is one of eleven brief textbooks making up a series entitled FOUNDATIONS OF MODERN BIOLOGY. We shall cite each of these excellent books at one point or another, and some of them (including this one) will be suggested in connection with more than one chapter. For present purposes, the author's first and tenth chapters, entitled "The Chemistry of Cell Contents" and "Enzymes," respectively, are especially recommended.

SWANSON, C. P. *The Cell.* Englewood Cliffs, N.J.: Prentice-Hall, Inc., 1960. This is another in the FOUNDATIONS OF MODERN BIOLOGY series described above. The author's first three chapters are particularly appropriate in connection with our present chapter.

In addition to the books listed above, the following articles from *Scientific American* are recommended.

CRICK, F. H. C. "Nucleic Acids," Volume 197 (September, 1957), p. 188. This article, by one of two men who proposed a model of the nucleic acid molecule that is now widely accepted (see Fig. 13 of our present chapter), explains some aspects of the nature of these unusual molecules.

FRIEDEN, E. "The Enzyme-substrate Complex," Volume 201 (August, 1959), p. 119. The student will find this article to be of interest in connection with this present chapter.

GAY, HELEN. "Nuclear Control of the Cell," Volume 202 (January, 1960), p. 126. The author discusses the role of the nucleus and its relation to the cytoplasm.

SCHMITT, F. O. "Giant Molecules in Cells and Tissues," Volume 197, September, 1957, p. 204. The chemistry of protoplasm receives a close look in this article.

SIEKEVITZ, P. "Powerhouse of the Cell," Volume 197 (July, 1957), p. 131. The structure and function of the mitochondrion are discussed at some length.

ZAMECNIC, P. C. "The Microsome," Volume 198 (March, 1958), p. 118. The nature and function of microsomes are discussed in this article.

The Classification
of Organisms

Thus far, our attention has been directed toward generalizations regarding living organisms and toward microscopic and sub-microscopic aspects of organization. In Chapters 6 through 9, we shall relate cells to organisms in terms of fundamental activity, but before attempting to do this, it becomes necessary to gain some idea of the variety of living forms, their structural and functional relationships to each other, and some insights which have been gained through attempts at their classification. The present chapter, therefore, constitutes something of a departure from the main stream of our thought, but we will need this information in succeeding chapters for purposes of exemplification. Hence, we feel justified in such a departure at this point.

KARL VON LINNÉ AND THE SCIENCE OF TAXONOMY

It is obvious that the student of living forms is obliged to develop some system both in regard to nomenclature and to classification; otherwise, his work would be aimless and chaotic. Furthermore, if his system were entirely different from those of other such investigators, there would be no common basis for understanding the work of the many individuals so engaged.

This confusing situation largely prevailed before the time of Karl von Linné, a Swedish botanist (1707–1778). Although some attention had been directed toward the problem by other biologists, Linné (or Linnaeus, as he preferred to be called after having suggested Latin as the universal language of taxonomy) was able to introduce a system of naming and classification, the major features of which are employed to the present day.

Essentially, this system is based on two major premises, namely, the employment of Latin or latinized names and the classification of living forms according to a hierarchy of categories ranging from the most specific groups which ordinarily need to be recognized taxonomically (species) to the most general (kingdoms). The selection of Latin as the language of taxonomy has proved to be most fortunate since it is no longer a vernacular language and, therefore, is not subject to basic grammatical changes. Furthermore, it has been employed for centuries as the language of scholarship and thus has always found acceptance among civilized peoples. Although the original categories erected by Linnaeus and his contemporaries have been altered to suit the needs of succeeding generations of taxonomists, the fact that the system itself remains highly workable is a tribute to its founder.

Taxonomists employ the following major categories: kingdom, phylum, class, order, family, genus, and species. Quite frequently, intermediate categories such as sub-phylum, super-order, and so on, are created to fill specific needs. Thus, it is the goal of taxonomy to place every organism in a species, every species in a genus, every genus in a family, and so on.

By way of illustration, let us consider the classification of an animal common to every-day experience, the domesticated house cat. In distinguishing it as a kind (or species) of organism different from all other organisms, we can best start with the most general category of classification and proceed toward the most specific. There are two great kingdoms into which most organisms fit readily on the basis of characteristics that will be defined later on. These are the **plant** and the **animal** kingdoms,[1] and our specimen is classified in the latter group. Of the

---

[1] In separating the animal and plant kingdoms, it should be pointed out that some organisms do not fit readily into either group, inasmuch as they exhibit characteristics of both groups. Some biologists consider these as a separate kingdom, the **Protista,** and the organisms which are included are called **protists.** Fortunately, there are relatively few such organisms, and they need not be considered at this point. Those groups which are considered in this chapter include organisms that are universally recognized to be either plants or animals. A consideration of the criteria which may be used in distinguishing plants from animals is presented in Chapter 5.

many phyla which taxonomists recognize in this kingdom, we find that the cat possesses those characteristics generally accepted for the phylum **Chordata,** a group that is made to include all animals exhibiting, among other features, a structure called a **notochord** at some time during their lives. Of such animals, one group, the vertebrates, are able to replace the notochord with a vertebral column and hence comprise the sub-phylum **Vertebrata.** Within this sub-phylum, several classes are recognized. Our animal is placed in the class **Mammalia** along with all other vertebrates whose young are nourished by means of milk and who produce hair as an external body covering, to mention two of their characteristics. This class is divided into several orders, one of which, the order **Carnivora,** is made to include those mammals whose natural food is the flesh of other animals. The carnivores differ so much among themselves that a number of families have been established taxonomically, and the cat is placed with other carnivores to which it bears a strong resemblance in the family **Felidae** (the cat family). Within this family, two genera are recognized; one of these is the genus *Felis,* which includes all "true" cats. There are several species belonging to this genus: *Felis leo* ("lion cat"), *Felis tigris* ("tiger cat"), and so on. Our cat differs from these, however, in one respect that has been selected for descriptive purposes. It can be tamed, and hence it is called *Felis domestica* ("domesticated cat").

By way of summary, let us arrange the classification of the house cat according to the following scheme:

Kingdom—Animalia
Phylum—Chordata
Sub-phylum—Vertebrata
Class—Mammalia
Order—Carnivora
Family—Felidae
Genus—*Felis*
Species—*domestica*

It may be pointed out that generic and specific names constitute something of a Latin or latinized[2] description of an organism, the generic name being a noun and the specific name usually a descriptive adjective. Because of this emphasis on a pair of names, the Linnaean system is sometimes referred to as one of **binomial nomenclature.** In keeping with correct grammatical usage, the generic name is to be capitalized, but the specific name is not except in certain unusual instances. For emphasis, both names are italicized in print. Sometimes the generic-specific binomial is referred to by lay persons as the **scientific name.** In some cases there

[2] Occasionally, a Greek name is used.

is no special need to cite the specific name; for example, it may not be known, or the person involved may wish to refer to a characteristic common to all species belonging to the genus. Under such circumstances, it is perfectly in order to cite only the generic name. A specific name is never used apart from a generic name, however.

Occasionally, it becomes necessary to recognize **varieties** or **sub-species** within a species. These categories assume considerable importance to taxonomists, but they are not ordinarily considered in classifying an organism.

It should be emphasized that taxonomic categories are abstractions since only organisms really exist in nature. Furthermore, the exact limits of these categories sometimes become rather arbitrary. A phylum is a group of similar classes, a class is a group of similar orders, and so on, but the degree of similarity required must be decided, in the final analysis, by some taxonomist. At the species level, the matter of definition becomes particularly vexing because it is at this point that terminology must bridge the abstract and the concrete. It is not enough simply to say that a species is a group of similar organisms, although this is true as far as it goes. Taxonomists have failed to supply a definition of the species which is universally satisfactory because it is not entirely an arbitrary matter. Two organisms may appear to be identical in morphology, but hidden physiological differences might be sufficiently great that they do not belong to the same breeding group, for example. At this point, it is sufficient that the student consider a species to be a group of organisms that are sufficiently similar morphologically, physiologically, and genetically to have been thus grouped together by some taxonomist. This is a very superficial definition, however, and will require revisions whenever one speaks of species from different standpoints.

ARTIFICIAL AND NATURAL SYSTEMS OF CLASSIFICATION

At the time that Linnaeus introduced the system of classification described above, the idea prevailed that species were static in nature and were not subject to change. Closely associated with this concept was the belief, held by Linnaeus and most other biologists of his day, that the ancestors of all extant animals and plants bore no actual genetic kinship to each other.

Since then, and especially within the past one hundred years, a different viewpoint has been adopted by most biologists. Present-day organisms are deemed to be descendants of common ancestors, and similarities or differences are interpreted as evidence of close or distant genetic kinship, as the case may be. This change in viewpoint has influenced taxonomy profoundly.

To Linnaeus, the goal of taxonomy lay in arranging categories in such a way as to allow for rapid identification of any given organism. Although this is a worthy goal and one that is still sought, the modern taxonomist attempts to relate organisms to one another **phylogenetically,** or according to ancestral history, as nearly as evidence allows him. Hence, present-day taxonomy strives to establish a **natural** system of classification wherein each category relates itself to the others according to ancestral relationships. Since it is often very difficult or even impossible to establish such relationships with any degree of certainty, a natural system is more a goal than a reality, especially above the species level.

From a practical standpoint, systems of classification still tend to be largely **artificial,** in spite of the change in emphasis that has taken place. While searching for evidences of relationship in some particular group or other, the taxonomist is obliged to formulate a tentative or working system. Nevertheless, the adoption of the "natural" viewpoint has been exceedingly profitable for biology since it has brought many areas of endeavor to bear upon the problems of taxonomy which formerly were not considered.

THE VARIETY OF LIVING FORMS

Well over a million species of animals and approximately three hundred fifty thousand species of plants have been classified, and it is certain that there are many which have not come to the attention of taxonomists. Furthermore, it seems evident that new species arise from time to time, perhaps slowly but surely, and for these reasons, no system of classification is complete or absolutely up-to-date.

Even competent taxonomists cannot be expected to know more than a relatively small number of separate species and their individual characteristics. Usually, a person becomes specialized in the study of one taxonomic group, perhaps an order, a family, or even a single genus, and does not attempt to become expert in the classification of other groups. Thus, it is not possible to gain a very broad knowledge of the variety of animals and plants within a short space of time, but the student of biology should gain some concept of the major groups which are recognized.

A BRIEF SURVEY OF THE ANIMAL KINGDOM

Most zoologists recognize the existence of some twenty-five or more phyla, many of which contain a relatively small number of species. Ten phyla are usually considered "major" phyla in that they include most animals which are commonly encountered and represent important dif-

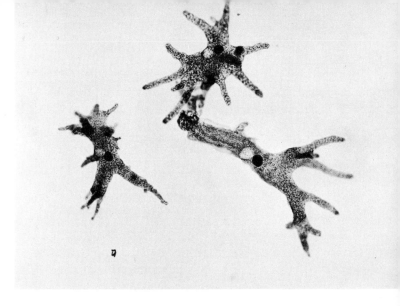

15 *Amoeba proteus*, three individuals shown with numerous pseudopodia extended. Note dark nucleus in cell at lower right, with light contractile vacuole near it. The cytoplasm contains numerous granules. (Courtesy Carolina Biological Supply Company)

ferences among animals. These are discussed below according to their exhibition of increased structural complexity.

Unicellular Animals

THE PHYLUM PROTOZOA (Gr. *protos*, first, + *zoon*, animal). Members of this phylum are recognized as those animals which are **unicellular.** The remainder of the animal kingdom are sometimes referred to as the **metazoa** (Gr. *meta*, after + *zoon*), a term which has no formal taxonomic status.[3] The metazoa simply include all **multicellular** animals. The several classes of the phylum are distinguished from each other on the basis of locomotion. For example, members of the class to which *Amoeba* (Fig. 15) belongs move by extending portions of the protoplasm in one direction. Such protoplasmic extensions are called **pseudopodia.** The ciliates (Fig. 16) move by means of numerous hair-like projections termed **cilia,** which beat in a coordinated pattern. The flagellates (Fig. 17) exhibit one or several locomotor structures known as **flagella.** As a structure, a flagellum is somewhat longer and more complex than a cilium. Several species of protozoa are responsible for certain human diseases; malaria,

[3] Some zoologists separate the animal kingdom into the sub-kingdoms Protozoa and Metazoa, and then establish phyla under each category. We shall regard the Protozoa as a phylum, however, and the metazoa as an informal group.

16 *Paramecium caudatum.* Note cilia extending from surface of cell. (Courtesy Carolina Biological Supply Company)

amoebic dysentary, and African sleeping sickness are examples of such diseases. Since protozoans are independent protoplasmic units, many of them lend themselves readily to cell studies, and they have been widely used in biological research.

Multicellular Animals

Before proceeding with descriptions of animal groups according to phyla, let us note several important features of multicellular animals that are of taxonomic significance. One of these has to do with the tendency of most multicellular animals to display some sort of orderly arrangement, or **symmetry.** Basically, there are two types of symmetry, **radial** and **bilateral.** If the body of an animal is so organized that it

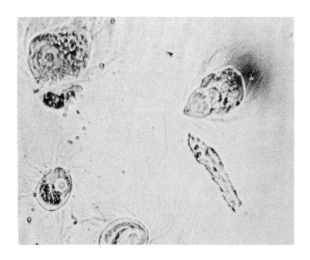

17 Several flagellated protozoa from the intestinal tract of a termite. Long, slender flagella may be seen extending from some of these cells.

can be divided into approximate mirror images by cutting in one plane
and one plane only, it is said to be **bilaterally symmetrical.** Such a
plane (called a **mid-sagittal** plane) would divide the animal into left
and right halves. A plane cut at right angles to a mid-sagittal plane
(**frontal**) would also divide an animal into two halves, but they would
not be approximate mirror images. The outer surfaces of the two halves
produced by a frontal plane are called **dorsal** and **ventral** surfaces, respectively. In the normal posture of most bilaterally symmetrical animals,
the dorsal surface is situated uppermost, and the ventral surface is lowermost. Since man assumes an upright position, the human body is an exception to this rule even though it is bilaterally symmetrical. A plane cut
perpendicular to mid-sagittal and frontal planes is called a **transverse**
plane, which divides the bilaterally symmetrical animal into **anterior**
and **posterior** portions (Fig. 18). In its over-all movement, the anterior
portion normally is situated so that it is forward, with the posterior portion bringing up the rear.

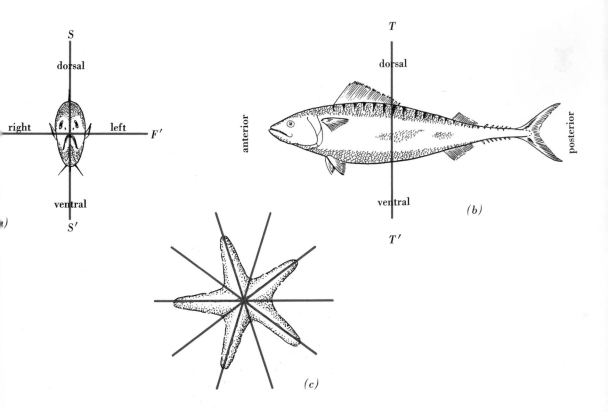

18   A comparison of bilaterally and radially symmetrical animals. a, sagittal (S—S′) section and frontal (F—F′) section as they would be described for a fish. b, transverse
(T—T′) section. c, radial symmetry as seen in a starfish.

In contrast to this type of organization, a **radially symmetrical** animal can be cut in a number of planes with the production of approximate mirror images (Fig. 18). In other words, the arrangement is something like the wheel of a wagon, with parts radiating outward from a central point. This type of symmetry may also be expressed in a three-dimensional way, as in animals whose bodies are spherical. The terms which were introduced above in regard to bilateral symmetry are meaningless, of course, in relation to radially symmetrical animals. There are no left and right sides, no anterior and posterior ends, nor any dorsal and ventral surfaces. Whenever two surfaces or ends are to be distinguished in a radially symmetrical animal, the terms **oral** and **aboral** are used in relation to the location of the mouth opening; that is, the oral surface or end is that upon which the mouth is located. Generally speaking, radial symmetry is characteristic of animals which are lowest in the phylogenetic scale.

Another principle regarding the structural organization of multicellular animals should be emphasized at this point. In their embryonic development, cells become differentiated very early into two or three tissue types called **primary germ layers.** If an animal exhibits only two of these possible three, it is said to be **diploblastic** (Gr. *diploos,* double + *blastos,* sprout), and the germ layers are called **endoderm** (Gr. *endon,* within + *derma,* skin) and **ectoderm** (Gr. *ektos,* without + *derma*). In **triploblastic** animals, a third layer, the **mesoderm** (Gr. *mesos,* middle + *derma*) develops.

THE PHYLUM PORIFERA (L. *porus,* pore + *ferre,* to bear). Members of this phylum are called **sponges,** and their bodies are perforated by pores which lead to some sort of central canal. They are really little more than colonies of cells which function more or less independently but which have contrived to share a common skeletal structure. In some forms, the skeleton with its system of pores is capable of absorbing large quantities of water after the cells have died, which accounts for the commercial value of certain of the larger sponges. Members of this group are diploblastic, and body structure is fundamentally radial in its organization; however, the basic radial symmetry is somewhat obscured in many forms. Most sponges live in warm, shallow ocean waters; very few are found in the deeper areas of the sea. Although the vast majority of species are marine, a few are adapted to living in fresh water.

THE PHYLUM COELENTERATA (Gr. *koilos,* hollow + *enteron,* an intestine). Coelenterates, as these animals are called, are the simplest multicellular animals to exhibit a body cavity where foodstuffs are broken down by chemical action, a characteristic also seen in all animals which are higher in the scale of complexity. Coelenterates possess only one open-

19 Some typical sponges. (Courtesy Carolina Biological Supply Company)

ing to this cavity, a **mouth,** through which must pass both the food they receive and any residues of digestion moving out of the body. They are radially symmetrical, and although not all forms are strictly diploblastic, this is a general characteristic of the group. Most coelenterates are marine, but several species are found in fresh-water environments. Representative members are the fresh-water hydra (Figs. 20 and 21), jellyfish, and corals (Fig. 22).

20 A fresh-water hydra with a bud extending from its body. Note tentacles at oral end, bulb-shaped basal disc at aboral end. The bud will ultimately become separated from the "parent" organism and will establish an independent existence. (Courtesy Carolina Biological Supply Company)

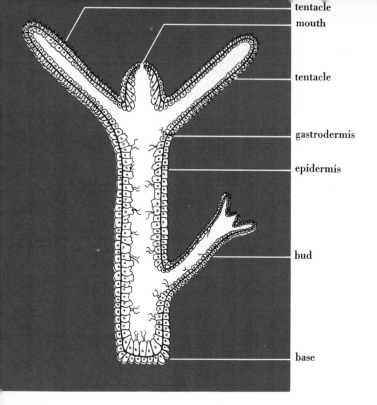

tentacle
mouth

tentacle

gastrodermis

epidermis

bud

base

21 *Hydra* as seen in longitudinal section.

22 A coral formation. Originally, several hundred hydra-like coelenterates occupied this formation, each within its individual
"hole." The organisms have long since died, but the holes
remain.

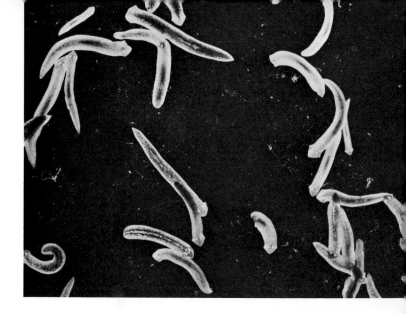

23 Several planaria, magnified about ten times, shown moving about on the bottom of a culture dish. (Courtesy Carolina Biological Supply Company)

THE PHYLUM PLATYHELMINTHES (Gr. *platys,* flat + *helminthos,* worm). The flatworms, as these animals are commonly called, are the least advanced of the bilaterally symmetrical animals. One outstanding characteristic which they possess in varying degrees is a dorso-ventral flattening that gives many of them a ribbon-like appearance. They are triploblastic, a characteristic which, along with bilateral symmetry, is exhibited by animals higher in the scale of complexity (Phyla Nematoda through Chordata, but see Phyla Mollusca and Echinodermata below in regard to symmetry). There is a digestive cavity with only a mouth opening. Members of two classes, **flukes** and **tapeworms,**[4] respectively, live upon or within the bodies of other animals in the relationship of **parasitism.** Members of a third class, exemplified by the fresh water planaria (Fig. 23) are free living.

THE PHYLUM NEMATODA (Gr. *nematos,* thread). Commonly called roundworms, members of this phylum are very widespread in nature. Also, a large number of species are known. Many of these worms are free living, some are parasitic on certain plants, and others parasitize various animals. Representative of this last group is *Ascaris lumbricoides* (Fig. 24), which may be found in the digestive tracts of the pig and man.

Roundworms are the first animals in the scale of complexity, of those discussed here, to exhibit a **tube-within-a-tube** body plan (Fig.

[4] Tapeworms do not possess a digestive tract. They absorb foods in solution from their hosts.

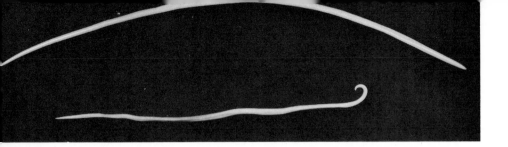

24 *Ascaris lumbricoides*, a parasitic roundworm shown about one-half life size. The male is smaller than the female, and has a hooked posterior end. (Courtesy Carolina Biological Supply Company)

25). With some structural variations, it is seen in all phyla which are yet to be discussed. Fundamentally, this type of body organization features a digestive tract with a mouth at one end and a second opening, the **anus,** serving as a portal of exit at the opposite end. This digestive tract is the inner "tube," and a surrounding body wall constitutes the outer, there being a space or cavity between the two. This space may be occupied by body organs or fluids. Whenever such a cavity is lined with a thin tissue of mesodermal origin called a **peritoneum,** it is termed a **coelome;** if it is not so lined, it is a **pseudocoelome.** Roundworms are pseudocoelomate, while animals belonging to Phyla Mollusca through Chordata, of those discussed here, are coelomate.

THE PHYLUM MOLLUSCA (L. *molluscus,* soft). This phylum is made up of animals whose soft bodies are covered with a **mantle,** which secretes a firm, calcareous shell in many species. Individually, members of the phylum are called **mollusks.** They exhibit a coelome, as do representatives of Phyla Annelida through Chordata, although in the case of the mollusks this body cavity is greatly reduced. Certain adult forms, of which

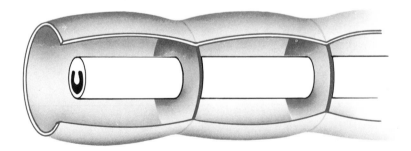

25 A portion of a typical "tube-within-a-tube" body plan. This is a somewhat diagrammatic representation of a portion of the body wall and intestine of an earthworm.

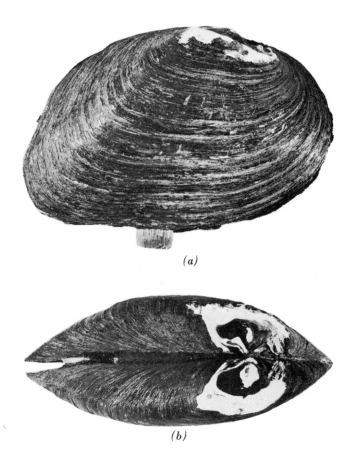

(a)

(b)

26 A fresh-water mussel. a, dorsal view. b, as seen from the "hinge" side of the two shell halves. (Courtesy Carolina Biological Supply Company)

the snails are representative, depart from the fundamental bilateral symmetry that is characteristic of the group and exhibit a coiling of the shell and other body parts. A ventral muscular mass, the **foot,** is usually present. There is a decided increase in complexity and specialization of organ systems over the phyla that have already been discussed; there are well-developed digestive, circulatory, excretory, and nervous systems. The phylum is quite large and includes such varied forms as clams, oysters, snails, squids, and octopuses.

THE PHYLUM ANNELIDA (L. *anellus,* a ring). **Annelids,** or **segmented worms,** exhibit a series of segments, all of which are approximately identical from external appearance, with certain exceptions. Almost all members of the phylum bear small, non-jointed appendages called **setae.**

27   *Loligo*, a squid. The broad portion of the body is the posterior end; note tentacles with suction cups at anterior end. Although the specimen shown here is only about a foot long, some forms attain a length of fifty feet or more. (Courtesy Carolina Biological Supply Company)

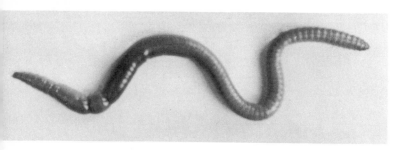

28   The earthworm, *Lumbricus terrestris*. Note segments, which are the distinguishing marks of the Phylum Annelida. The thick band near the anterior end (at left) is the clitellum, which functions in reproduction.

29   An aquatic leech, photographed at the bottom of an aquarium. (Courtesy General Biological Supply House, Inc.)

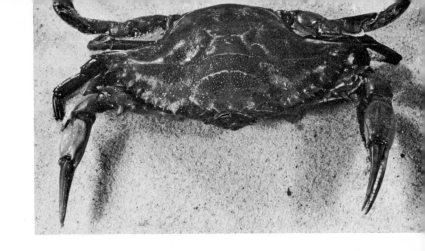

30 *Callinectes*, the edible blue crab. (Courtesy Carolina Biological Supply Company)

31 Several representative insects.

The coelome is quite extensive (Fig. 25), and systems are remarkably well-developed. The wide range of adaptability among members of this group is seen in the variety of habitats occupied. Representative forms are earthworms, clamworms, and leeches.

THE PHYLUM ARTHROPODA (Gr. *arthron*, joint + *podos*, foot). In number of species, the **arthropods** outweigh all other animal phyla combined. They are highly successful as a group, occupying every known type of habitat and exhibiting a wide variety of body types. The characteristic around which they are grouped is the possession of paired, jointed appendages, but they exhibit many other distinctive features. There is a hard **exoskeleton** composed of a material known as **chitin,** which is shed periodically to allow for growth. The coelome is much reduced, somewhat as in the mollusks. Segmentation is not nearly so obvious as in annelids, but is quite marked. **Cephalization,** which may be defined as the accumulation of nervous and sensory tissues at the

32 *Centruroides sculpturatus,* a deadly scorpion of the southwestern United States. This scorpion is usually less than three inches in length, yet the sting of even a small specimen may be fatal to a human. Note sting poised above body. (Courtesy Carolina Biological Supply Company)

33 The tarantula, a large spider of the southern United States and the tropics. Its bite is painful, but not particularly dangerous to man. (Courtesy General Biological Supply House, Inc.)

anterior end of the body, is evident to a degree not seen in the phyla that have been surveyed to this point. An accompaniment of cephalization is the presence of compound eyes which function in the reception of visual impulses. Body systems are quite complex and highly efficient. A number of classes and other taxonomic groups have been erected to distinguish between such forms as crustaceans, insects, spiders, scorpions, mites, ticks, centipedes, and millipedes.

THE PHYLUM ECHINODERMATA (Gr. *echinos,* spiny + *dermatos,* skin). Members of this phylum are characterized by the presence of calcareous plates or **ossicles** which are imbedded in the dermis, thus giving them a rough, prickly external appearance. Because adult forms are radially

34 *Scolopendra,* a large centipede. (Courtesy Carolina Biological Supply Company)

35   *Spirobolus*, a common millipede of the southern United States.
(Courtesy Carolina Biological Supply Company)

symmetrical and because many of the body systems do not approach the
degree of complexity exhibited by most members of the higher phyla,
they were formerly assigned a much lower place in the animal kingdom.
However, embryological and biochemical evidence point to a close relationship to the chordates, and most zoologists now regard them in this light.
This is a good example of an attempt at natural classification, since
a purely artificial approach based on external, adult morphology would
place echinoderms far down the scale. As a matter of fact, zoologists rely
heavily upon embryological characteristics in classifying animals since
relationships are often more clearly evident during early stages than in
adult forms. Echinoderms exhibit an extensive coelome and a simple
nervous system but no specialized circulatory or excretory systems. One
unique feature of these animals is a **water vascular system,** a sort of
hydraulic arrangement which makes locomotion and certain other functions possible. The starfish is perhaps the most familiar representative of
the phylum; other echinoderms are brittlestars, sea urchins, sand dollars,
and sea cucumbers. All members of the phylum are exclusively marine.

THE PHYLUM CHORDATA (L. *chorda,* cord). This phylum derives its name
from the characteristic of all representatives to exhibit, at some stage of
development, a dorsal rod-like structure called the **notochord.** In higher
forms, the notochord is replaced by a dorsal column of vertebrae during
embryonic development. All such chordates are called **vertebrates.**

(a)

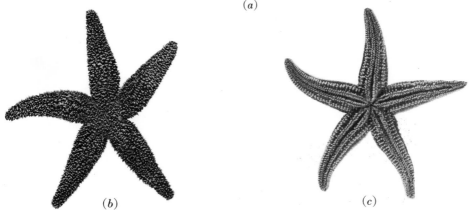

(b)   (c)

36 Representative echinoderms. a, sea urchin (upper left), sand dollar (lower left), sea cucumber (upper right) and starfish (lower right). b, another view of starfish, aboral aspect. The circular structure on the central portion of the body is the opening to the water vascular system. c, oral aspect of starfish. Note rows of suctorial **tube feet** extending from each ray. (b and c courtesy Carolina Biological Supply Company)

Some zoologists speak of the chordates in which the notochord is not replaced by vertebrae as **protochordates.** There are relatively few species of protochordates as compared with the vertebrates. In addition to the notochord, chordates exhibit at some stage a dorsal, tubular **nerve cord,** which lies just above the notochord in normal body position, and paired **pharyngeal pouches.**[5] Possession of these three characteristics is limited to members of the Phylum Chordata. In addition, there are characteristics which are shared to some extent with other animals. Body systems reach a high point of development, especially in the more advanced classes of the phylum. The coelome is quite extensive, and cephalization becomes very pronounced. Although serial segmentation is not nearly as evident in adult chordates as in annelids or even arthropods, it figures prominently among most members of the phylum. The vertebrates exhibit a cartilaginous or bony endoskeleton.

Inasmuch as the vertebrate group of the Phylum Chordata is made up of animals which are probably of greatest interest to most students, the several classes will be described at this point.

CLASS AGNATHA (*a-,* not + Gr. *gnathos,* jaw). This is the first of three classes usually recognized by zoologists as being **fishes,** which are restricted to water. As an adaptation to their environment, all fishes possess **gills** which enable oxygen to pass from the water into the blood stream. The agnatha derive their name from their failure, unlike other fishes, to develop jaws; the mouth is a round, suctorial opening adapted to a parasitic existence. Although there is a poorly developed cartilaginous vertebral column, the notochord persists throughout life. Representative forms are lampreys, which may occupy marine or fresh-water habitats, or both, and hagfishes, which are exclusively marine.

37 A lamprey. Note the seven openings near the anterior end which allow water to pass over the gills. The mouth, which is ventral, is not seen in this view. (Courtesy Carolina Biological Supply Company)

[5] The pharyngeal pouches are often erroneously called *gill slits.* In those vertebrates that develop gills (Classes Agnatha through Amphibia below) the pouches do become slits, but in the land vertebrates (Classes Reptilia through Mammalia below) they do not normally do so.

38 A skate, dorsal view. (Courtesy Carolina Biological Supply Company)

CLASS CHONDRICHTHYES (Gr. *chondros*, cartilage + *ichthys*, fish). Although members of the preceding class exhibit cartilaginous skeletons, and cartilage comprises a part of the adult skeleton of many higher vertebrates, including man, this characteristic has been selected as a basis for separating this class from those fishes which possess bony skeletons. The notochord is present in adult forms, but it is greatly modified by the vertebral column.[6] Most members of this class are marine. Sharks, skates, and rays are perhaps the best known cartilaginous fishes. Certain sharks attain considerable size; whale sharks sometimes reach a length of fifty feet and are the largest fishes (*not* the largest aquatic vertebrates) known.

[6] Although every chordate exhibits a notochord during embryonic life, this structure becomes less and less prominent in adult forms as one ascends the vertebrate scale of complexity. It is more reduced in the bony fishes, discussed below, than in chondrichthians, still more reduced in amphibians, and most reptiles retain no trace of the notochord as adults. In all birds and mammals, the notochord is replaced entirely by a vertebral column during embryonic development.

CLASS OSTEICHTHYES (Gr. *osteon,* bone + *ichthys*). Members of this class exhibit skeletons that are largely composed of bone, and for this reason they are called the **bony fishes** to distinguish them from members of the preceding two classes. A large number of species have been described; of the 50,000 or so species of vertebrates that are known, over half are members of this class. There are a number of structural differences between bony fishes and those described above, many of which are quite obvious. However, there is considerable variation in external morphology. In these fishes, the gills are covered by a plate, the **operculum,** which functions in passing a current of water over the gills. Another outstanding structural feature is the presence of a **swim bladder,** which arises as a ventral outpushing of the pharynx. This organ serves to regulate hydrostatic pressure, which helps to maintain buoyancy, and in certain unusual forms, the lungfishes, it has a limited function as a lung. Although the majority of species are marine, a large number occupy fresh-water habitats, with a few being able to alternate between the two.

CLASS AMPHIBIA (Gr. *amphi,* both + *bios,* life). A number of technical characteristics separate these vertebrates from the fishes which precede them in the phylogenetic scale and the reptiles, which follow them. The feature used as a basis for naming this group, however, is their dependency upon an aqueous environment during their early stages, at which time gills are present, followed in many forms (but not all) by a stage in which the development of lungs makes it possible for them to become land-dwellers. Salamanders, newts, toads, and frogs are common amphibians.

CLASS REPTILIA (L. *reptum,* to creep). Reptiles derive their name from the feature that they are relatively slow-moving animals, with the snakes

39 The white crappie, a typical fresh-water fish. (Courtesy Arkansas Game and Fish Commission)

40 *Rana grylio*, the Southern bullfrog. When fully grown, this frog attains a body length of about six inches. (Courtesy Carolina Biological Supply Company)

failing to exhibit appendages at all. They may be distinguished from the amphibia by their possession of scales and claws, as a group, which amphibia do not exhibit. Perhaps these are the most obvious structural differences between the two groups. A number of anatomical, embryological, and physiological traits are sufficiently unique to delimit them as a class. Representative reptiles are lizards, snakes, turtles, alligators, and crocodiles.

CLASS AVES (L. *avis*, bird). Since birds are feathered bipeds, it is not difficult to see why they are rather definitely set apart from other vertebrates as a class. In addition to these features, most of them exhibit forelimbs that are adapted into wings for flight, and there are many other structural modifications which are accompaniments of this unusual ability. For example, the bones of birds are very light, with large central cavities, and the breast muscles are highly developed. Unlike all other animals which have been discussed to this point, and like the mammals which are introduced below, the body temperature of birds does not vary with the environment. For this reason, they are often said to be "warm-blooded,"

41 *Ambystoma maculatum*, the spotted salamander. (Courtesy Carolina Biological Supply Company)

a term which is somewhat misleading. A large number of orders within the class are recognized.

CLASS MAMMALIA (G. *mamma*, breast). This class of vertebrates has been named for one of its most outstanding characteristics, namely, that the young are nourished during early stages of post-natal life by milk secreted from mammary glands. The production of hair as an external body covering, which occurs in varying degrees among species, is also a distinguishing characteristic. Except for one primitive group, they are **viviparous,** giving birth to more or less well-developed young, whereas other vertebrates are **oviparous,** producing eggs varying in size but all of which are relatively large as compared with those of mammals. Body systems reach the acme of morphological and physiological complexity in this group, the nervous system in particular becoming highly efficient. The human species derives its supremacy largely because the nervous system of man is the most highly developed in the animal kingdom. A great deal of variety exists among mammals, as exemplified by the monotremes (egg layers), the marsupials (pouched mammals), the bats, which are capable of flight, the aquatic forms such as whales and porpoises, and the primates, of which man is a member, to mention only a few outstanding forms.

By way of summary, let us represent graphically some of the features of the ten phyla which we have introduced. It will be seen (Fig. 49) that there is a gradual increase in complexity from the Protozoa to the Chordata and that successful adaptations tend to "accumulate." In a metaphorical sense, it is as though nature experimented and found that some things work and others do not. Those that do, she retained. As we

42 A turtle, photographed on land. Many turtles spend a great deal of time in the water, although they breathe by means of lungs. (Courtesy Carolina Biological Supply Company)

43 A sparrow hawk in swooping position. (Photograph by George Purvis, courtesy Arkansas Game and Fish Commission)

44 The duckbill platypus, an egg-laying mammal. (Photograph courtesy New York Zoological Society)

45 A kangaroo with young in pouch. (Photograph courtesy New
York Zoological Society)

shall emphasize later, evidence is overwhelming that the various animal
groups arose on earth at different times, with a given phylum preceding
another in almost direct proportion of time to degree of complexity. That
some of them arose from others or from ancestors common to all is certain,
which explains the "accumulation" principle.

46 *Myotis*, the brown bat, shown in flight. (Photograph courtesy
New York Zoological Society)

47 A white-tailed deer, which belongs to a large order of mammals that includes pigs, sheep and cattle. (Photograph by George Purvis, courtesy Arkansas Game and Fish Commission)

A porpoise, trained to ring a bell, performing at a marine aquarium. Being mammals, these animals are extremely intelligent. (Courtesy *Marine Life, Inc.*, Gulfport, Mississippi)

48 White-faced chimpanzee, a primate. (Photograph courtesy New York Zoological Society)

Though being far from complete, this brief survey of the animal kingdom should serve as a basis for distinguishing the most common animals. A further study of zoology will, of course, greatly enlarge the student's knowledge and appreciation.

A BRIEF SURVEY OF THE PLANT KINGDOM

Botanists have experienced considerably greater difficulty in establishing major plant divisions[7] which are generally accepted than

[7] Botanists have traditionally preferred the term "division" at this level, thus lending to the term "phylum" a zoological connotation. However, many modern botanists have abandoned this distinction, and their systems of classification employ "phylum" as the major taxonomic category.

have zoologists for animal phyla. This is because evidences of phylogenetic relationships between plants and plant groups seem to be far less convincing, in general, than are those which have been elucidated for the animal kingdom. For many years, four plant divisions were recognized:

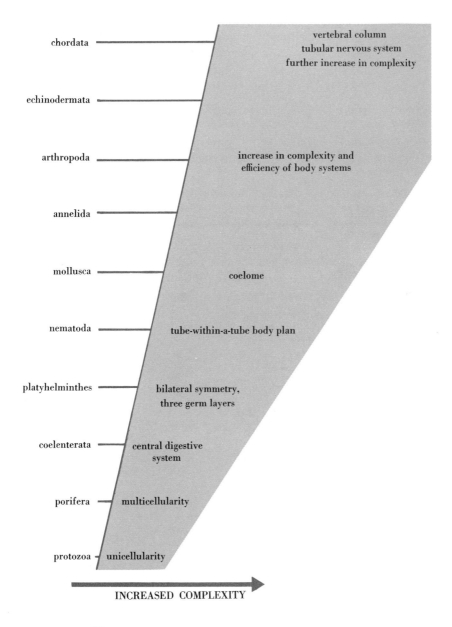

49 Graphic representation of the "accumulation" principle as shown by major animal phyla in regard to several important structural features. As pointed out in the text, members of the Phylum Echinodermata deviate from the general principle in certain respects.

Division Thallophyta, which included the algae, fungi, and lichens; Division Bryophyta, the mosses and liverworts; Division Pteridophyta, the ferns and their "allies"; and Division Spermatophyta, the seed plants.

Botanists have long recognized, however, that these groups are highly artificial. Hence, a tendency has developed toward the establishment of many plant divisions or phyla in the belief that this represents a more natural type of classification when viewed from the standpoint of present knowledge regarding plant relationships. At best, however, agreement among botanists as to just how many major divisions or phyla should be recognized is by no means as complete as it is among zoologists for the animal kingdom. In view of this, it is considered best in this text to present a brief survey of the plant kingdom in terms of seven plant groups. It should not be thought that these represent formal taxonomic categories; they merely serve as a convenient system by means of which some understanding of the plant kingdom may be gained.

ALGAE. These plants, which are relatively simple in structure and whose cells possess the green pigment **chlorophyll,** are widely distributed in nature. They grow most abundantly in marine and fresh-water habitats, but they also occur in and upon soil. Some are present within or upon the bodies of certain plants and animals. Several different groups of algae exist, some of the more important of which are discussed below.

The **blue-green** algae contain the pigments **phycocyanin** (blue) and **phycoerythrin** (red) which, along with chlorophyll, characteristically give these plants a blue-green color. They are further marked

50 Microscopic view of *Nostoc*, a blue-green alga. The cells of this plant grow in chains, which are imbedded in this particular form within a gelatinous ball. The top edge of the ball is shown here in sectional view. (Courtesy General Biological Supply House, Inc.)

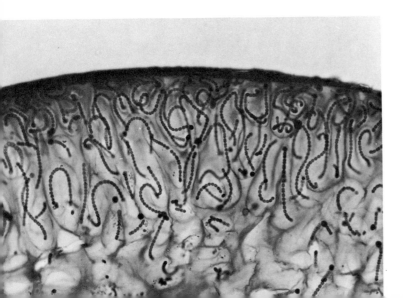

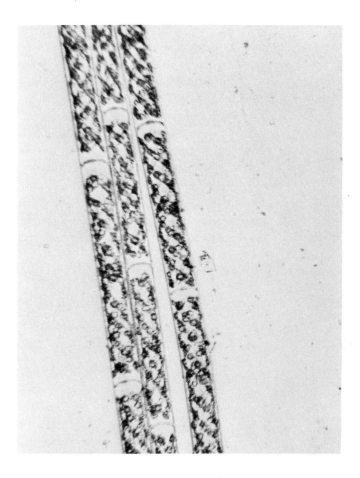

51 A common green alga, *Spirogyra*, whose filaments are shown here as they appear using the lowest power of a compound microscope.

by the failure of their cells to exhibit clearly delineated nuclei characteristic of most cells. As a result, their chromatin is more diffuse.

The **green** algae possess chiefly the pigment chlorophyll within their cells; this imparts a characteristic grass-green appearance to these plants. Unlike blue-green algae, their cells exhibit nuclei, as do those of all plants whose descriptions follow. A number of different forms of green algae are known; there are many unicellular species, certain of which achieve motility by means of flagella, while others are colonial, filamentous, or of even more complex form.

The **brown** algae are so called because of their characteristic coloring, which results from the presence of a brown pigment, **fucoxanthin,** in addition to chlorophyll. These plants are almost exclusively marine. They achieve a degree of complexity that is unusual for algae; some species, the kelps, exceed forest trees in size. Many "seaweeds" commonly seen washed up on beaches are members of this group.

The **red** algae possess phycoerythrin in large amounts in addition to chlorophyll. Some representatives are not red but are included within the group because of other characteristics. The group is predominantly marine, but there are a number of widely distributed fresh-water forms. Most are filamentous, but some exhibit a broad, foliaceous organization.

Although these four major groups include most species of algae, there are many commonly encountered forms which represent still other types. The algae comprise a quite varied group and a very important one from the standpoint of ecological balance in nature. Many of them serve as the primary basis for various **food chains** of animals; all aquatic,

52 *Fucus vesiculosis*, a brown alga. This plant is marine, and is found attached to rocks where low tides expose them to view. (Courtesy General Biological Supply House, Inc.)

53 *Polysiphonia,* a red alga. (Courtesy General Biological Supply House, Inc.)

higher animals depend ultimately upon algae as a food source. Much attention has been devoted within recent years to the utilization of certain algae as a direct source of food for man. Finally, it should be mentioned that many algae, like some protozoa, lend themselves very readily to cytological and biochemical studies, and certain species have been investigated extensively in these connections.

FUNGI. Members of this group are relatively simple in structure as compared with plants belonging to those groups which are yet to be discussed. In this respect, they are similar to the algae, from which they differ as a group in being devoid of chlorophyll, a characteristic that renders them dependent upon organic compounds as a source of carbon, rather than upon carbon dioxide, which algae and all green plants are able to utilize.[8] The fungi discussed below are major representative types.

[8] A few species of bacteria are capable of utilizing carbon dioxide for this purpose rather than being dependent upon sources of organic compounds.

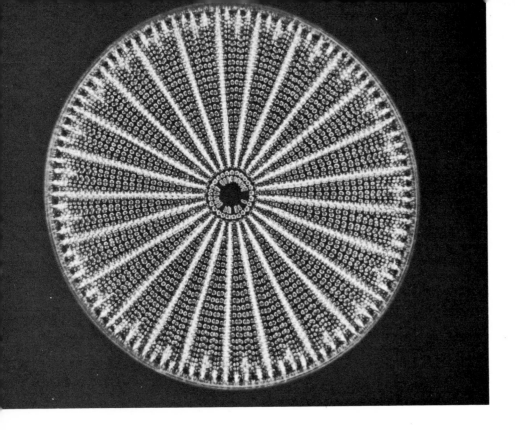

54 A diatom, greatly magnified. The diatoms, which constitute a group of algae not discussed in this text, are unicellular organisms whose shells, containing silicon, are frequently sculptured elaborately. (Courtesy General Biological Supply House, Inc.)

The **bacteria** appear to be the simplest of all organisms from a purely morphological standpoint, although there are certain forms, the "higher" bacteria, which become relatively complex in their growth and development. Most bacteria exist as small, unicellular spheres (**cocci**), rods (**bacilli**), or spirals (**spirilla**) as shown in Fig. 55. Because of their ubiquity and their varied physiological habits, they assume tremendous importance to man and to all other organisms. Perhaps the most notable distinction between bacteria and other fungi is a cellular one; nuclear material in bacterial cells is rather atypical, a definite nucleus being difficult to demonstrate by the use of ordinary nuclear staining techniques. In all other fungi, nuclei are readily demonstrable within cells.

Another group of unicellular fungi, the **yeasts,** are considerably larger than bacteria, and exhibit certain morphological features which distinguish them from other fungi by appearance alone (Fig. 56). Many yeasts are commercially important to man because of their ability to ferment sugars with the production of ethyl alcohol, their production of carbon dioxide, and their synthesis of certain vitamins.

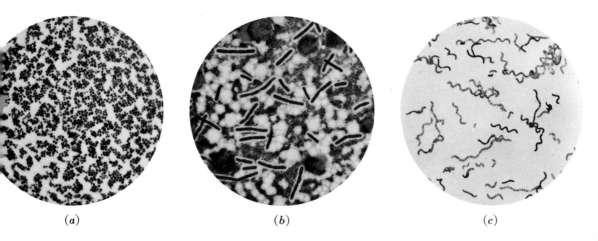

(a) (b) (c)

55 Three morphologically different types of bacteria, greatly magnified. a, cocci. b, bacilli. c, spirilla. (Courtesy General Biological Supply House, Inc.)

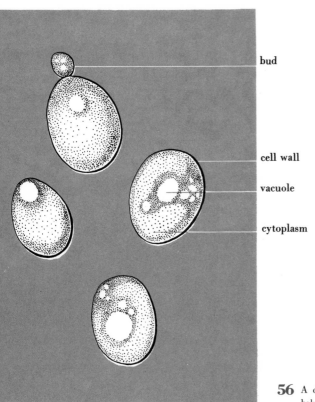

bud

cell wall

vacuole

cytoplasm

56 A drawing of some typical cells of common baker's yeast, showing the production of buds.

Molds and **mildews** are fungi which produce elaborate branching systems, or **mycelia,** and hence are often fuzzy in appearance. Although the filaments of some molds and mildews are not divided by cross walls into cells, others are definitely multicellular, a distinction which has been utilized for taxonomic purposes. The molds and mildews are of considerable economic importance to man, both positively and negatively. Mildews may seriously injure or destroy valuable crop and ornamental plants upon which they are parasitic; molds are frequently involved in food spoilage, or they may injure cloth, leather, and other materials upon which they are able to grow. In contrast, man has used a number of molds in the manufacture of food and medicinal products, and certain molds have become extremely valuable in genetical and biochemical research. Typical molds are shown in Figs. 57 and 58.

Another group of fungi includes the **rusts** and **smuts,** which are parasitic on higher plants. They are filamentous in form, and they inflict severe damage to certain important crop plants, particularly the cereal grains.

Certain fleshy forms, notably the **cup fungi, mushrooms,** and **puff balls,** are widely distributed in nature, and some of them achieve considerable individual size as compared to the microscopic aspect of most fungi which have been discussed to this point. Actually, the fleshy structure characteristic of a given species is only one part of a fairly complex reproductive cycle, its development having been preceded by what is frequently a long period of activity on the part of mold-like filaments. Once started, the fleshy body may enlarge at an incredibly fast rate, a phenomenon that has made the mushroom a symbol for rapid growth. These **fruiting bodies,** as botanists call them, are producers of great numbers of **spores,** which are reproductive cells.

As a group, the fungi occupy a position of considerable importance in the world of life because of their mode of nutrition. Obliged as they are to exist on organic compounds obtained from their environments, they are active in the decomposition of various materials. As a result, they play a vital role in the great matter and energy cycle which is operating in nature. In their nutritive habits, some parasitic bacteria and other microscopic fungi are sufficiently irritating to the tissues of other plants or to those of animals, including man, that they are causative agents of diseases. Relatively few species of bacteria and other fungi are disease-producing, or **pathogenic,** however. Most members of this group exist in nature by decomposing organic matter that is no longer a part of a living system.

LICHENS. Although lichens constitute a relatively small plant group, they deserve special mention because of their unusual nature. A lichen is a dual plant, being a sort of cooperative enterprise between an algal and a fungal component. The species thus involved form a plant body which

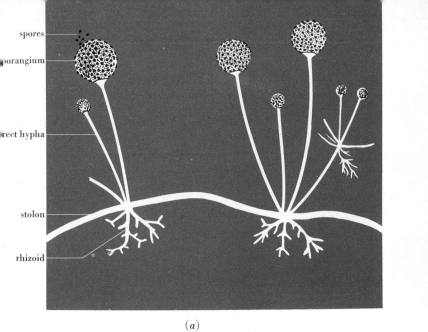

spores

sporangium

erect hypha

stolon

rhizoid

(a)

(b)

57 The bread mold, *Rhizopus stolonifer*. a, drawing of this mold showing several structures. b, appearance as seen using lowest magnification of compound microscope.

58 A colony, or mycelium, of *Penicillium chrysogenum*, one strain of which produces most of the world's penicillin. The dark central area is blue-green in color, and the border is white. (Photograph courtesy Chas. Pfizer and Co., Inc.)

59 *Amanita*, a poisonous mushroom. Fruiting bodies are seen in various stages of growth. (Courtesy General Biological Supply House, Inc.)

differs in appearance from either algae or fungi, and because a given lichen reproduces itself consistently, it is considered a true species in its own right. The relationship between the alga and fungus which compose a lichen is not completely understood, but in some habitats it enables both to do together what neither can do alone since lichens thrive in a great many places where other plants do not exist. They may be found growing on rocks, which they gradually decompose, and on the barks of certain trees. Some species grow in arctic regions where few other plants are found. In the general economy of nature, lichens assume a position of some importance in the formation of soil and in serving as a source of food for certain animals which live in extreme northern regions. Because of their unusual nature, lichens have proved to be of value in some types of biochemical research.

LIVERWORTS. Plants belonging to this group were originally called by this name because some forms are lobed and thus bear a slight resemblance to the livers of higher animals. Although they are primarily land-dwellers, they are largely restricted to moist habitats due to the absence of specialized conducting tissues. As is true of plants which are morphologically more complex (the mosses, ferns, and seed plants), they possess chlorophyll and hence are not dependent upon other organisms for organic compounds. Another feature shared with plants of these groups (and with certain algae) is the exhibition of a dimorphic life cycle, in which a spore-producing phase, the **sporophyte,** alternates with a gamete-producing phase, the **gametophyte.** In the liverworts, the gametophyte is far larger and more conspicuous than the sporophyte, the latter being attached to the former throughout its existence.

60 Typical lichens growing on the bark of a tree limb. (Courtesy Carolina Biological Supply Company)

61 *Marchantia*, a liverwort. Living specimens are bright green in color. (Courtesy Carolina Biological Supply Company)

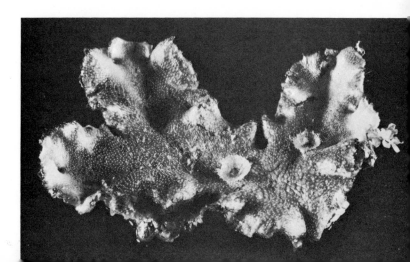

MOSSES. The mosses are quite similar to the liverworts in regard to habitat, dominance of the gametophyte over the sporophyte, and various morphological features. In contrast, there are distinct differences, one of the most important being that the moss sporophyte is generally more prominent and complex than that of liverworts. Mosses are not as restricted to moist habitats as liverworts and are more widely distributed in nature.

FERNS AND FERN-LIKE PLANTS. Members of this group differ from all plants described to this point in their possession of complex tissues called **xylem** and **phloem,** a distinction that is shared with members of the seed plants (see below). Because these tissues make possible the transport throughout the plant body of water and of substances in solution, plants which possess them are called **vascular plants.** This attribute has made possible the development of plant bodies which are quite large and whose tissues may exist many feet from a source of water.

62 *Polytrichum,* a moss. The leafy portion of each plant is the gametophyte, and the stalked portion is the sporophyte. (Courtesy General Biological Supply House, Inc.)

63 A fern as seen in growth habit near a fresh-water pond.

The ferns themselves usually do not attain great size, although the tree ferns of the tropics may reach a height of eighty feet, and it is known that species which are now extinct were much larger than any present-day ferns. In common species of the temperate zone, the sporophytic plant exhibits a subterranean stem called a **rhizome,** from which roots project in a positive response to gravity and from which leaves, called **fronds,** extend upward. In contrast to liverworts and mosses, the sporophyte of ferns is the dominant phase, the gametophyte being relatively small and short-lived.

SEED PLANTS. Like liverworts, mosses, ferns, and some algae, these plants exhibit a life cycle in which there is an alternation of sporophytic and gametophytic phases. In this group, however, embryonic sporophytes become surrounded by food materials, each unit containing one embryo with its associated storage materials being called a **seed.** Thus, such plants are quite distinct from all those discussed previously which do not form seeds. In seed plants, a further dominance of sporophyte over gametophyte is seen, the latter existing entirely within tissues of the former.

Beyond doubt, members of this group are the most successful plants in nature as a whole. Over 200,000 species are known, which means that only some 150,000 species are divided among the other six groups that we have discussed. Species vary in size and form all the way from extremely small plants to giant trees, and as a group they occupy virtually all types of habitats.

The seed plants may be conveniently divided into two groups on the basis of their reproductive structures. One group, the **gymnosperms**

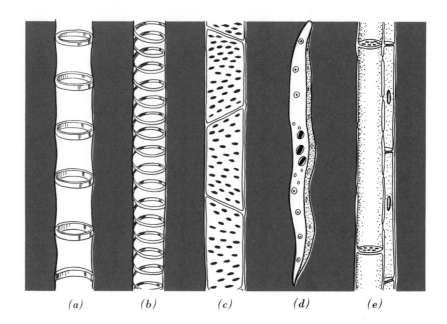

(a)   (b)   (c)   (d)   (e)

64 Some typical vascular, or conducting, structures. a-c, conducting vessels of xylem showing some of the patterns seen in their walls. d, a conducting structure of xylem called
a **tracheid,** enlarged somewhat from its actual proportion to a, b, c and e. e, phloem
tissue. The column of larger cells is called a **sieve tube,** because the walls between
cells are perforated. The more slender cells are called **companion cells.** These figures
were all drawn from vascular tissues of flowering plants.

(Gr. *gymnos,* naked + *sperma,* seed), bear seeds which usually are exposed
on the plant. Although several types of gymnosperms are recognized,
the **conifers** represent the largest group. These are trees or shrubs
which bear their seeds within structures called cones. The vast majority,
of which pine, fir, and spruce are representative, are **evergreens,** but a
few species such as larch and cypress are **deciduous.** Many species of
conifers assume considerable importance as a source of wood and other
products. In contrast to the gymnosperms, the **angiosperms** (Gr.
angeion, vessel + *sperma*), or **flowering plants,** bear seeds enclosed
within a structure which arises from a part of the flower. Within the seed
plant group, the angiosperms are by far more successful and numerous
than the gymnosperms. The latter number less than one thousand species,
and it can thus be said that there are about 200,000 known species of
flowering plants. Hence, they are more numerous than all other plants
combined, which explains why most individual plants encountered in
nature belong to this group. Virtually all species cultivated by man are
flowering plants, as are all trees except gymnospermous species. There is
great variety of form and habitat within the group. Many species are
perennial, and individuals sometimes attain great size and age.

65 A stand of young pine trees, showing typical slender growth of trunks.

66 A contrast between the seed-bearing habits of gymnosperms and angiosperms. The seeds of pine, which are winged, are borne upon the scales of cones, which open to release them. The bean pods shown are ripened ovaries of flowers, and the seeds are borne within them.

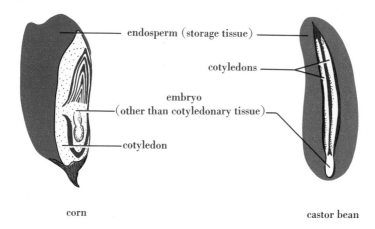

endosperm (storage tissue)

cotyledons

embryo
(other than cotyledonary tissue)

cotyledon

corn   castor bean

67 Contrast of corn seed (monocotyledonous) with castor bean seed
(dicotyledonous). Each seed is drawn as it was sectioned in
such a manner as to show the embryonic sporophytic plant in
each case.

The structure common to all species of angiosperms, the flower,
is a plant organ whose function is the formation of seeds in reproduction. There is a considerable variety in flower form, the typical structure
being a showy, symmetrical aggregation of spore-bearing and sterile parts.
Many flowers, however, such as those of grasses, do not exhibit such
prominence.

68 A floral arrangement of Easter lilies. Note the slender leaves
characteristic of monocotyledons. (Photograph by Sam Fausett,
courtesy Idlehour Florist, Conway, Arkansas)

The flowering plants usually are divided into two groups, the **monocotyledons** and **dicotyledons,** which are names describing embryonic structure in the respective groups. A **cotyledon** may be described as a **seed leaf** of the embryonic sporophyte; monocotyledonous plants possess one such structure, whereas dicotyledonous plants exhibit two (Fig. 67). In general, the monocotyledons are plants whose leaves are slender with veins running parallel to each other, such as grasses, cereal grains, and certain ornamental plants (Fig. 68). The dicotyledons usually exhibit leaves which are broader and whose veins are not parallel; cotton, beans, and oak trees exemplify dicotyledons (Fig. 69).

69 A bean plant, showing the broad leaves and netted arrangement of veins characteristic of dicotyledons. Note the two shrivelled cotyledons still attached to the stem; in beans, these structures are carried above ground by the emerging shoot, and they eventually fall off.

Although "accumulation" of adaptations is perhaps less obvious among plants than is the case in the animal kingdom, we can trace a few important structural advances from the simplest plants to those that are most complex (Fig. 70). This indicates a certain kinship among plants, just as with animals, and we shall see later on that there are other evidences which tend to verify this principle.

This brief survey of the plant kingdom should serve to aid in distinguishing between plants of the major groups that we have described. The field of botany is vast in its scope, embracing many different aspects of the plant world, and the student is encouraged to enlarge his knowledge and appreciation of the field through further reading from appropriate sources.

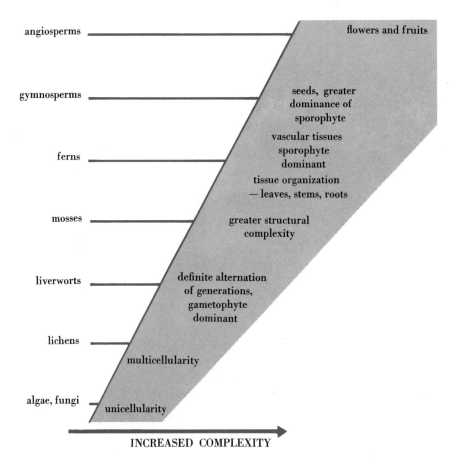

70   Graphic representation of the "accumulation" principle as shown by major plant groups in regard to several important features.

CONCLUSION

The aim of this chapter has been that of presenting certain basic principles of taxonomy and their application. Inasmuch as the material of subsequent chapters will frequently depend upon a knowledge of these principles, and upon an acquaintance of plant and animal forms that will be used as examples, it is imperative that the contents of this chapter be learned thoroughly. Aside from this immediate motive for learning, however, is the fact that a well-educated person should be aware of and generally familiar with the forms of life which he observes about him, and with some of the methods which professional biologists employ in studying organisms. Although this material only introduces the student to these forms and methods, it is hoped that it may open to him an area that will command his continued interest.

QUESTIONS

Multiple Choice

1. Which of the following is a member of the Phylum Mollusca? (a) an earthworm, (b) a sponge, (c) an insect, (d) a coral animal, (e) an octopus.

2. Which of the animals above belongs to a phylum that includes more species than does any other phylum?

3. Which of the following is first to break the proper sequence? (a) class, (b) family, (c) order, (d) genus, (e) species.

4. In classifying an organism, which of the names above would not be capitalized?

5. Which of the following plants is characterized by the presence of vascular tissues? (a) a moss, (b) a fern, (c) a liverwort, (d) a fungus, (e) an alga.

6. Which of the above would you expect to possess no chlorophyll?

7. Animals that give birth to more or less well-developed young are said to be (a) coelomate, (b) triploblastic, (c) viviparous, (d) amphibious, (e) abnormal.

8. Which of the following is an animal whose body temperature does not fluctuate with that of the environment? (a) a fish, (b) a frog, (c) an insect, (d) a bird, (e) an echinoderm.

9. Which of the following classes of the Phylum Chordata includes the largest number of species? (a) Chondrichthyes, (b) Osteichthyes, (c) Reptilia, (d) Aves, (e) Mammalia.

10. Which of the following plant groups includes more species than all the others combined? (a) algae, (b) fungi, (c) mosses, (d) ferns, (e) seed plants.

11. Only one of the following animals exhibits a "tube-within-a-tube" body plan. Which is it? (a) sponge, (b) coelenterate, (c) flatworm, (d) roundworm, (e) protozoan.

12. In chordates, there is a dorsal, elastic rod at some stage of development. This structure is called the (a) spinal cord, (b) spinal column, (c) backbone, (d) dorsal blood vessel, (e) notochord.

13. An angiosperm is a plant which (a) produces seeds in cones, (b) does not produce seeds in cones, (c) bears no flowers, (d) possesses no chlorophyll, (e) exhibits no vascular tissues.

14. The oak tree is (a) a fern, (b) a gymnosperm, (c) a lichen, (d) a flowering plant, (e) none of these.

15. The animal known as the lamprey belongs to the same class of vertebrates as (a) the shark, (b) the frog, (c) the bony fishes, (d) the snakes, (e) none of these listed.

16. Monocotyledons and dicotyledons are distinguished from each other, in the final analysis, on the basis of differences in their (a) leaves, (b) stems, (c) roots, (d) flowers, (e) embryos.

17. Which of the following statements is *not* true of bacteria? (a) They are fungi. (b) They all cause diseases. (c) Most of them are unicellular. (d) Their nuclei are difficult to demonstrate by ordinary nuclear staining techniques. (e) Many of them decompose materials in nature.

18. How many of the following are characterized by radial symmetry? (a) Coelenterata, (b) Platyhelminthes, (c) Mollusca, (d) Echinodermata, (e) Chordata.

19. Which of the following animals has a dorsal, tubular nerve cord? (a) earthworm, (b) starfish, (c) tapeworm, (d) shark, (e) crab.

20. Which of the animals above has a water-vascular system?

True-false

1. Members of the Class Chondrichthyes possess skeletons composed entirely of cartilage.

2. The Phylum Metazoa includes all multicellular animals.

3. All plants which possess chlorophyll rely upon carbon dioxide as a source of carbon.

4. A pine tree is a gymnosperm.

5. Most sponges inhabit relatively deep areas of the ocean; few are found in shallow water.

6. Linnaeus is credited with introducing the natural viewpoint into taxonomy.

7. Arthropods are distinguished from other animals chiefly by their possession of paired, jointed appendages.

8. Like liverworts and mosses, ferns exhibit a sporophytic phase which is much more obvious and outstanding than the gametophytic phase.

9. The domesticated cat is included within the Class Mammalia because its natural food is the flesh of other animals.

10. Cells of green algae exhibit nuclei that are definite and distinct from the cytoplasm.

11. Not all fungi are strictly dependent upon organic compounds for their carbon.

12. There are about 1,000,000 known plant species.

13. The Phylum Platyhelminthes is the first phylum to exhibit a coelome, as a group.

14. Cephalization reaches its highest development in the flowering plants.

15. Crustaceans, insects, spiders, scorpions, ticks, and centipedes all belong to the same phylum.

16. The flowers of ferns are not very large, and hence are often missed entirely by the amateur observer.

17. Some algae exhibit a dimorphic life cycle.

18. A starfish does not have dorsal and ventral surfaces; these terms are meaningless in relation to such animals.

19. Segmentation is more pronounced in annelids than in any other animal group.

20. The so-called "scientific name" of an organism is actually a binomial which includes the name of its genus and its family.

Questions for Consideration and Discussion

1. Define the following terms: rhizome, cilia, coelome, binomial nomenclature, mid-sagittal plane, cotyledon, seed, protochordate, phycoerythrin, xylem.

2. Name the ten phyla of animals discussed in this chapter and the major characteristics of each.

3. Name the seven classes of vertebrates discussed in this chapter and the major characteristics of each.

4. What unusual feature is exhibited by lichens?

5. How many features can you think of that are shared in common by green algae and flowering plants? In what ways do they differ?

6. Distinguish properly between natural and artificial systems of classification.

7. Since members of the Phylum Echinodermata are radially symmetrical, why is the phylum given the place that it is in the scale of animal complexity?

8. Name some diseases that are caused by protozoa.

9. Distinguish properly between radial and bilateral symmetry.

10. Name some fungi that are of commercial value and list the products associated with each.

REFERENCES

BOLD, H. C. *The Plant Kingdom.* Englewood Cliffs, N.J.: Prentice-Hall, Inc., 1960. This book, which is one of the FOUNDATIONS OF MODERN BIOLOGY series, will prove very helpful to the student who wishes to expand his knowledge of plants and plant types.

BUCHSBAUM, RALPH. *Animals without Backbones,* 2nd ed. Chicago: The University of Chicago Press. 1948. A survey of the invertebrate phyla, written and illustrated in a very fine manner.

CRONQUIST, ARTHUR. *Introductory Botany.* New York: Harper & Brothers, Publishers, 1960. A thorough, well-organized textbook of general botany.

HANSON, E. D. *Animal Diversity.* Englewood Cliffs, N.J.: Prentice-Hall, Inc., 1961. One of the FOUNDATIONS OF MODERN BIOLOGY series, this book will serve to enlarge the student's knowledge of the animal kingdom.

MILNE, L. J. and M. M. MILNE. *Animal Life.* Englewood Cliffs, N.J.: Prentice-Hall, Inc., 1959. A beautifully illustrated, concise textbook of general zoology.

————. *Plant Life.* Englewood Cliffs, N.J.: Prentice-Hall, Inc., 1959. A complementary textbook of general botany to that listed above, with similar features.

ORR, R. T. *Vertebrate Biology.* Philadelphia: W. B. Saunders Co., 1961. A study of North American vertebrates; the biology of fishes, amphibians, reptiles, birds and mammals.

STORER, T. I. and R. L. USINGER. *General Zoology,* 3rd ed. New York: McGraw-Hill Book Co., Inc., 1957. An outstanding textbook of general zoology.

CHAPTER

Metabolism

As was noted previously, living organisms are characterized by certain manifestations which set them apart from anything in the non-living world. One of these is the phenomenon of **metabolism,** a word that basically applies to the chemical activities occurring in a given cell. As applied to a multicellular organism, it is used to describe the chemical activities of the entire body of cells.

Since chemical activity centers around energy storage and release, and because it is necessary that the organism have at its disposal energy-yielding compounds that may be utilized, the study of nutrition must of necessity be closely allied with that of metabolism. It is the purpose of this chapter to acquaint the student with fundamentals of these processes as they occur in living forms.

THE MOVEMENT OF MATERIALS THROUGH CELL MEMBRANES

Under most conditions, the living cell is in a constant state of dynamic activity. This. includes movement into the cell of substances which may enter into such activity and the movement outward of materials that would otherwise tend to accumulate and inhibit the metabolic machinery.

Diffusion

Basic to the movement of such substances is the physical phenomenon of **diffusion,** which for purposes of the present discussion may be defined as the movement of molecules or ions due to their innate kinetic energy. This phenomenon is exhibited by molecules or ions in all states of matter, although movement is much more rapid in a gas than in a liquid, and is slowest in a solid.

A moment's reflection will produce the realization that diffusion is a very common phenomenon. If a vial of perfume is opened at the front of a room, its odor may be detected at the back of the room within a short time due to the diffusion of its molecules through the air. Of course, under most conditions, there are air currents which aid in the distribution of molecules released in this fashion, but carefully controlled experiments indicate that diffusion eventually occurs on its own. To cite another example, a cube of sugar dropped into a cup of coffee will dissociate into individual molecules, which go into solution throughout the liquid and which will in time become uniformly distributed throughout the medium.

It will be noted that there is a tendency toward equalization of diffusing ions or molecules throughout a medium which is not difficult to understand. For purposes of illustration, let us suppose that the molecules of perfume mentioned above are as large as marbles and that they possess built-in motors which drive them aimlessly. When perhaps a thousand such units are released at the front of the room, they immediately go flying off in every direction. Some of them collide and thus deflect each other's courses, some bounce off the walls, floor, and ceiling, and so on, but by random movement they very rapidly become uniformly distributed throughout the room. Unless some other factor enters in, they will remain uniformly distributed, since the "laws of chance" dictate that about as many continue to move in one direction as another. Because of this tendency toward equalization, molecules of any diffusing substance are inclined toward a net movement from a region of greater concentration to regions of lesser concentration, as in the examples of perfume and sugar given above.

Now let us assume a situation in which diffusing molecules must pass through a partition capable of admitting them but which will prevent the diffusion of other molecules present in the medium. It so happens that cellophane is made in such a way that there are tiny openings, far too small to be seen even with the highest power of an ordinary microscope, through which molecules of water will pass but not those of sucrose. If the bulb of a thistle tube is filled with table syrup, which is a

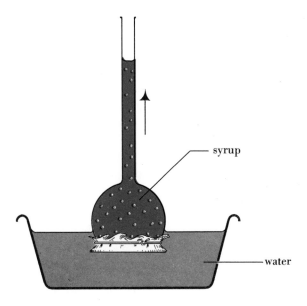

syrup

water

71 The rise of syrup in a tube due to the net movement of water
molecules from a region of their greater concentration to one of
a lesser concentration.

concentrated aqueous solution of sucrose, a piece of cellophane tied in
place across the open end of the bulb, and the bulb immersed in a beaker
of water (Fig. 71), a striking phenomenon occurs. Within a very short
time, the syrup will be seen to rise in the tube, a process that may continue until a considerable height is reached.

This result can be explained in terms of diffusion. In their
motion, the molecules of water which are outside the thistle tube bombard the cellophane membrane. Most of them do not happen to "hit" an
opening and thus bounce back into the medium, but some of them do
and thus enter the bulb. Of course, there are water molecules inside the
bulb, but due to the presence of the numerous sucrose molecules there
are not as many of them to bombard the cellophane from that side, and
hence there will be even fewer "hits" than occur from the outside.
Furthermore, the sucrose molecules seem to inhibit the freedom of movement of whatever water molecules are present, and so there is a *net increase* in water molecules within the bulb and a *net decrease* within the
beaker. This causes the syrup to become diluted, of course, and forces
some of it up into the tube.

By way of illustration, let us compare this situation to that which
would exist if a room were divided by a partition containing several round

holes measuring six inches in diameter. Ten men with a baseball each are placed on one side of the partition; five men with a baseball each and five men with a basketball each are placed on the other side. At a given signal, all the men start throwing their balls toward the partition, those men who throw baseballs having the privilege of picking up baseballs from the floor as they either come through the openings or as they bounce back from the partition, with the basketball men continuing to throw at random also. The net result would, of course, be an increase in number of baseballs on the side where the basketballs are in play, since the latter not only cut down on the number of "diffusible" balls, but they also interfere with those baseballs which are thrown from that side by occasionally deflecting them.

The cellophane covering the bulb of the thistle tube, like the partition in the illustration, is permeable to only one of the two types of objects bombarding it, which accounts for the net movement of the permeating substance from one side to the other. Hence, such a partition as cellophane is said to be **differentially permeable** because it can be permeated by one type of molecule making up the sucrose solution but not by the other. In other words, the membrane "differentiates," in this case, between water and sucrose molecules.

It may occur to the student to wonder, at this point, what these examples regarding diffusion have to do with the living cell and its activities. A vast amount of research has shown that the limiting surfaces of cells behave as differentially permeable membranes, allowing some substances to pass through and inhibiting the passage of others.[1] There is one important difference between a membrane such as cellophane and the membranes of cells, however; cell membranes are living and are vastly more complex than non-living membranes such as cellophane. There are factors which govern the entrance of ions and molecules besides their sizes and the sizes of the openings through which they must pass, although these factors apparently are involved to some extent. There is still a great deal to be learned regarding the movement of substances across cell membranes, but a few influencing factors are known. The net electrical charge of a ion or molecule may determine its ability to pass through the membrane. The degree to which a substance is chemically similar to the materials which make up the membrane is another factor. Some substances may be "pumped" through by the expenditure of energy on the part of a cell, a phenomenon known as **active transport.**

[1] In the cell, only protoplasmic membranes behave in this fashion. Whenever a cell wall or pellicle is present on one surface of a cell membrane, there is no interference with permeability because these structures seem to be universally permeable to all substances in solution.

Different types of cells differ in permeability of their membranes to many substances, and even similar cells may vary in this respect under different environmental conditions. However, it is obvious that a number of factors are responsible for the relative ease with which some substances penetrate cell membranes as compared with others. Hence, protoplasmic membranes are differentially permeable, as is cellophane, but not entirely for the same reasons.

A Special Case of Diffusion: Osmosis

At this point, it is important to understand something of the role of water in relation to the passage of substances into and out of cells. Water is the common solvent for materials which are of importance to the cell; not only is a given cell composed of perhaps seventy-five to eighty-five per cent water, but it is surrounded by an aqueous medium. In the case of aquatic organisms, this is obvious, but it may not occur to the student that living cells at the tops of trees or that cells which lie deeply within the body of a mammal, for example, are also dependent upon such a medium with which to exchange materials. Water is one of only a few substances (carbon dioxide and oxygen are others) to which cell membranes are freely permeable. Because of the importance of water as a diffusing substance, a special term is used to describe its movement through a differentially permeable membrane. Whenever molecules of water diffuse across a differentially permeable membrane in such a way that a net increase is realized on one side of the membrane, **osmosis** is said to occur.[2]

In the experiment illustrated by Fig. 71, osmosis is responsible for the rise of syrup in the tube. Sufficient pressure may be exerted under the conditions of this experiment to force a column of dilute syrup to a height of several feet. Now it might be supposed that as long as more water were added to the beaker, this process could go on indefinitely since the solution within the thistle tube would never be pure water theoretically. Hence, osmosis could be expected to occur in the direction of the solution indefinitely. However, a point is reached at which the column exerts sufficient pressure downward that those water molecules which are freely diffusible from inside the tube gain in momentum and establish an equilibrium with incoming water molecules. At this point, osmosis stops, even though diffusion of water molecules continues.

[2] The physical chemist uses the term osmosis to describe such activity shown by any solvent. However, since water is the only solvent which needs to be considered in osmotic phenomena as exhibited by living cells, the term is used in biology to describe a special type of diffusion, that of water molecules under the conditions indicated above.

Whenever osmosis takes place, the solution from which a net movement of water molecules occurs is said to be **hypotonic** to the other solution, and the solution that shows a net gain in the process is said to be **hypertonic** to the other. Hence, in Fig. 71, the water is hypotonic to the syrup, which is, of course, hypertonic to the water. A solution that is equal to another in diffusible water molecules is said to be **isotonic** to it.

In order to demonstrate that living cells are subject to osmotic pressures, let us consider a cell such as that of *Spirogyra* (Figs. 51, 72), a filamentous green alga which thrives in ponds of fresh water. Although its surrounding medium is never absolutely pure water, it is nevertheless sufficiently concentrated in water molecules to be hypotonic to the protoplasmic contents of the cell. There is thus a continual tendency for osmosis to occur inward. Why, it might be asked, does the cell not increase in size until it bursts? The reason lies in the rigidity of the cellulose cell wall, which is sufficient to resist bursting under these conditions. Enough pressure builds up inside the cell to establish such an osmotic equilibrium as that produced by the column of syrup in the experiment described above. Whenever a cell exhibits an internal pressure due to osmosis, it is said to be **turgid,** and such pressure (resulting from osmosis) is called **turgor pressure.**

Now suppose that a filament of *Spirogyra* is put into a solution prepared by dissolving five grams of sodium chloride in sufficient water to make the entire solution equal one hundred milliliters (about one-fourth pint). This solution proves to be hypertonic to the protoplasm of

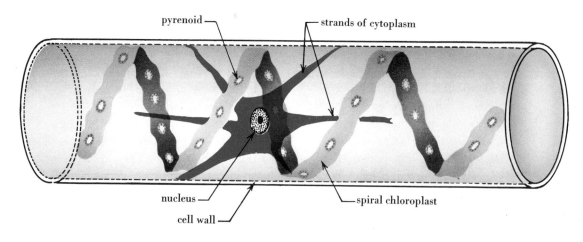

pyrenoid — strands of cytoplasm

nucleus — cell wall — spiral chloroplast

72 Cell of *Spirogyra*. Compare with Figs. 51 and 73.

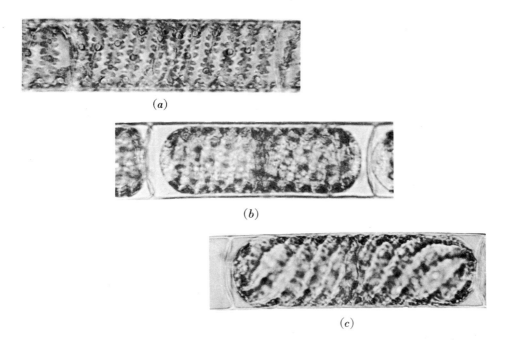

(a)

(b)

(c)

73 Plasmolysis in *Spirogyra*. a, appearance of cell growing in pond water. b, appearance of the same cell about twenty seconds after it was subjected to a five per cent solution of sodium chloride. Note that the protoplast, surrounded by the plasma membrane, has pulled away from the cell wall. c, deplasmolysis of a cell, accomplished by surrounding a plasmolyzed cell with tap water. Note that the protoplast is returning to its normal position.

the cells, and within a matter of seconds sufficient water leaves a given cell to cause a shrinking of the protoplast. The cell wall, being rigid, remains in place and the plasma membrane actually draws away from it (Fig. 73b). This loss of turgidity on the part of the cell due to osmosis is called **plasmolysis,** and a cell whose turgidity is less than that experienced in its normal environment is said to be **flaccid.** Unless plasmolysis has occurred to a critical degree, normal turgidity may be restored to the cells of the *Spirogyra* filament by replacing the sodium chloride solution with pond or tap water, thus reversing the direction of osmosis (Fig. 73c).

Many fresh-water organisms which do not exhibit rigid cell walls manage to withstand turgor pressures by "bailing out" excess water. *Amoeba* and *Paramecium*, for example, exhibit **contractile vacuoles** which function as pumps in this respect (Fig. 74). Were it not for this mechanism, such delicate cells would soon burst. In higher animals, cells

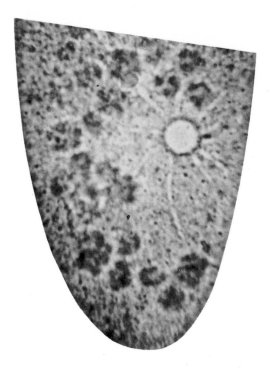

74 Portion of a cell of *Paramecium*, showing a contractile vacuole. The canals that extend outward from it into the cytoplasm apparently convey water from the cytoplasm into the vacuole, and it is pumped out of the cell at this point.

are surrounded by fluids which are isotonic to the protoplasm. The delicate red blood cells of man, for example, can be made to swell and burst if removed from their normal environment and placed in a solution which is even slightly hypotonic to them.

Although water itself is not an energy-yielding substance, it is of paramount importance to the metabolic life of cells, and hence to organisms, in that it serves as a solvent for and a carrier of a variety of compounds both inside and outside the cell. Not only is this the case, but it makes possible enzymatic reactions which could not occur otherwise. Furthermore, its molecules actually enter into certain metabolic reactions.

The Role of Diffusion in Metabolism

In the final analysis, the metabolism of a given organism is directly and necessarily related to the movement of materials through cell membranes. Some of these are organic substances which are either produced by the cell in excess of its own requirements, or they may be materials that are brought into the cell from an external source in order to satisfy the metabolic needs of the cell. Others are ions of inorganic compounds, and still others are materials such as water, carbon dioxide, or oxygen which play an important part in the chemical activities of the cell. In view of this constant interchange of materials with its surrounding medium, it is important that the cell be considered a highly active unit of protoplasm which of necessity maintains lines of transportation to and from its surrounding medium.

PHYSIOLOGICAL ACTIVITIES ASSOCIATED WITH METABOLISM

The total activity of an organism might be compared to that of an army engaged in fighting a war. In such an effort, not all the men are engaged in actual combat; there are many who serve in a purely supporting role. In the same way, organisms carry on a variety of activities which are related directly or indirectly to metabolism, and it is most important that these be defined as exactly as possible. However, metabolism itself is the actual "combat"; regardless of how complex an organism may be, and some are composed of billions of cells, it is within the cells that the activity most essential to the organism occurs.

In view of the great variety of organisms, it is not surprising that both metabolism and the activities which support it vary considerably among living forms. Yet, there are certain activities which are common to all organisms, and these will be emphasized in the discussion which follows. Within a given topic, important differences among organisms in respect to the particular activity under consideration will receive attention.

The Acquisition of Food

By correct definition, any substance which may ultimately be broken down by an organism with an accompanying release of utilizable energy is said to be a **food** for that organism. Some organisms may utilize materials as food which other organisms do not. For example, cellulose is an organic compound which can be utilized by certain bacteria and protozoa but not by other organisms. Water is not a food for any organism, even though it is an essential substance for all living forms. Certain organic compounds such as vitamins may be very necessary to the metabolism of a given organism but not because they are utilized for the production of energy. Their role in the cell is one accessory to metabolism. Similarly, certain inorganic salts are necessary to the functioning of all cells but not because they are capable of yielding energy. Like vitamins, they serve to regulate metabolic processes.

THE NATURE OF FOOD SUBSTANCES. In Chapter 3, we discussed the organic compounds which are present in protoplasm and designated the carbohydrates, fats, and proteins as "fuel" compounds. This distinction is a valid one in terms of what usually goes on in a cell, but we must qualify the concept somewhat at this point. Actually, any organic molecule may be "burned" in a cell, and this includes vitamins, enzymes, nucleoproteins, and the various structural components of the cell. However, it appears that the cell is somewhat selective in this respect, and as long as carbohydrates and fats particularly are available, it utilizes them. Proteins are not as readily attacked, and their major function within the cell (and hence within the organism) is not that of serving as fuel but as a source of building material.

In spite of the principle that these three types of compounds are the real sources of energy in the cell, there is a rapid turnover of all organic molecules except for certain ones such as those of DNA which are somewhat isolated from the enzymatic machinery. This means that virtually everything in the cell is a "fuel" substance in the final analysis. To draw an analogy, let us suppose that a certain lumber dealer finds it necessary, for some reason, to keep a fire going in a furnace. Under ordinary circumstances, he uses coal or oil as fuels because they are cheap and readily available. He might use the furnace, since he has it anyway, to dispose of scrap lumber and assorted waste products, but he does not depend upon these for fuel. They are only *incidentally* burned. Now let us assume that his supply of coal and oil is cut off. He might be forced to use whatever he can find that will burn, and if maintenance of his fire is sufficiently important to him, he might even be obliged to burn his own valuable lumber. Of course, this analogy is only a rough one, since we do not ascribe consciousness and purpose to the cell as we do to a human being, but there are valid parallels. The coal and oil are analogous to carbohydrates and fats, the lumber to proteins, and the scraps of material to the various "used" molecules of the cell which are disposed of in the metabolic "fire."

Even though we cannot draw an exact distinction between "fuel" and "non-fuel" compounds, however, the original distinction is valid for all practical purposes. Carbohydrates and fats are the only materials that furnish energy to the cell in very large amounts, at least under most conditions. Proteins may or may not play a significant role in this respect, depending upon their quantity and the relative quantities of the other two fuels. Any other organic molecules that are broken down may yield some energy, but in amounts that are quite insignificant when compared with that furnished by carbohydrates, fats, and proteins.

A NUTRITIONAL CLASSIFICATION OF ORGANISMS. In the acquisition of these "fuel" substances, animals and plants differ fundamentally. The nutrition of animals is said to be **phagotrophic** (Gr. *phagos*, to eat + *trophikos*, nursing), inasmuch as it is characteristic of those organisms that are decidedly animals to take into their bodies foodstuffs which are in a non-diffusible form. Plants, in contrast, are of two types in regard to nutrition. There are those which are capable of synthesizing their own food substances from carbon dioxide and water, with sunlight usually serving as a source of energy for the process. Such plants are said to be **autotrophic** (Gr. *autos*, self + *trophikos*). Other plants are dependent upon outside sources for food, as are animals, but they are obliged to receive the food in such a form that it will diffuse through cell membranes. These plants are said to be **heterotrophic** (Gr. *heteros*, other + *trophikos*).

There are some exceptions to these nutritional rules. For example, an alga called *Chrysamoeba* possesses chlorophyll and thus is capable of manufacturing carbohydrates, but it also sends out pseudopodia, by means of which it ingests solid food particles much as protozoa do. Hence, it is both autotrophic and phagotrophic. The present tendency among biologists is to regard any organism that is autotrophic to any extent at all as a plant, however, and *Chrysamoeba* is generally so regarded. Certain fungi, the slime molds, are phagotrophic at one stage of their existence, but their reproductive habits are so distinctly plant-like that they are not considered animals. A few seed plants such as the Venus' fly trap (Fig. 156), although autotrophic, capture insects for food also, thus exhibiting phagotrophic nutrition of a sort. Certain animals, particularly forms which are adapted to a parasitic habit within the bodies of other animals, may receive food from the host in such a state that it will diffuse into their bodies, and thus they are not phagotrophic. The tapeworm is such an animal. However, such forms resemble definite animal groups so closely that there is no tendency to regard them as heterotrophic plants merely because of their nutrition. They are rather said to be **saprozoic** (Gr. *sapros*, decayed + *zoon*).

In spite of such exceptions, which are relatively few, the characteristic mode of nutrition of an organism constitutes the most reliable criterion for deciding whether it is a plant or an animal. On this basis of distinction, there are very few species that cannot be definitely assigned to either the plant or the animal kingdom.

AUTOTROPHIC NUTRITION. Except for a few species of unusual bacteria known as **chemoautotrophs,** which are able to capture energy from certain chemical reactions, autotrophic plants manufacture foods by virtue of their possession of chlorophyll. This substance makes possible the utilization of solar energy in combining carbon dioxide and water to form glucose or other carbohydrates, with oxygen also being produced in the process. Although many separate chemical reactions are involved, the over-all reaction may be represented as follows:

$$\text{Solar energy} + 6CO_2 + 6H_2O \xrightarrow{\text{chlorophyll}} C_6H_{12}O_6 + 6O_2$$

Thus, for every six molecules each of carbon dioxide and water that enter the reaction, one molecule of glucose and six molecules of oxygen are produced. This process is called **photosynthesis,** which literally means "putting together by means of light."

The importance of photosynthesis to the entire world of life can hardly be overestimated. Because green plants (including those algae whose other pigments mask their chlorophyll) are able to store the energy of sunlight within organic compounds, organisms which are unable to synthesize fuel substances are provided with a food source. Although animals may eat other animals, or bacteria may exist on a diet far removed from green plants, all life, except for the chemoautotrophic forms, is ultimately dependent upon photosynthesis, which in turn depends upon the sun as an energy source.

Although simple carbohydrates are the immediate products of photosynthesis, the green plant does not ordinarily build up great quantities of these substances. Rather, they serve as raw material for the further synthesis of organic compounds. They may be converted to more complex carbohydrates or to fats in the plant, or they may be combined with nitrogen and other elements available to the plant in its environment to form proteins. Vitamins, enzymes, and various materials essential to the well-being of the plant may finally be formed by such modification of these carbohydrates, and even more chlorophyll can be synthesized from them. It may be said that the green plant is a very able chemist, producing a variety of substances from these fundamental materials. The actual chemistry of reactions which occur in green plants is extremely complex and is still the subject of much intense research.

There is a common notion that green plants obtain their food from the soil, or, in the case of aquatic species such as algae, from the aqueous medium. This is a mistaken idea; reflection upon the foregoing discussion will lead to the realization that green plants are capable of manufacturing food from "non-food" materials. It is true that these plants depend upon their environments for essential substances such as water, carbon dioxide, and inorganic salts, but we do not classify these as foods. As for plants that grow in the soil, a simple experiment will show that it is not from the soil itself that the substance of a plant is chiefly derived. A container may be filled with dirt, oven-dried, and weighed. If the seed of some plant is inserted into the soil and thoroughly watered, the seed will germinate into a plant. After the plant has grown to a considerable size, it may be pulled up and separated from the soil in which it was growing. If great care has been taken to ensure that all the original soil is still present, and if all plant parts are removed from it, a second drying and weighing will indicate that the soil has lost only an extremely small percentage of its original weight. When the plant is weighed, it will be found that it is many times heavier than the soil which has been lost. Of course, much of the weight of the plant is accounted for by the water it has absorbed. However, even its dry weight will be found to equal many times that lost by the soil.

It was experiments such as the one described above that led early plant physiologists to the realization that the body of a land plant derives its mass from some source other than soil. As more and more carefully controlled experiments were performed, with methods being developed for the exact measurement of water and gases, the process of photosynthesis became known. Since the time of its initial discovery, biologists have probed more deeply into the complex intermediate steps involved in photosynthesis, and a great deal more is now known about it than was formerly.

For many years after the photosynthetic equation given above was known to be quantitatively accurate, it was supposed that carbon and oxygen separated during the process, with carbon becoming attached to water and with oxygen being released. The plausibility of this hypothesis can readily be seen if we reduce the equation to its simplest terms.

$$CO_2 + H_2O \longrightarrow CH_2O + O_2$$

It was supposed further that the (CH_2O) unit was "multiplied" in some fashion to form sugars. Six such units, for example, might form glucose. As is so often the case in scientific matters, however, the most attractive, plausible, or even popular hypothesis does not always prove to be the correct one. In this instance, direct evidence was not forthcoming until about 1940, when the principle of using isotopic tracers[3] was applied to

---

[3] Isotopes are atoms of the same element which differ in mass. Ordinary oxygen atoms, for example, have eight protons and eight neutrons in the nucleus. The chemist refers to this kind of oxygen as O^{16}. Another kind of oxygen atom (O^{18}) has eight protons and *ten* neutrons. Since the number of electrons is the same in both cases, there is no difference in their *chemical* properties, but they differ in their *physical* properties. Water molecules may be prepared using O^{18}, for example, and the fate of the oxygen can be "traced" by using instruments capable of detecting it through its physical properties. Most elements consist of different isotopes, which means that tracer techniques are available for use in attacking a great variety of biological problems.

this problem. By incorporating "heavy" oxygen into water molecules, investigators were able to trace its fate during photosynthesis. Contrary to the earlier idea, it was found that such oxygen became the O_2 of the photosynthetic equation. Clearly, then, the reaction did not involve a splitting of the CO_2 molecule to liberate oxygen. Furthermore, twice as much oxygen appeared from the reaction than *apparently* had gone into it, if all the liberated oxygen came from water, as it obviously did.

Step by step, the major features of the process became clear. It is now known that the first step in photosynthesis is **photolysis,** or the breakdown of water in the presence of chlorophyll, with light energy serving to activate the reaction:

$$2H_2O \xrightarrow[\text{chlorophyll}]{\text{light}} 4H + O_2$$

The oxygen produced in this reaction may escape into the immediate environment of the plant, or some of it may be used in the plant for other reactions. As for the hydrogen, it is captured by certain molecules that serve as **hydrogen acceptors** and is eventually delivered to a complex cycle of reactions which CO_2 also enters.

At this point, the second phase of photosynthesis, **CO_2 fixation,** begins. Carbon dioxide is taken up by a three-carbon compound, already present in the chloroplast, called **ribulose diphosphate (RDP)**. A molecule of RDP, one of CO_2, and one of water react to produce two three-carbon molecules of a compound called **phosphoglyceric acid (PGA)**. Each PGA molecule loses an oxygen atom (which is joined to hydrogen coming from photolysis) and becomes **phosphoglyceraldehyde (PGAL)**. By special transformation reactions, five out of six PGAL molecules produced in this fashion are changed to three of RDP, which then go on for another "load" of CO_2. One out of six is made available to the plant.

Actually, PGAL is the end product of photosynthesis, not glucose as the over-all equation would indicate. However, since PGAL *may* be converted to glucose (it may also be utilized as such by the plant, or be converted to other materials), it is sufficiently accurate for purposes of representation to balance the equation as we do. One correction must be made, however. Since all the oxygen produced during photosynthesis comes from water, and some water is produced during CO_2 fixation, it is more accurate to express the over-all process as follows:

$$\text{Solar energy} + 6CO_2 + 12H_2O \xrightarrow{\text{chlorophyll}} C_6H_{12}O_6 + 6O_2 + 6H_2O$$

Or, to be still more specific, we might express the process of photosynthesis by means of a diagram, as shown in Fig. 75, which is itself an oversimplification in terms of what actually happens. Nevertheless, it should be obvious that the capture of light energy and its storage in organic molecules is a process which is much more complex than our original equation might indicate.

The Utilization of Foods

Those green plants which exhibit bodies of considerable size and complexity generally produce more food in favorable seasons than they can use, and it may be stored in some form within one of the plant organs. The most common sites of storage are roots (as in sweet potatoes)

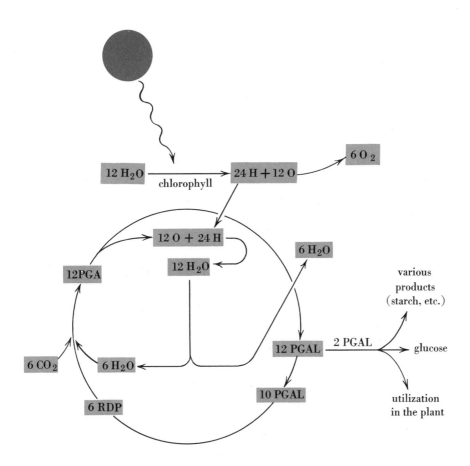

75 A diagrammatic representation of photosynthesis. See text for amplification.

and stems (as in sugar cane), but the leaves may also serve in this capacity. In seed plants the seeds (and often the fruits, in flowering plants) are sites of considerable food deposition. Under certain circumstances the plant may utilize these resources or, as is more frequently the case, they may serve in the propagation of the species. A seed, for example, is an embryonic plant surrounded by a relatively large quantity of stored food.

DIGESTION IN PLANTS. Whenever PGAL is produced by a plant in excess of its immediate requirements, it is converted to some form, such as starch, which is suitable for storage over long periods. Then, when the plant is obliged to draw on its resources, it must throw the machinery into reverse and convert these materials into glucose or some other diffusible substance. The situation is roughly analogous to that in which a person, during a season of rapid financial gain, invests his surplus cash in real estate. During harder times, he can "spend" his investment but only after he has converted it to legal tender.

As a typical example of food utilization in a plant, let us consider the germination of a seed such as that of wheat. Under suitable conditions of moisture and temperature, the embryonic wheat plant within the seed begins to undergo cellular activity. However, it cannot grow without a food source, and as yet it does not possess the ability to manufacture any. Under these conditions, it utilizes the stored but not diffusible starch which surrounds it by producing an enzyme, **diastase,** which is secreted into the storage material, where it hydrolyzes the large starch molecules to their component glucose links. Thus, the starch undergoes **digestion,** a term which is used in biology to describe the breakdown of nondiffusible food substances to a diffusible form.

Although the embryonic plants of autotrophic species become independent of external food supplies as soon as chlorophyll develops, heterotrophs are dependent upon such a source throughout the entire course of their existence. Bacteria, for example, cannot exist unless they have an available supply of energy-yielding materials. By way of illustrating heterotrophic nutrition, let us suppose that a medium is prepared by dissolving or suspending a variety of food materials in water. If this medium is exposed to the atmosphere, bacteria-laden particles of dust will enter the medium soon, and these bacteria will subsequently become surrounded by water containing potential food molecules. Some of the dissolved food substances may possibly be sufficiently simple to diffuse into the bacterial cells without being digested, but most of them must be acted upon chemically before this is possible. Bacterial cells are capable of producing digestive enzymes, however, which move from the

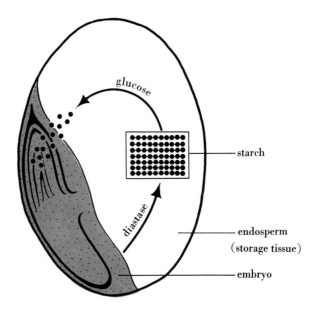

76 Diagram illustrating the digestion of starch in a seed. Enzyme molecules move from the embryo to the endosperm under proper environmental conditions, and the resulting glucose is then utilized by the embryo in its metabolism.

cells into the medium. Certain of the foods, depending on the enzymes which these particular bacteria are capable of producing, will be rendered diffusible by this action and hence will become available to the cells.

DIGESTION IN ANIMALS. In general, animal nutrition is similar to that carried on by nonautotrophic plants (including heterotrophs and embryonic seed plants) in that digestion is extracellular. Unlike plants, however, most animals exhibit elaborate digestive tracts or cavities into which enzymes are secreted from special **glands** or from the cells surrounding a given cavity. Foods are received through a mouth and are acted upon within such a specialized system, the products of digestion being absorbed into surrounding tissues. Certain of the lower animals, notably protozoa and sponges, exhibit a unique habit of acquiring food. Particles of food, or even entire organisms, are taken into the cells themselves and are digested within **food vacuoles** (Fig. 77).

Reception of food into the cell is necessary to the phago-trophic nutrition of protozoa since, if they receive non-diffusible food, it

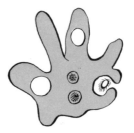

77 An amoeba in the process of capturing a smaller animal. The nucleus is shown near the center of the cell, and just below it is a food vacuole formed previously. A second food vacuole is formed around the ingested small animal. Also shown are two contractile vacuoles.

must of necessity enter the cell itself.[4] Certain of the cells which make up the body of a sponge also engulf food particles, a habit that accompanies the absence of a digestive cavity. Cellular engulfment is largely abandoned above this level of complexity, although it is seen in phagocytic cells of higher animals (for example, certain of the white blood cells, or **leucocytes,** of man and other vertebrates).

PRODUCTS OF DIGESTION AND THEIR FATES. Although a large number of different carbohydrates, fats, and proteins may serve as foods in the world of life, products of digestion do not vary greatly among organisms. Disaccharides and polysaccharides are broken down to monosaccharides, glucose being by far the most common product. The digestion of fats results in **glycerol** and **fatty acids,** both of which may pass into cells. Proteins yield amino acids in the process, and these are also diffusible.

The transport of diffusible food molecules from the site of digestion to all cells which require them is accomplished in a variety of ways among organisms. Being unicellular, bacteria simply receive them from the surrounding medium. Other heterotrophic plants exhibit fairly simple bodies, and apparently these substances diffuse from cell to cell throughout the plant. A certain amount of food transport is accomplished in autotrophic plants by diffusion from cell to cell and in vascular species by phloem tissue as well. The digestive tracts of such animals as coelenterates and flatworms are in sufficiently close contact with all body cells that dif-

---

[4] Actually, the ingested food does not penetrate the cell membrane, but is rather surrounded by it. In a sense, therefore, the protoplasm forms a sort of temporary digestive cavity. Nevertheless, nutrition is considered phagotrophic.

fusion is not a highly involved matter. Higher animals generally exhibit a blood-vascular system whose branches extend to outlying tissues, by means of which diffusible food substances are transported from the site of digestion to a point sufficiently close to any given cell that it may receive them.

FOOD MOLECULES AND THE CELL. Once inside a living cell, a given food molecule follows one of two possible courses. It may be chemically "shattered" through a series of reactions that make possible the release of its bound energy, or it may be used in the synthesis of a more complex substance by undergoing alteration and/or combination with other molecules, ions, or chemical groups. Since all chemical changes that occur in a cell are described by the term metabolism, it becomes convenient to distinguish between those which are constructive, or energy-consuming, from those which are destructive, or energy-releasing. The term **anabolism** is used to describe those reactions occurring in cells which result in the production of complex substances from simpler ones (energy consuming), and the term **catabolism** is applied to those which result in the breakdown of complex substances to simpler ones (energy releasing).

Anabolism. Because certain difficulties are inherent in the study of anabolism, biologists know far less about these reactions as a whole than about catabolism. At this point, it will be sufficient to understand that anabolic reactions are of two fundamental types in regard to an energy source. One type, represented by photosynthesis, utilizes an external energy source and results in the production of complex substances from the raw materials carbon dioxide and water, as we have seen. A second type utilizes an internal energy source, the energy released by catabolic reactions occurring within the same cell, and results in the production of complex substances from a variety of raw materials that may be available to it. By virtue of one or both of these types of reactions, a cell may build up a quantity of complex substances which are available to the organism for storage purposes, for repairing the metabolic machinery, for the synthesis of more protoplasm, or, in the case of multicellular organisms, for the transport to and nutrition of other cells in the body.

As an example of the cell's ability to manufacture complex materials from simpler ones by using an internal energy source, let us consider the sequence of events which transpire during protein synthesis. Nucleic acids control this process by serving as models, or templates, which ultimately determine the exact arrangement of proteins constructed by a given cell. Apparently, DNA molecules in the nucleus give rise to RNA copies, which become deposited in the microsomes. It is here that

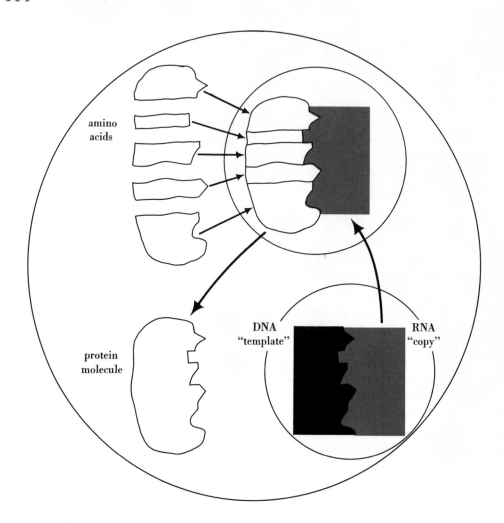

78 Representation of protein synthesis in a microsome and its control by DNA of the nucleus.

these copies serve as sub-templates, and amino acids available in the cytoplasm are somehow drawn to the microsomes and "fall in" according to the template pattern (Fig. 78). This is not accomplished without an expenditure of energy on the part of the cell. Such energy must ultimately be furnished by catabolic reactions. The important feature of this process, however, is that the original DNA templates of the nucleus are the master minds of the whole sequence of events and thus control the synthesis of proteins.

In other ways, the synthesis of fats and carbohydrates occurs. Furthermore, many products which are combinations or derivatives of the three "fuel" types of compounds are built up by virtue of complex anabolic processes. In photosynthetic plants, chlorophyll is one of these. Cells may produce certain substances in such quantities that they are either stored within the cell or **secreted** outward. All of these anabolic activities are in some way under the control of finely adjusted mechanisms which are localized within cells.

Catabolism. It will be recalled that carbon is a rather unique element in its ability to undergo changes that are associated with storage and release of energy. As organic compounds are synthesized within the cell, their carbon atoms "bind" the energy which is given to them by forming alliances with each other and with other atoms, especially those of hydrogen. It is quite beyond the scope of this text to attempt an explanation of why this is possible, but let us consider the carbon atom a sort of safe with four money boxes, into which money (energy) may be put. The atom may either place lids (hydrogen atoms) on the boxes or it may attach its boxes to those of other carbon atoms, with each serving as a lid for the other (Fig. 79).

If the analogy is carried further, catabolism may be considered the exact opposite of this. It begins with full money boxes, each tightly capped, and it proceeds only when keys (enzymes) to the lids are provided by the cell. Having "unlocked" the boxes, the cell is faced with two difficulties. It must dispose of the lids (hydrogen atoms) and it must convert the storage money (energy) into usable currency. We shall consider the latter process first.

79 Illustration representing the storage of energy in chemical bonds.

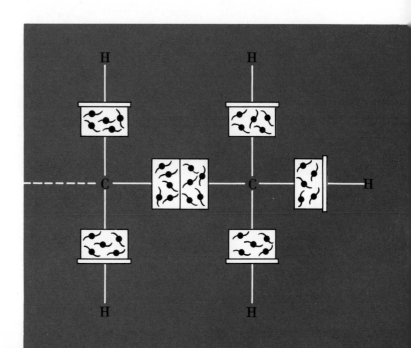

Apparently, all types of cells make use of a pair of "money-changers," **adenosine diphosphate** and **adenosine triphosphate,** abbreviated **ADP** and **ATP,** respectively. These compounds are identical except that ADP exhibits two phosphate groups on each of its molecules, while ATP displays three (Fig. 80). Now it so happens that when ATP loses one of its phosphate groups and becomes ADP, tremendous energy is made available to the cell in a form that can be used. The resulting ADP molecules and phosphate groups then become recombined by utilizing energy obtained from other processes and are used all over again. Hence, the "money" released from the carbon-hydrogen bonds is spent on attaching phosphate groups to ADP molecules to form ATP again, which thus becomes a source of readily available energy. This process is represented as an energy cycle in Fig. 81.

Ideally, a cell disposes of hydrogen atoms by attaching them to oxygen. This results in the formation of water, a substance that is not

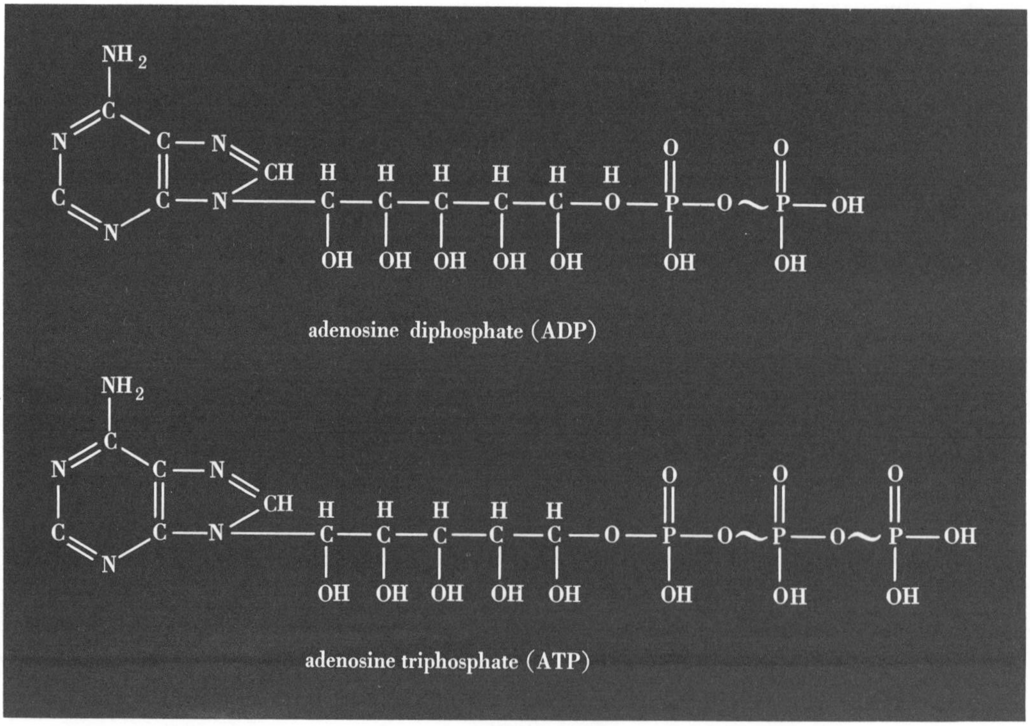

adenosine diphosphate (ADP)

adenosine triphosphate (ATP)

80 Structural formulas of adenosine diphosphate and adenosine triphosphate. The bonds (~), of which ADP possesses one and ATP two, signify "high-energy" bonds. In the ordinary functioning of the ADP-ATP energy cycle, only the terminal high-energy bond of ATP is broken to release energy.

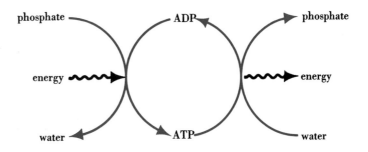

81 The ADP-ATP energy cycle.

only non-toxic to the cell, but is highly useful, as we have seen. This process is not as easily accomplished as might be supposed, however. It is only by virtue of a complex series of enzymatic reactions that it occurs, with corresponding energy release (and consequently, ATP synthesis) taking place step by step.

Let us consider the catabolism of carbohydrates. As we have learned, these "fuel" substances enter the cell in the form of monosaccharides. At this point, they are subjected to a series of reactions which result in the splitting of each six-carbon molecule into two three-carbon molecules. A phosphate group becomes attached to each of these two molecules during the process, and each becomes **phosphoglyceraldehyde** (PGAL), which we encountered in photosynthesis. Each molecule of PGAL is next converted to **phosphoglyceric acid** (PGA) by the net gain of one oxygen atom. This substance then proceeds to lose its phosphate group to ADP, forming ATP, and by other reactions which have occurred along the line, a net loss of two hydrogen atoms has been realized. The resulting product is **pyruvic acid** ($C_3H_4O_3$), of which there are two molecules for every one of glucose (or other monosaccharides) that entered this reaction sequence. This series of reactions from carbohydrate substrates to pyruvic acid is called **glycolysis,** and it is important to observe that *the end product of glycolysis is pyruvic acid.* In abbreviated form, glycolysis may be illustrated as follows:

$$C_6H_{12}O_6 \longrightarrow 2 \text{ PGAL} \longrightarrow 2 \text{ PGA} \longrightarrow 2 \text{ } C_3H_4O_3 + 4H$$

Thus far, we have said nothing about the loss of hydrogen which occurs during glycolysis. This substance is taken up by a special type of nucleotide[5] present in the cell and is held until it can be released

---

[5] This type of nucleotide also serves in photosynthesis to transport hydrogen atoms from the "split" H_2O to the point at which they join the oxygen coming from the conversion of PGA to PGAL (see page 108).

to gaseous oxygen. This is the usual pathway for hydrogen released in glycolysis, with pyruvic acid being further degraded, and we shall give attention presently to this further aspect of catabolism. First however, let us see what happens in a cell if the hydrogen produced in glycolysis cannot be given to gaseous oxygen. In most cells, this simply ties up all of the available nucleotide hydrogen acceptor with which it can combine. The damming-up of hydrogen eventually poisons the cell. This explains why most organisms cannot live for very long in the absence of gaseous oxygen. However, there are cells and even organisms that are capable of living in a total absence of oxygen. Hence, they are said to be **anaerobic,** which means "without oxygen."

Just what do cells existing under anaerobic conditions do with their hydrogen atoms? They simply give them to pyruvic acid, forming either **lactic acid** or **ethyl alcohol:**

$$C_3H_4O_3 + 2H \longrightarrow C_3H_6O_3 \qquad \text{(animal cells and certain bacteria)}$$

pyruvic   lactic
   acid   acid

$$C_3H_4O_3 + 2H \longrightarrow C_2H_6O + CO_2 \quad \text{(plant cells)}$$

pyruvic   ethyl
   acid   alcohol

It should be kept in mind that not all cells possess enzymes for making one or the other of these conversions. In fact, relatively few cells can do so. If a cell *does* possess this capability, and hence produces lactic acid or ethyl alcohol under anaerobic conditions, it is said to carry on **fermentation.** If this is the *only* catabolic pathway open to an organism, it is obliged to forego the greater part of the energy which is bound up in carbohydrate molecules and must make up for this by fermenting more carbohydrate if it is to carry on an equivalent degree of metabolism to that which would be possible if it were capable of utilizing oxygen. For example, when yeast cells[6] are grown under anaerobic conditions, they consume much more carbohydrate in producing a given number of cells than is required under aerobic conditions. To be exact, only about five per cent of the potential energy in a glucose molecule is made available to a cell in fermentation. For this reason, it is apparently not by accident that the great majority of organisms possess mechanisms which make oxygen utilization possible, since this ability renders a species far more

[6] Some organisms, such as yeasts, may live either aerobically (utilizing gaseous oxygen as a hydrogen acceptor) or anaerobically (utilizing its own pyruvic acid as a hydrogen acceptor). Others, such as certain bacteria, are said to be **obligately anaerobic** because gaseous oxygen is actually poisonous to them. Most organisms are, of course, obligate aerobes.

capable of maintaining itself in nature where it is obliged to compete with other species. That there are relatively few anaerobic species is testimony to this principle.

In spite of the principle that the more complex organisms are dependent upon oxygen as a hydrogen acceptor, there are circumstances under which certain cells or tissues may function anaerobically. In muscle cells of man and other vertebrates, for example, energy for contraction is normally provided by the breakdown of ATP to ADP, which is in turn recharged to ATP by a series of steps connected with the complete breakdown of the polysaccharide **glycogen** to carbon dioxide and water. However, under conditions of great activity, the blood stream cannot supply the muscles with oxygen at a rate sufficient to keep up with hydrogen production, and lactic acid (the end product of fermentation in this case) accumulates. In man, at least, this lactic acid is eventually carried to the liver, where it may be completely oxidized. Under these conditions, therefore, the muscle cells are obliged to function anaerobically, which greatly lowers their efficiency for the time being in terms of glycogen utilization.

As far as man is concerned, the fermentation of carbohydrates by yeasts or bacteria may be turned to his advantage. Ethyl alcohol and lactic acid products have long been valued, and the accumulation of these substances in the immediate environments of their producers is made possible through their inability to pass their waste hydrogen on to oxygen.

In summary, glycolysis is the anaerobic catabolism of carbohydrates, with pyruvic acid being the end product of the process. Pyruvic acid may then go in either of two directions. If the accumulated hydrogen cannot be given to gaseous oxygen, glycolysis continues as fermentation. If gaseous oxygen is able to combine with hydrogen in the cell, then **respiration** of pyruvic acid occurs, a process which may be defined as the aerobic phase of catabolism. These alternate pathways are illustrated in Fig. 82. We shall now turn our attention to this second possible phase of catabolism, respiration.

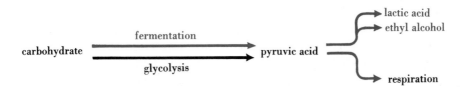

82 The possible fates of a carbohydrate in catabolism. Note that fermentation and glycolysis are identical processes, except that glycolysis ends with the formation of pyruvic acid, and fermentation ends with the formation of either ethyl alcohol or lactic acid.

Cells that carry on respiration do so by virtue of their ability to obtain either products of digestion or glycolysis, which they pass through a further series of reactions. During this process, hydrogen atoms are removed from molecules, and carbon dioxide is formed from the carbon and oxygen remaining on the molecules. Carbohydrates which enter the cell must first pass through the series of changes associated with glycolysis, of course, and they enter the respiratory phase as pyruvic acid. Each molecule of this substance is then joined to a molecule of coenzyme A (see page 37), after which it loses one of its carbon atoms. Some very complex reactions occur at this point, but what is left of the original pyruvic acid molecule remains attached to Co-A, and this two-carbon complex is called **acetyl Co-A.** This transformation may be represented in a highly abbreviated form as follows:

$$\text{Pyruvic acid} + \text{Co-A} \longrightarrow \text{acetyl Co-A} + CO_2$$

Acetyl Co-A then combines with oxaloacetic acid ($C_4H_4O_5$), which is present in the cell, to form **citric acid** ($C_6H_8O_7$), and Co-A is released to re-combine with more pyruvic acid. Several reactions follow, during which a sort of give-and-take process occurs involving water, hydrogen, and carbon dioxide. As a result, two additional molecules of carbon dioxide are thrown off, accompanied by a net loss of four hydrogen atoms. This results in the formation of oxaloacetic acid, which is then ready to react with a fresh molecule of acetyl Co-A, thus forming a new molecule of citric acid. Because this series begins at this point, it is called the **citric acid cycle** (Fig. 83).

A great many substances may enter the citric acid cycle by some means other than the pyruvic acid gateway. Fatty acids from fat digestion enter it as acetic acid ($C_2H_4O_2$), which then becomes transformed to acetyl Co-A.[7] Amino acids may enter at various places along the citric acid cycle after having their nitrogen groups removed. Since carbohydrates are the major fuels for most cells, however, the main pathway of catabolism is by way of glycolysis coupled with respiration.

Carbon dioxide formed in respiration presents no problem to the cell, since it diffuses readily through cell membranes. Thus, whenever a concentration of carbon dioxide builds up within a cell so that a net diffusion occurs outward, the cell is relieved of this waste substance. Disposal of hydrogen atoms presents a much greater problem, however. Ultimately, they are attached to gaseous oxygen with the result that water is formed, but this can occur only after hydrogen is passed along a series of compounds. The first of these are the special hydrogen-accepting nucleotides which we encountered in photosynthesis and glycolysis, the

---

[7] Glycerol, the other fraction of fat digestion, enters the glycolytic sequence by undergoing transformation to PGAL (Fig. 85).

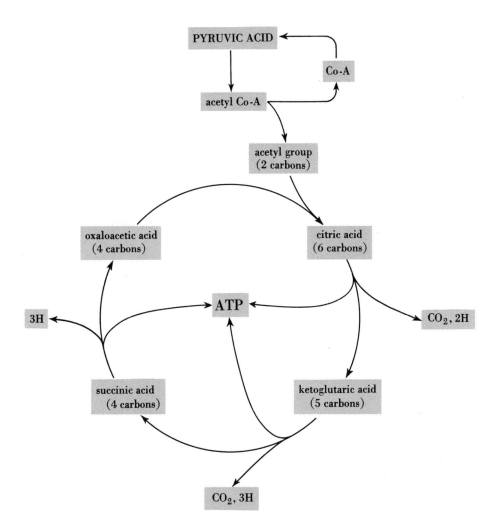

83 Citric acid cycle in abbreviated form. Pyruvic acid, the end product of glycolysis, undergoes respiration by virtue of the reactions shown here. Hydrogen atoms, illustrated as being produced at three points in the cycle, combine with nucleotide acceptors and eventually join with oxygen to form water. Compare with Figs. 84 and 85.

second is **flavoprotein,** which is a derivative of the vitamin **riboflavin,** and the third is a five-member series called **cytochromes.** Actually, it is only the electron of each hydrogen atom that is transported. The hydrogen atoms dissociate into hydrogen ions and electrons when they are cut loose from their parent molecules. We might represent this dissociation as follows:

$$H \longrightarrow H^+ + e^-$$

Although only electrons are involved, with the hydrogen ions being re-joined to them when oxygen enters the picture, we shall ignore this technical point for the present and illustrate the process of hydrogen transfer as though the entire atom were involved. However, this dissociation is very important because it is the passage of electrons that yields much of the total energy of respiration. For thermodynamic reasons that we shall not attempt to explain, energy "levels" are attained gradually by electron transfers, with the result that ADP is joined with phosphate to form ATP. The cell thus "captures" some of this energy, which would all be lost as heat were hydrogen joined directly to oxygen. It should be mentioned that not only is hydrogen from respiration passed along the nucleotide-flavoprotein-cytochrome sequence, but also that hydrogen resulting from glycolysis, already having been picked up by nucleotides, becomes involved, and all hydrogen moves along this common pathway until it joins oxygen. This process is illustrated in Fig. 84, where it is related to catabolism in general.

As a result of this activity, the cell is "rewarded" for furnishing the machinery involved (enzymes, nucleotides, flavoprotein, cytochromes, and so on) by a yield of ATP which it can store. As a secondary compensation, the hydrogen atoms joined to oxygen form water, which is useful to the cell.

Experimental evidence indicates that respiratory enzymes and their associated hydrogen acceptors, when present in the cell, are localized in the mitochondria, whereas those enzymes which make glycolysis possible are present in the surrounding cytoplasm. This, along with certain other lines of evidence, shows that cells are rather highly organized in respect both to structure and function. During the catabolism of a food molecule such as glucose it is first attacked by enzymes present in the cytoplasm. The resulting pyruvic acid is then acted upon in the mitochondria, in cells that possess respiratory enzymes, with the resulting production of carbon dioxide and water. Thus, the mitochondrion assumes a role of considerable importance in the cell, being a unit wherein the respiratory enzymes may function as an organized system.

As is true of fermentation, glycolysis releases only a small part of the potential energy of a food molecule subjected to both phases of catabolism. According to experimental data, a total of thirty-eight molecules of ATP are formed from a corresponding number of ADP molecules during the complete catabolism of a glucose molecule. Only two of these are formed during glycolysis. Thus, in the case of glucose, about ninety-five per cent of the potential energy is released during respiration (Fig. 84).

At this point, we are prepared to summarize catabolism by means of an equation. Since glucose is by far the most common substrate acted upon in cells, we shall use it in the equation:

$$C_6H_{12}O_6 + 6O_2 \xrightarrow[\text{enzymes}]{\text{intracellular}} 6CO_2 + 6H_2O + \text{energy (in the form of ATP)}$$

It should be remembered that this equation actually represents many reactions, and there is a danger that it oversimplifies the process

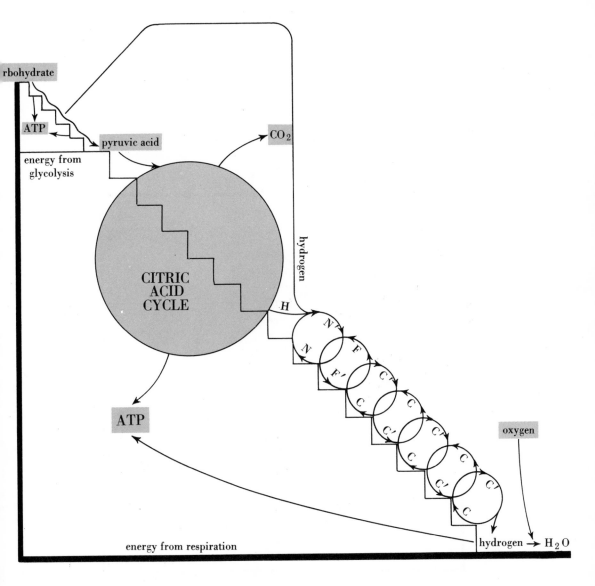

84 Schematic representation of the complete catabolism of carbohydrate to carbon dioxide and water according to a concept of energy levels. N—nucleotide; F—flavoprotein; C—cytochrome. The prime letters (N', F', C') represent reduced, or hydrogen-laden, molecules.

for this reason. However, there is an advantage in being able to see the net result of a series of reactions, and the equation tells us that in the complete breakdown of a molecule of glucose, twelve atoms of oxygen are required. By the time all the energy is realized from the molecule, this oxygen and all atoms originally bound up within the molecule reappear as six molecules of carbon dioxide and six molecules of water. A more complete summary is given in Fig. 85.

A Comparison of Catabolism and Photosynthesis. It will occur to the thoughtful student that the equation given above representing the complete catabolism of glucose is exactly opposite to that illustrating photo-

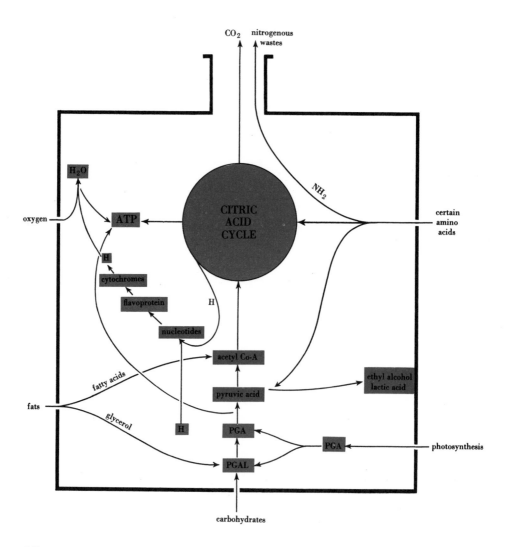

85 A representation of catabolism according to the concept of a furnace.

synthesis, except that solar energy is put into the photosynthetic equation, and energy which is bound up in ATP molecules (usable currency for the cell, in terms of our former analogy) appears after respiration is completed. There is great significance in the similarity that these equations bear to each other; it means that anabolism and catabolism balance each other in nature, with carbon, hydrogen, and oxygen traveling an endless cycle back and forth between the two phases. Hence, the world of life apparently is involved in a sort of suspended matter-energy cycle wherein neither matter nor energy are created or destroyed; they are merely changed. By means of this convenient mechanism, all types of organisms are able to profit from the energy coming to our planet from the sun.

In more specific detail, photosynthesis and catabolism involve many of the same types of enzymes, hydrogen carriers, and intermediate compounds. As we have seen, the special nucleotides to which hydrogen becomes attached are involved in both instances. The compounds PGA and PGAL play important roles in both photosynthesis and catabolism. Glucose, one possible end product of photosynthesis, is the most common substrate of catabolism. Energy transfer and storage in both sequences centers around the ADP-ATP cycle. From the standpoint of energetics, water is split in photolysis only by virtue of the ability of chlorophyll to capture light energy and apply it specifically to separate hydrogen from oxygen. In a much-abbreviated sense, all the reactions that go on between photolysis and the formation of water in respiration are simply a means for getting the energy of sunlight into ATP molecules. In other words, the splitting of water is an energy-consuming (anabolic) process, and the formation of water from hydrogen and oxygen is an energy-releasing (catabolic) process. Figures 85 and 86 illustrate the metabolic link between photosynthesis and catabolism.

One final point of comparison should be made. Because photosynthesis occurs in green plants, there is a prevalent but erroneous belief that respiration occurs only in animals. Perhaps this idea has its roots in attempts on the part of authors and teachers to simplify metabolism by saying that animals "breathe" oxygen and plants "breathe" carbon dioxide. As is the case with many erroneous ideas, there is some truth to such a viewpoint, since animals *do* consume oxygen from their environments, and plants that are active in photosynthesis exhibit a net intake of carbon dioxide over that of oxygen. However, it is obvious at this point that whenever a plant derives energy from a foodstuff it is obliged to consume oxygen (if it is an aerobe) *exactly as an animal does*. This may easily be demonstrated by allowing a number of seeds to germinate within a closed container. It will be found that they deplete the oxygen in the atmosphere of their container within a short time and will stop growing until they are supplied with more. Another way of showing this is to

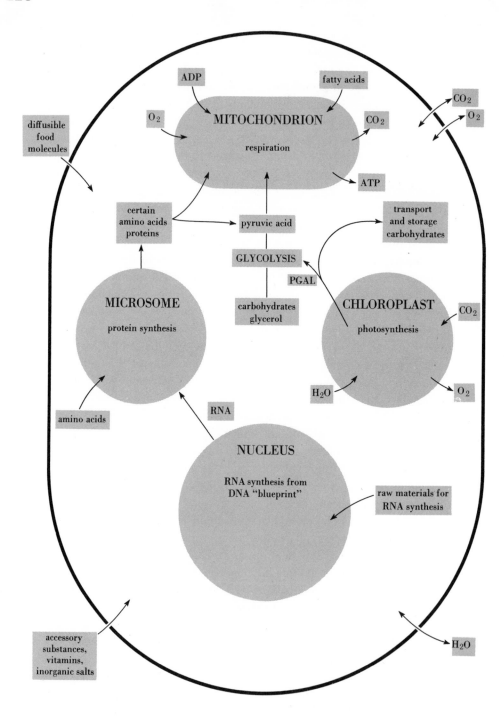

86 Metabolism in terms of a generalized cell, showing the division of labor among cell organelles. It should be kept in mind that this is a schematic representation, and that many cells do not carry on all of these activities.

measure gaseous exchange in a green plant which is maintained for a time in darkness. Under these conditions, it will be found that oxygen is utilized, and carbon dioxide is produced. Finally, heterotrophic plants are unable to utilize carbon dioxide in photosynthesis, and their metabolism is essentially like that of animals.

Energy Expenditure. Thus far, we have only described mechanisms whereby solar energy becomes the readily available energy of ATP molecules. It will be recalled that energy is defined as the capacity to do work, and it behooves us at this point to gain some understanding of the uses to which energy may be put in the organism.

First of all, it should be understood that cells are not one hundred per cent efficient in capturing the total potential energy of food molecules and binding it into ATP molecules. If one hundred eighty grams of glucose (an amount called a **gram molecular weight** of glucose by the chemist) are burned in a device which is capable of measuring precisely the total amount of energy released in terms of calories,[8] it is found that 686,000 such units are made available upon the complete catabolism of this amount of glucose to carbon dioxide and water. Only about 170,000 calories actually become available to the cell, however, the remainder being lost in the form of heat. Thus, the cell is only about twenty-five per cent efficient in the capture of energy made available in catabolism. Few inanimate machines achieve more efficiency than this from their fuels, however, and this yield is thus in line with general thermodynamic expectations. Hence, a large part of the energy to which the cell has access is in the form of heat, and with the exception of birds and mammals, who maintain constant body temperatures, this is of little or no value to the organism.

Of the energy which cells manage to capture, much of it is spent on anabolic reactions. When an organism exhibits an increase in mass as a result of growth, energy must be put into this increase. Even in green plants, where anabolism feeds on sunlight instead of energy derived entirely from ATP molecules, the conversion of PGAL into storage products, cell walls or protoplasm through alteration or combination with other substances involves an expenditure of energy coming from the cells themselves. In non-autotrophic organisms, of course, all anabolic reactions occur at the expense of cellular energy.

Another large area of energy expenditure lies in the various movements exhibited by living organisms. In the case of higher animals,

---

[8] The calorie is rigorously defined as that amount of heat necessary to raise the temperature of one gram water one degree centigrade. The large Calorie, always capitalized in print, represents a thousand small calories. Human physiologists and nutritionists generally use the large Calorie as a unit of heat measurement.

it is quite obvious that the muscles are responsible for expending much of the available energy since food intake becomes almost directly proportional to muscular activity after basal metabolism is accounted for. Even the movement of body fluids in those animals exhibiting blood-vascular systems depends upon the expenditure of energy since heart muscle must perform work in pumping these fluids. Plant organs such as roots and stems display various movements in their growth and in their responses to various external stimuli. These movements depend upon energy expenditure. It is a matter of common experience, for example, that roots often move or break very heavy rocks. Such work on the part of the plant is accomplished only through energy release. Those microorganisms which achieve motility by means of cilia or flagella use energy in the process. Even cytoplasmic movement (**cyclosis**) within cells requires energy.

A variety of activities such as osmosis, filtration, secretion, active transport, and impulse transmission, occurring in varying degrees among different organisms, require relatively small amounts of energy as compared with that expended in anabolism and movement, but their importance is not to be underestimated since they are vital processes wherever they occur. More rarely, organisms expend energy in producing electricity (as does *Narcacion nobiliana,* the electric torpedo, or ray) or light (as does *Photinus pyralis,* the fire-fly).

Whatever the form taken when energy is expended in an organism, ATP is changed to ADP with the release of phosphate groups, recombination to form ATP occurring at a later time in the organism through the catabolic channels which were described above. The importance of this mechanism to the world of life can hardly be overestimated. In spite of the variety of forms that energy expenditure takes in organisms, ATP is apparently involved in all such reactions. It is worthy of note that living organisms have this mechanism in common, which is an indication that all of them are more nearly alike than superficial differences have often led us to believe. We shall encounter other common characteristics that lend support to this view.

The Elimination of Wastes

Metabolism and its accompanying processes result in the accumulation of substances within organisms which are of no further use to them. Ordinarily, such materials become poisonous to the organism producing them unless they are removed, and the elimination of such wastes is therefore an essential function.

THE ELIMINATION OF METABOLIC WASTES. We have already observed that respiration of food molecules is completed with the production of water and carbon dioxide. Since water is not a waste substance, inasmuch as it is of further benefit to the organism, there is no special problem in regard to it. As we have seen, carbon dioxide requires no mechanism on the part of the cell other than simple diffusion for its elimination since it moves readily through the plasma membrane. Merely because the cell rids itself of this metabolic product does not mean, however, that an organism composed of possibly billions of cells can eliminate it without difficulty. While plants and the simpler animals generally require no special organs for getting rid of carbon dioxide (or of other wastes), animals whose body mass renders the elimination of this substance very difficult exhibit mechanisms which are suited to this function. In the vertebrates, carbon dioxide combines with water to produce carbonic acid, which ionizes in the blood stream to form hydrogen ions and bicarbonate ions:

$$CO_2 + H_2O \longrightarrow H_2CO_3 \longrightarrow H^+ + (HCO_3)^-$$

Carbon dioxide is thus transported through the blood stream in the form of bicarbonate ions. Eventually, a reversal of this series of reactions makes possible the release of carbon dioxide to the outside environment through the gills or lungs.

Another group of substances which are of importance in this respect are nitrogenous wastes resulting from the catabolism of proteins. In mammals, for example, nitrogen is removed from amino acids in cells of the liver and is converted first to ammonia (NH_3), which in turn forms urea [$CO(NH_2)_2$]. This substance is collected from the blood stream by the **kidneys,** from whence it passes to the outside of the body in the **urine.**

A variety of other catabolic end products accumulate in cells, depending on the substrate acted on and the enzyme system of any given organism. Such products may diffuse to the external environment in plants and simple animals, or they may eventually find their way to the kidneys in higher animals. By far the most important waste substances which result from the catabolic breakdown of foodstuffs, however, are carbon dioxide and nitrogenous wastes.

All the waste substances described thus far arise within cells and thus are products of metabolism. The term **excretion** is applied to the elimination of this class of waste substances, which distinguishes them from those that are not metabolic in nature, that is, those originating in extracellular rather than intracellular chemical reactions.

THE ELIMINATION OF NON-METABOLIC WASTES. Since animals receive entire food particles into their bodies, it is inevitable that certain portions of such ingested material will prove to be resistant to digestion and hence cannot pass through cell membranes. Under such conditions, the organism is obliged to eliminate such materials as remain after all digestion has been accomplished that is possible. However, elimination of this sort is not excretion, since this term applies to the elimination of metabolic wastes. Such digestive residues are called **feces,** and their elimination is termed **defecation.**

It will be recalled that protozoans carry on digestion in surrounded, extracellular pockets called food vacuoles. Such food molecules as have undergone the digestive process move into the protoplasm of the cell, and the residue is eventually eliminated in a fashion that is somewhat the reverse process of the original ingestion. By virtue of this mechanism, protozoa carry on defecation, even though they are not multicellular. In sponges, cells which are capable of food ingestion carry on defecation in much the same manner as do protozoa. Ceolenterates and free-living flatworms possess only one opening into the digestive cavity, and undigested residues escape from the mouth. In animals exhibiting a tube-within-a-tube type of body plan, feces are eliminated from the posterior opening.

A SUMMARY OF METABOLISM: THE HISTORY OF FOODS IN MAN

In order to coordinate the separate aspects of metabolism which have been discussed to this point, it will be profitable to consider a concrete example of food breakdown and utilization in a higher animal. Since the student is probably more familiar with the structure and function of the human body than with that of any other animal, and because a natural interest may be expected in the identification of metabolic principles with man himself, it is to this subject that we shall now direct our attention.

The Gastro-intestinal Tract and Digestion

Being one of the animals that possess a tube-within-a-tube body plan, man exhibits a gastro-intestinal tract beginning with a mouth and ending with an anus. During embryonic development, the tract grows in length at a more rapid rate than does the body wall, which causes it to be thrown into folds. In a mature human being, it averages about thirty feet in length. Certain accessory organs of digestion, the **salivary glands, liver, gall bladder,** and **pancreas,** develop as outpushings from the embryonic tract, and, when fully developed, they lie in close proximity to it. The digestive tube itself consists of the cavity just posterior to the mouth (properly called the **oral cavity**), the **pharynx, esophagus, stomach, small intestine** (consisting of the **duodenum,**

jejunum, and **ileum,** in that order), and the **large intestine.** Figure 87 shows the relationship of these several organs to each other.

Food enters the mouth, and any solid portions are retained within the oral cavity for a time, where the teeth render them more susceptible to the chemical action which follows by dividing them into smaller pieces. Simultaneously, the secretion of the salivary glands moistens the food mass, making passage along the esophagus possible, and an enzyme, **salivary amylase,** begins a process of hydrolysis whereby the polysaccharide carbohydrates glycogen and starch, if present, are broken down to the disaccharide maltose. Fats and proteins are not chemically affected in the oral cavity.

By the act of swallowing, the moistened food passes through the pharynx and esophagus, entering the stomach through a muscle-enclosed opening. Here it encounters an acid environment, due to the presence of hydrochloric acid in the **gastric juice** secreted by tiny glands in the stomach wall. The salivary amylase, which is inactivated by acid, continues to hydrolyze starch or glycogen for a time, however, because penetration of the food mass by the acid is not instantaneous. Although the gastric juice contains no enzymes capable of acting on carbohydrates, a degree of hydrolysis occurs through the action of hydrochloric acid on some of the bonds that link monosaccharide units together. It appears that very little digestion of fats occurs in the stomach, although they are softened. Protein digestion begins in the stomach through the action of **pepsin,** an enzyme present in gastric juice which acts specifically on certain bonds within protein molecules, thus hydrolyzing many of them to shorter chains.

Whenever a quantity of food is present in the stomach, liquified portions are released at intervals into the duodenum through an opening similar to the one between the esophagus and the stomach. There is usually sufficient alkalinity in the secretions that collect in the small intestine to counteract the acid nature of the liquified food as it comes from the stomach, thus rendering it near the point of neutrality in reaction. It is in the small intestine that the major portion of digestion occurs, the stomach having served chiefly as a site of storage. Secretions from the pancreas and the liver enter the duodenum. Small glands located within the intestinal wall secrete enzymes also. As a result of pancreatic and intestinal secretion, the food mass is exposed to a large number of enzymes in the small intestine, each of which is rather specific for certain types of chemical bonds.

Molecules of starch or glycogen which escaped the action of salivary amylase are hydrolyzed to maltose by an amylase secreted by the pancreas. Maltose and other undigested disaccharides are split to their component monosaccharides by enzymes which form a part of the in-

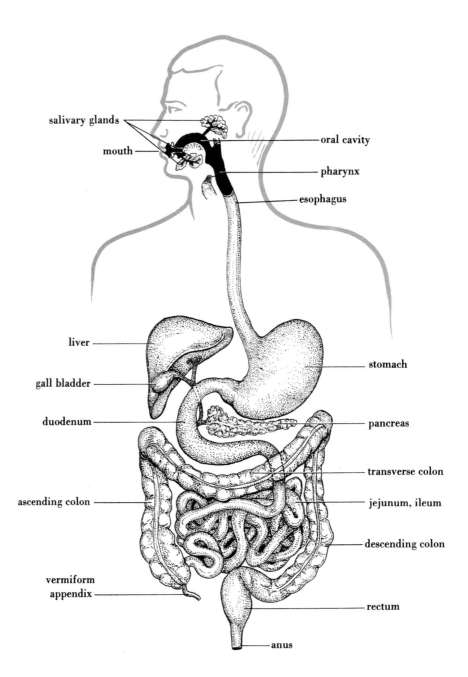

salivary glands

mouth

oral cavity

pharynx

esophagus

liver

gall bladder

duodenum

stomach

pancreas

transverse colon

ascending colon

jejunum, ileum

descending colon

vermiform
appendix

rectum

anus

87 The human gastro-intestinal tract with its associated organs. For illustrative purposes, the several organs of this system are somewhat separated from each other. In their normal positions, they are much more intimately associated.

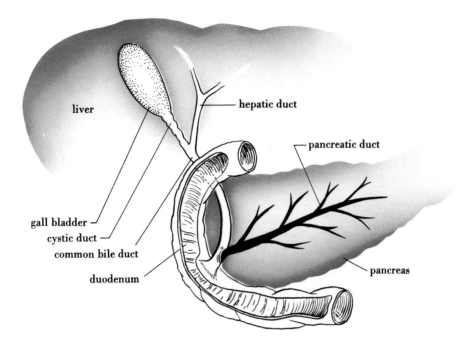

88 The relationship of the liver, gall bladder, pancreas and duodenum. Bile, produced in the liver, is stored in the gall bladder. It and the pancreatic secretion enter the duodenum at the same point.

testinal secretion. Carbohydrate digestion is completed with the production of monosaccharides, since these are diffusible.

It will be recalled that virtually no digestion of fats occurs prior to the time that these enter the small intestine. At this point, however, **lipases** of the pancreatic and intestinal secretions hydrolyze some of the fat molecules to glycerol and fatty acids, both of which are diffusible. Perhaps more than half of the fat is not hydrolyzed but is finely emulsified to molecular aggregates called **chylomicrons,** which eventually pass through the membranes of the cells lining the inner lumen of the intestine.[9] It appears that this emulsification is made possible by the combined action of bile salts, found in the secretion of the liver which empties into the duodenum, and the products of fat digestion resulting from the action of lipases. Thus, the first step in the breakdown of fats is

[9] Ordinarily, molecules as large as those of fats, to say nothing of several such molecules in aggregate, do not penetrate cell membranes. However, due to the constitution of the plasma membrane (largely fatty materials) such aggregates seem to "squeeze" themselves in by combining with other fatty materials in the membrane.

the hydrolytic production of glycerol and fatty acids, which then proceed to emulsify the remaining fat with the help of the bile salts.

By the time proteins reach the small intestine, hydrolysis has occurred to an extent through the action of pepsin. The pancreatic enzymes **trypsin** and **chymotrypsin** render the protein chains still shorter by acting upon links for which they are specific, with the result that **peptides** consisting of relatively few amino acids are produced. Various peptidases (enzymes) of pancreatic and intestinal origin then remove amino acids one at a time, and digestion of proteins is completed since amino acids are able to penetrate the cell membranes of the intestinal lining.

The Fate of Digestive Products

ABSORPTION. Monosaccharides, fatty acids, glycerol, chylomicrons, and amino acids are absorbed into the cells that line the inner surface of the small intestine and pass on to still deeper cells. Eventually, they reach small blood capillaries and lymph vessels which transport them from the intestine. Some of the absorption can be accounted for by simple diffusion, but it is known that under certain conditions active absorption against concentration gradients occurs, at least in the case of certain monosaccharides. The small intestine is well adapted to the process; not only is there a great deal of surface by virtue of its considerable length (about twenty feet), but the lining is characterized by the presence of folds and by finger-like projections known as **villi** (Fig. 89), an arrangement which offers a tremendous amount of surface to the digested food.

TRANSPORT. At this point, let us digress from our main stream of thought and consider more fully the **circulatory** system of man. Early in embryonic life, a **heart** and **blood vessels** form, connect, and in time become functional. At the time of birth (although circulation has already been going on for some months in the individual), the system is ready to begin its work of serving a food-receiving, metabolically active body. The four-chambered heart (Fig. 90) is so organized that its two upper chambers serve as receiving stations, and its two lower ones pump blood outward. Two types of vessels attach to the heart: those which convey blood away from the heart are called **arteries,** and those which conduct blood to the heart are called **veins.** The large arteries, in coursing away from the heart, branch into smaller and smaller vessels and eventually end in the tissues as **capillaries,** which are of microscopic size. As far as the diffusion of food molecules, gases and wastes are concerned, the capillaries constitute the functional portion of the blood-vascular system since their walls are very thin. Ultimately, the capillaries

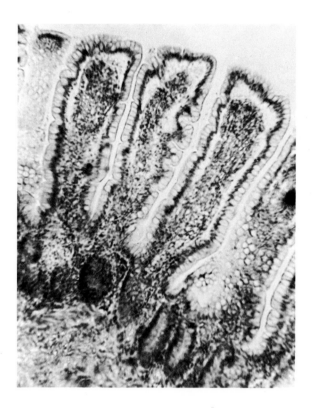

89 Section of human ileum, showing several villi. Note the extent to which the intestinal surface is increased by virtue of their presence.

join in a pattern opposite to their original branching, and form the veins.

In its flow through the heart, blood is returned from the tissues through two large veins that enter the **right atrium.** From this chamber, it passes to the **right ventricle** through a valve and is then pumped through the **pulmonary artery** to the lungs. After coursing through the capillary network there, it returns to the **left atrium** by way of two **pulmonary veins,** each of which branches into two veins before reaching the heart, and continues through a valve into the **left ventricle.** From here, it is pumped through the **aorta,** the largest artery in the body, to the many branch vessels of the arterial system. After passing through the capillary network, it returns to the heart by way of the venous system (Fig. 91). Although the velocity of blood flow varies with a number of factors, including degree of physical activity, a given blood cell completes this cycle, on the average, in a little over a minute's time.

Distinct from the blood-vascular system, but a vital part of cir-

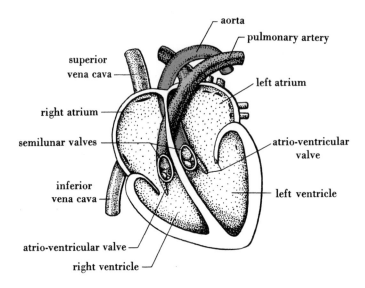

aorta

pulmonary artery

superior
vena cava

left atrium

right atrium

semilunar valves

atrio-ventricular
valve

inferior
vena cava

left ventricle

atrio-ventricular valve

right ventricle

90 Diagrammatic representation of the human heart in frontal section, as it would be viewed from the ventral surface of the body. In its cycle of contraction, the two atria force blood simultaneously into the two ventricles, the wave of contraction spreads downward, and the two ventricles force the blood through the pulmonary artery and the aorta at the same time.

culation, is the lymphatic system. The vessels of this system branch into capillaries, but unlike those of the blood-vascular system, they are "blind." In other words, they do not connect with others, but simply end in the tissues (Fig. 92). They play an important part in returning fluids from the tissues (a result of filtration, diffusion and osmosis outward from the blood-vascular capillaries) to the main circulatory system. Eventually, the **lymph,** as tissue fluid is called after its collection in these capillaries, is carried to certain large veins near the heart, chiefly through two main lymphatic vessels.

Regarding the digestive process, the small intestine is richly vascularized by capillaries which merge to form veins, and these in turn eventually form one vessel, the **hepatic portal vein** (Fig. 91). This vessel conducts blood from the intestine to the liver, where it branches

91 Simplified diagram of human circulatory system showing the relationship between veins and arteries within several organs. Note that the hepatic portal vein begins and ends in capillaries.

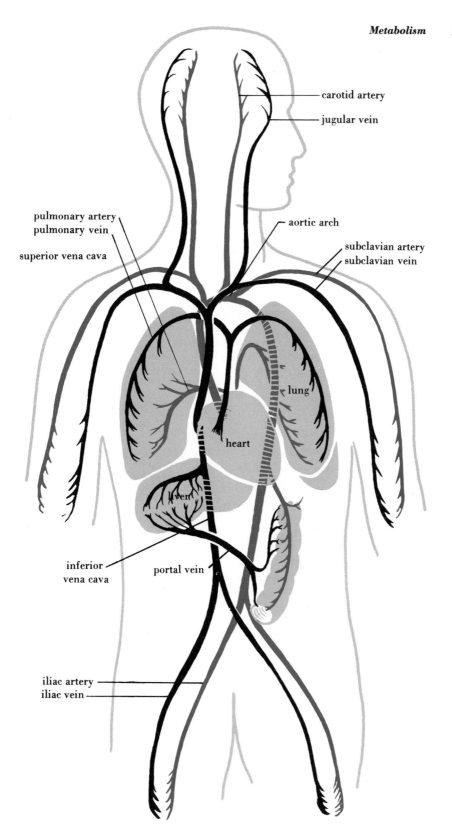

carotid artery

jugular vein

pulmonary artery
pulmonary vein

superior vena cava

aortic arch

subclavian artery
subclavian vein

lung

heart

liver

inferior
vena cava

portal vein

iliac artery
iliac vein

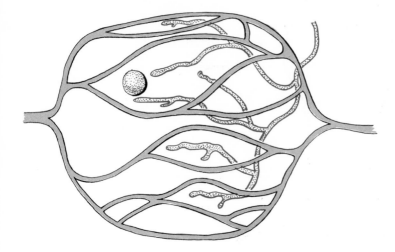

92 A comparison of blood capillaries, which form a continuous network, and lymphatic capillaries, which are "blind." Notice that both are in very close connection with cells, whose metabolic requirements they serve.

into smaller and smaller vessels until capillaries are again formed. Thus any products of digestion reaching the intestinal capillaries are carried to the liver. This is the course taken by monosaccharides and amino acids. Although it appears that fatty acid molecules which are relatively small largely follow this same route, the usual pathway taken by products of fat digestion is that provided by capillaries of the lymphatic system, whose main ducts eventually empty into the blood stream. Hence, these products reach the main circulation without going to the liver as do monosaccharides and amino acids.

UTILIZATION. The chief function of digested carbohydrates is that of furnishing the body with a ready source of energy. Toward this end, the blood stream maintains a fairly constant level of glucose under normal dietary conditions. If this level has fallen during a period of fasting or starvation, glucose and other monosaccharides received from the small intestine are picked up directly from the liver without alteration and are carried to the tissues. Under normal circumstances, however, they are converted in the liver to glycogen by a process known as **glycogenesis** and are stored by the liver in this form. Liver glycogen may be built up to a point of saturation, and spare glucose is then converted to fat in certain tissues of the body. Thus, the carbohydrate "money" of the body exists either as usable currency (glucose), as readily-convertible stocks and bonds (glycogen), or as a storage commodity (fat). Although the liver is the central "bank" for glycogen in the body, this substance may be maintained to some extent in "branch banks" such as muscles. Once glycogen is formed in the liver, however, it must be hydrolyzed to glucose by a process called **glycogenolysis** before it can be transported to such tissues, where a reverse process results in its re-formation into glycogen.

Under normal conditions, it appears that glycerol, fatty acids, and chylomicrons travel directly from the intestine to sites of storage called **fat depots,** of which the mesenteries and the tissues just beneath the skin are most important. Glycerol and fatty acids are recombined into fats which, together with the chylomicrons, serve as raw materials for the synthesis of the particular type of fat characteristic of the human species. Whenever the energy requirement of the body is such that carbohydrate intake is insufficient to meet it and to maintain a normal level of glycogen in the liver and other tissues, these fat stores are called upon. It appears that they are transported under these conditions to the liver, where they are split to glycerol and fatty acids, which then become available to the cells of the body.

Although carbohydrates and fats are involved to a certain extent in anabolic processes within cells, their primary function is that of energy release and storage in the body. In the case of proteins, the reverse is true. The primary function of amino acids as they are absorbed from the intestine is that of growth and repair, as well as utilization in processes which have to do with the general maintenance of body cells. After these needs are met, excess amino acids are converted in the liver to other readily utilizable substances. There is virtually no storage of proteins and amino acids in the body, and these substances must be taken into the body at fairly frequent intervals. If the needs of cells for these materials are not met, the body is obliged to satisfy these requirements by utilizing certain of its own tissues. Under conditions of a normal diet, however, the intake of protein is somewhat greater than that necessary to maintain the tissues. This results in an excess of amino acids in terms of their primary function, and it is these units that enter into transformations in the liver. The conversion of amino acids to other substances or their entrance into the citric acid cycle involves the loss of their NH_2 groups, which are eventually excreted in the form of urea.

In spite of the inability of the body to build up amino acids from fats and carbohydrates alone, since these possess no nitrogen, a certain amount of amino acid synthesis takes place. Some are formed through modification of others, and some are produced from non-protein materials. Certain of the amino acids, however, cannot be made; these must be included in the diet, hence they are termed **essential amino acids.** Eight of the twenty-odd amino acids which make up the proteins of the human diet are essential to man. Not only must these be included in the diet, but they must be present in amounts sufficient to meet the anabolic needs of the body. It is therefore possible that the body may receive amounts of protein which are more than adequate in terms of purely quantitative needs, but if there is a deficiency in even one essential amino acid, the result is a break in the nutritional chain. Fortunately, most proteins are complete in their inclusion of essential amino acids, although not all are equally rich in them. In general, proteins of animal origin are richer than those of plants in this respect, which means that the daily intake of protein must be larger when plant products are chiefly or exclusively utilized as a source.

With the build-up of fat, glycogen, and blood glucose, the body is equipped with immediate and reserve fuels with which to stoke the catabolic fires. Respiration is made possible in the cells through the passage of hydrogen to gaseous oxygen, this final acceptor being transported to the cells by way of the blood stream in loose chemical combination with **hemoglobin,** a pigment present in red blood cells. In addition to a catabolic function, glucose and certain types of fat molecules may also enter into anabolic reactions of various sorts. Growth, repair, and maintenance are made possible by the diffusion of amino acids from the blood stream into cells, and any surplus of these is diverted to the function of energy production through loss of their nitrogen in the liver.

In addition to its intake of carbohydrates, fats, and proteins, the body requires certain inorganic salts whose ions perform a regulatory function in cellular metabolism, and these must be included in the diet. Also essential to the normal functioning of the body is the presence of certain vitamins, which the body is unable to synthesize for itself.[10] These must also be supplied in the diet. Finally, a quantity of water must be received in order to serve the many functions to which this substance is put in the body. Water, vitamins, and inorganic salts require no digestion because their molecules are capable of diffusing through the intestinal lining.

Excretion

As we have emphasized, carbon dioxide and nitrogenous materials (in the form of urea in man) constitute the chief catabolic waste products

[10] Two vitamins, D and K, are synthesized in quantity within the human body. The action of sunlight on a substance in the skin called **ergosterol** changes it to vitamin D, and bacteria of the intestinal tract manufacture vitamin K, which is absorbed when their cells disintegrate. Apparently, no other vitamins are manufactured by the body or obtained from bacterial synthesis in the intestine, at least in appreciable quantities.

of cells. There are two distinct pairs of organs in the human body for eliminating these substances. The **lungs,** which also serve to introduce oxygen into the blood stream, are responsible for the final collection of carbon dioxide; the **kidneys** collect and eliminate urea, as well as certain other metabolic wastes.

The breathing system of man is so constructed that a pair of lungs occupy the **thoracic cavity** which are held open or inflated by the below-atmospheric pressure of the cavity. Each lung is supplied with branches of an air-tube, the **bronchus,** and the two bronchi join to form the **trachea** which opens into the pharynx at the point where the esophagus begins (Fig. 93). As the **diaphragm** and certain muscles of the chest undergo contraction, the thoracic cavity is expanded. Air rushes into the lungs in response to the partial vacuum created by such action, and oxygen is thus made available to the cells of the lungs. Relaxation of the muscles causes the lungs to undergo partial collapse due to their own elasticity, and a quantity of air is expelled.

Functionally, gaseous exchange occurs in the lungs by virtue of the thinness of the lung tissues and of the walls of capillaries which supply them. This exchange is apparently a matter of simple diffusion;

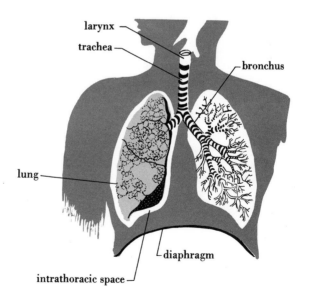

93 A diagram of the human breathing system. Contraction of a broad muscle, the diaphragm, creates a pressure deficit in the intrathoracic space, and air rushes into the lungs. Relaxation of the diaphragm allows the lungs to partially deflate through their own elasticity. By this means, air is inhaled and exhaled alternately.

there is a continual tendency for oxygen to move into the capillaries, and for carbon dioxide to move into the lungs. Intimate contact of cells makes it possible for this exchange to occur (Fig. 94). As would be expected, inhaled air contains more oxygen and less carbon dioxide than exhaled air. As a matter of fact, the air of the atmosphere, as it is inhaled, contains about twenty per cent oxygen and .03 per cent carbon dioxide, whereas exhaled air contains about sixteen per cent oxygen and four per cent carbon dioxide.

Of course, the lungs are concerned as much with respiration as with excretion, and we discuss their function at this point only as a matter of convenience. However, the dual function of these organs is often overlooked, and perhaps we should emphasize their role in excretion for this reason.

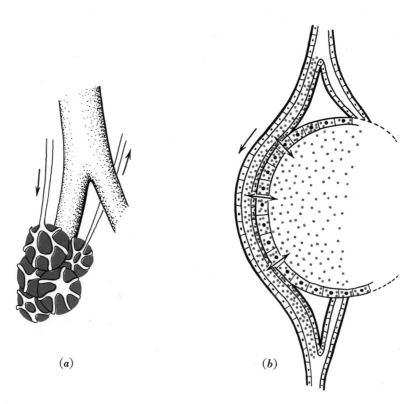

(a)   (b)

94 Gaseous exchange in the lung. a, capillary network surrounding air sacs of lung. Close proximity of cells allows gaseous exchange to occur. b, diagram showing the net diffusion of oxygen (∘) from air sac to capillary, and that of carbon dioxide ( ) in the opposite direction.

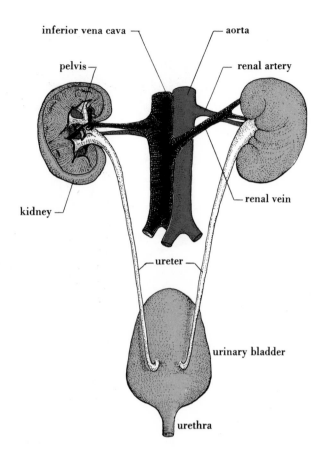

inferior vena cava

aorta

pelvis

renal artery

kidney

renal vein

ureter

urinary bladder

urethra

95 Diagram of human urinary system.

The paired kidneys are located near the dorsal body wall at about the level of the waist. Each is supplied with an artery and a vein, and a urinary duct, the **ureter,** leads from each to the **urinary bladder.** From this site of temporary urine storage, a single tube, the **urethra,** leads to the outside of the body (Fig. 95).

Functionally, the kidney operates in extracting nitrogenous wastes by virtue of an intimate relationship between the capillary bed of its blood vessels and the functional units of the kidney, called **nephrons** (Fig. 96). There are about a million nephrons in each kidney, all of which eventually empty into the pelvis, or collecting space (Fig. 95). Each nephron consists of a **capsule,** which looks like a cup in cutaway view, and a long **tubule,** which connects with others to afford a common drainage into the kidney pelvis. The capsule is filled with a tuft of arterial

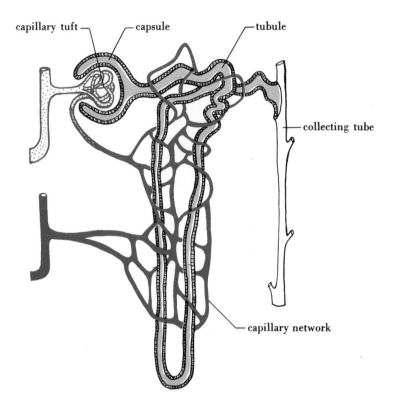

capillary tuft — capsule — tubule

— collecting tube

— capillary network

96 A single nephron of the human kidney and its relationship to the blood-vascular system. For purposes of representation, the tubule is made somewhat shorter here than it actually is.

capillaries, and it is here that removal of materials from the blood stream actually occurs. The walls of both the capillaries and the capsule are extremely thin, and blood pressure causes filtration of materials to occur from the blood stream into the tubule by way of the capsule. How, it might be asked, does the tubule differentiate between waste materials and those in the blood which are of further use to the body? The answer is, it does not. The capsule removes quantities of water, glucose, salts, and other materials. In fact, anything in the blood may filter through except the "formed" materials of the blood (cell and platelets) and the so-called plasma proteins, or normal proteins of the blood, whose molecules are too large to filter through the plasma membranes of the cells involved. As a result of total filtration in both kidneys, thirty-five to forty gallons of fluid are collected in a twenty-four-hour period! Obviously the body cannot spare this much fluid, and we must look for some mechanism whereby some of it is reclaimed. This mechanism resides in the tubules of the nephrons, where a capillary net lies in close proximity to each tubule (Fig. 96). It is here that most of the water and many of the other materials originally filtered out are reclaimed by the blood stream through a process of active absorption. Under normal conditions, the kidneys retain only urea, some other waste products, a small quantity of salts, and enough water to make a total of about a quart and a half of urine produced within a twenty-four-hour period.

Although the lungs and the kidneys are responsible for eliminating the major portion of metabolic wastes, there are a few other mechanisms that should be mentioned. The sweat glands, whose major function is that of temperature regulation, ordinarily remove a little more than a pint of fluid per day from the body. This fluid contains small amounts of urea and other wastes. The liver secretes bile, which contains a number of metabolic residues from the liver. In this case, the distinction which we have drawn between excretion and defecation breaks down somewhat, inasmuch as bile is released into the duodenum and eliminated with the feces. Finally, it should be mentioned that many other tissues, such as the lining of the nasal cavities, may function in a limited excretory capacity through their production of fluids containing small amounts of waste material.

Defecation

After absorption of diffusible food molecules from the small intestine is complete, the residue passes into the large intestine. At this point, the material consists of such indigestible substances as cellulose, which is not attacked by any of the digestive enzymes, and various particles which proved to be resistant to breakdown by virtue of size or texture. A considerable amount of water is also present. Although digestion has already proceeded as far as it can go, myriads of bacteria present in the large intestine attack many of the substances still remaining and thus build up their own populations in that region. Bacterial cells are eliminated as a part of the feces, and it has been estimated that some fifty per cent of the mass as it eventually leaves the body may be represented by living or dead bacteria. During the several hours spent by the fecal material in the large intestine, much of the water is absorbed from it into the blood stream, and the final product is eliminated as a relatively compact mass.

The Ultimate Fate of Human Wastes

Although man is not involved directly, the matter and energy cycles of which his excretory and fecal products become a part are of vital concern to his own metabolism. Carbon dioxide, eliminated by him and by other organisms as a product of respiration, is utilized by autotrophic plants in the formation of new organic compounds. Various bacteria finally convert urinary and fecal wastes to compounds which are used in anabolic processes by these same autotrophs. Although the diet of man is not derived entirely from plant products as such, he depends upon a food chain which of necessity has its roots in the synthesized products of plants. Thus he becomes a part of a grand system of elemental cycles which make possible the necessary metabolic balance that characterizes the world of life. The cycles exhibited by carbon and nitrogen are discussed and figured as typical ones in a later chapter (Chapter 9). Similar cycles occur, of course, for all those elements which are ever incorporated into protoplasm.

CONCLUSION

As we have seen, the phenomenon of metabolism with its accompanying activities is an exceedingly intricate process involving chemical and physical principles which attain to a high degree of complexity. It seems, in fact, that one result of further gains in knowledge of these processes is a greater insight into the vastness of our ignorance on the subject, which is frequently the case in many areas of learning. For example, it was common at one time to speak of the "simple one-celled animals" or the "simple bacteria." Biologists no longer feel as free to speak of simplicity, except in relative terms regarding external morphology, as was once the case. On the basis of present knowledge, it is realized that the simplest of living organisms is really most complex, biochemically, and if metabolism occurs at all, it requires a vast array of mechanisms to make it possible. It is also realized that great gaps exist in our knowledge of these mechanisms and probably will for a long time to come.

Nevertheless, much is known about the chemical and physical activities which characterize organisms, and the importance of these to the world of life is more fully appreciated now than formerly. Although those which are presented in this chapter are elementary, perhaps they will lead the student to a partial understanding of (and quite possibly a thorough appreciation for) this manifestation of life.

QUESTIONS

Multiple Choice

1. Amoeba is considered an animal because (a) it moves, (b) it lacks chlorophyll, (c) it is autotrophic, (d) it is heterotrophic, (e) it is phagotrophic.

2. In the process of photosynthesis, the "by-product" is (a) PGA, (b) PGAL, (c) oxygen, (d) carbon dioxide, (e) chlorophyll.

3. Which of the following is an enzyme that attacks certain carbohydrates? (a) trypsin, (b) chymotrypsin, (c) salivary amylase, (d) pepsin, (e) pancreatic lipase.

4. Which of the enzymes above requires an acid medium for its action?

5. The anaerobic phase of catabolism is called (a) glycolysis, (b) respiration, (c) anabolism, (d) excretion, (e) hydrolysis.

6. Energy obtained by a cell from catabolic reactions is stored immediately in the form of (a) glucose, (b) glycogen, (c) pyruvic acid, (d) DNA, (e) ATP.

7. Of the following, which probably represents the greatest expenditure of energy, considering the entire world of life? (a) secretion, (b) osmosis, (c) impulse transmission, (d) movement, (e) the production of light.

8. Which of the following best explains re-absorption in the tubules of nephrons? (a) osmosis, (b) simple diffusion, (c) filtration, (d) active transport, (e) hydrolysis.

9. Finger-like projections increase the secretory and absorptive area of the small intestine. These are known as (a) chylomicrons, (b) veins, (c) villi, (d) bronchi, (e) tubules.

10. Which of the following best defines the term digestion? (a) the breakdown of foods in the gastro-intestinal tract, (b) the utilization of food by cells, (c) the action of enzymes upon a food mass in the small intestine, (d) the breakdown of foods to a point at which gaseous oxygen serves to combine with hydrogen atoms, (e) the breakdown of food molecules to a soluble and diffusible state.

11. In photosynthesis, the energy of sunlight is utilized specifically by chlorophyll to (a) change PGA to PGAL, (b) change PGAL to glucose, (c) change ADP to ATP, (d) split water to hydrogen and oxygen, (e) attach hydrogen to oxygen.

12. Which of the following is an end product of fat digestion? (a) glucose, (b) fatty acids, (c) amino acids, (d) glycogen, (e) bile salts.

13. In cells, hydrogen is passed along a series of compounds called (a) cytochromes, (b) chlorophylls, (c) hemoglobins, (d) enzymes, (e) vitamins.

14. Which of the following affords the best explanation of osmosis? (a) the diffusion of water, (b) the passage of water from a region of greater concentration through a differentially permeable membrane to a region of lesser concentration, (c) a process wherein water and carbon dioxide are combined to form sugar, (d) a process in which water is raised in a column through pressures that are inherent in solutions, (e) a process in which sugar in solution passes from a region of lesser concentration to a region of greater concentration through a differentially permeable membrane.

15. Which of the following is absorbed in quantity from the large intestine? (a) glucose, (b) urea, (c) amino acids, (d) fatty acids, (e) water.

16. Air enters the lungs because (a) the lungs are elastic, (b) certain muscles contract, (c) certain muscles relax, (d) lung tissues are very thin, (e) the body needs oxygen.

17. The end product of glycolysis is (a) pyruvic acid, (b) citric acid, (c) PGAL, (d) ATP, (e) acetyl Co-A.

18. Atoms of the same element which differ in mass are called (a) ions, (b) isotopes, (c) tracers, (d) salts, (e) co-enzymes.

19. Blood returns from the lungs in the human and is received into the (a) right atrium, (b) right ventricle, (c) left atrium, (d) left ventricle, (e) none of these.

20. When the fat stores of the human body are utilized, they are first broken down to fatty acids and glycerol in the (a) small intestine, (b) large intestine, (c) pancreas, (d) liver, (e) lymphatic vessels.

True-false

1. Photosynthesis represents one type of anabolism.

2. In the growth of a plant, most of the total mass (excluding water) is derived from the soil.

3. In the human gastro-intestinal tract, some of the fat which is present in the food mass is not broken down to fatty acids and glycerol at all.

4. In catabolism, pyruvic acid is changed in one reaction to citric acid which is then broken down to carbon dioxide and water.

5. No organism can exist for very long without a source of gaseous oxygen.

6. Defecation is actually one type of excretion.

7. Apparently, protein synthesis in cells is controlled primarily by DNA molecules of the nucleus.

8. Oxygen is one substance that enters cells readily by osmosis.

9. About fifty per cent of the human fecal mass may be composed of bacteria.

10. Oxygen travels in the human blood stream chiefly in association with the pigment hemoglobin, whereas carbon dioxide is present chiefly in the form of bicarbonates.

11. In the thistle tube experiment, fluid rises in the tube because the water is hypertonic to the syrup.

12. One fundamental difference between plants and animals is that animals carry on digestion, whereas plants do not.

13. It is entirely possible for a food molecule to enter the citric acid cycle at some point other than by the pyruvic acid gateway.

14. Products of carbohydrate and protein digestion enter the blood stream in man, but most products of fat digestion enter the lymph stream.

15. Most proteins are complete in their inclusion of essential amino acids.

16. Lymphatic capillaries connect directly with arterial capillaries, and circulation is continued in this manner.

17. The oxygen liberated during photosynthesis comes from the carbon dioxide that is broken down during the over-all process.

18. The terms fermentation and glycolysis are synonymous.

19. It is actually the electrons of hydrogen atoms, rather than the atoms themselves, that are passed along the nucleotide-flavoprotein-cytochrome system.

20. Both pancreatic juice and bile enter the gastrointestinal tract at the duodenum.

Questions For Consideration and Discussion

1. Define the following terms: respiration, metabolism, excretion, photolysis, photosynthesis, heterotrophic nutrition, anaerobe, plasmolysis, active transport, glycogenesis.

2. Criticize this statement: "Animals breathe oxygen, and plants breathe carbon dioxide."

3. Exactly why did fluid rise in the thistle tube under the conditions outlined in the beginning portion of this chapter?

4. Trace the pathway of a bite of food containing all three food types from the time that it enters the mouth of a human to the time that its components are absorbed through the intestinal wall. Now assume that one glucose molecule enters a cell and is subjected to complete catabolism. Tell what happens in this process.

5. Write the over-all equation for photosynthesis; for complete catabolism.

6. What are the main waste products of catabolism in animals?

7. Some organisms do not adhere strictly to the nutritional "rules" governing animals and plants. Name some of these exceptions.

8. Discuss the roles played by ADP and ATP in metabolism.

9. What is the normal course of action in the human body when food intake is greater than that necessary to satisfy the immediate needs of the body? What occurs when the reverse situation exists? Discuss this over-all process thoroughly.

10. Why are biologists hesitant to speak of bacteria and protozoa as being "simple" organisms?

REFERENCES

CARLSON, A. J., VICTOR JOHNSON and **H. M. CAVERT.** *The Machinery of the Body,* 5th ed. Chicago: The University of Chicago Press, 1961. A clear, forthright presentation of human biology that will serve as good collateral reading for parts of this chapter.

GALSTON, A. W. *The Life of the Green Plant.* Englewood Cliffs, N.J.: Prentice-Hall, Inc., 1961. One of the FOUNDATIONS OF MODERN BIOLOGY series, this book will be especially helpful at this point in regard to photosynthesis.

MC ELROY, W. D. *Cellular Physiology and Biochemistry* (see reference at end of Chapter 3). This book is recommended in its entirety to be read in connection with this chapter.

SCHMIDT-NIELSON, KNUT. *Animal Physiology.* Englewood Cliffs, N.J.: Prentice-Hall, Inc., 1960. This book is another in the FOUNDATIONS OF MODERN BIOLOGY series; much of it is devoted to topics that are covered in this chapter.

In addition to the books above, the following articles from *Scientific American* are recommended.

ARNON, D. I. "The Role of Light in Photosynthesis," Volume 203 (November, 1960), p. 104. Some of the mechanisms involved in the transformation of light energy into the potential energy of carbohydrates are discussed in this article.

FENN, W. O. "The Mechanism of Breathing," Volume 202 (January, 1960), p. 138. The structure and function of the human lungs and their accessory structures are discussed.

HOAGLAND, M. B. "Nucleic Acids and Proteins," Volume 201 (December, 1959), p. 55. An article dealing with the role of nucleic acids in protein synthesis.

LEHNINGER, A. L. "Energy Transformation in the Cell." Volume 202 (May, 1960), p. 102. The role of ATP in cellular reactions.

SMITH, H. W. "The Kidney," Volume 188 (January, 1953), p. 40. An account of the structure and function of the human kidney.

WIGGERS. C. J. "The Heart," Volume 196 (May, 1957), p. 74. An account of the structure and function of the human heart.

CHAPTER 6

Growth

Having discussed the phenomenon of metabolism and the activities which accompany it, we are now in position to comprehend a second characteristic of living matter, growth, which is made possible in an organism by virtue of anabolic processes resulting in the synthesis of protoplasm. The ability to utilize materials found in its environment for the production of more complex substances gives protoplasm a unique distinction; although crystals or rocks may "grow" by the accumulation of various materials, this is hardly comparable to the complex metabolic activities exhibited by protoplasm in adding to its own total quantity. It becomes our present task to direct attention to different circumstances under which growth may occur, various types of growth, and the specialization of cells and tissues which occurs in the phenomenon called **differentiation.**

THE BIOLOGICAL MEANING OF GROWTH

By definition, growth simply means *increase in mass.* However, when the biologist states that growth is a characteristic of life, he does not mean that every living organism is adding to its total quantity at all times or that every cell in a complex body is synthesizing more proto-

plasm. Whereas most plants continue to grow as long as they live, it is characteristic of the higher animals to reach a certain size at which point further over-all growth is not necessarily demonstrated. The statement that growth is a characteristic of life means that protoplasm exhibits the *potentiality* of growth, although in cases where cells are sufficiently specialized as to have lost the ability to increase their total mass, growth occurs only in the extremely limited sense that cellular parts are replaced as they wear out.

Over-all growth of a multicellular organism may occur in two ways. Its cells may simply become larger, as is the case in a human being when fat is stored, or its cells may increase in number by growing individually and dividing. Unless it is defined otherwise in its usage, biologists generally employ the term in the latter sense, that is, to mean an increase in number of cells. In unicellular organisms, such growth results in an increase in number of individuals, of course and is thus a process of reproduction at that level.

THE PROCESS OF CELL DIVISION

As we have noted, cells may divide to form other cells under certain circumstances. The forces which initiate this process are not entirely clear, but division is usually preceded in a given cell by the synthesis of sufficient protoplasm that when the cell reaches its maximum size, division occurs to produce two daughter cells from the original one. Cells exhibiting a high degree of metabolic activity, for example bacterial cells under optimal conditions, may divide as frequently as every fifteen or twenty minutes. There is remarkable uniformity among organisms in regard to the mechanics of cell division. With the exception of certain forms whose nuclear materials are atypical, such as blue-green algae, division may be said to consist of two processes, namely, nuclear division or **mitosis** and cytoplasmic division or **cytokinesis.**

Division of the Nucleus—Mitosis

The first indication that a cell is about to undergo division is a visible change in the chromatin "network" of the nucleus. Special staining or microscopical techniques reveal that this material is not really a network at all but that it consists of elongated threads which are distinct from each other. As the nucleus undergoes further change, these threads gradually condense and thicken. Because this is the first and most obvious of the nuclear changes associated with division of the nucleus, early cytologists settled upon the name mitosis (Gr. *mitos,* a thread) to describe the entire process of nuclear division. From the beginning of the mitotic process to the formation of two daughter nuclei, four progressive and interconnected stages or phases are recognized.

PROPHASE. This stage begins with the condensation of the chromatin threads, which are called **chromosomes** as they become distinctly visible (Figs. 97, 98). The number of chromosomes which finally make their appearance at late prophase is generally constant for a species; for example, the cells of onion (*Allium cepa*) exhibit sixteen chromosomes, and those of the parasitic roundworm *Ascaris lumbricoides* possess only four. These two species are mentioned as examples because they are frequently used to demonstrate mitosis to beginning students. The chromosome number per cell in man is forty-six. In the cells of some organisms, the chromosomes number into the hundreds. Apparently, there is no correlation between chromosome number and degree of complexity of an organism.

Great variation in chromosomal morphology occurs among species, there being differences both in size and shape. Even within a species, the chromosomes can often be distinguished from one another, and can be named or numbered on that basis. In the cells of the great majority of organisms, a given chromosome is seen to have a morpho-

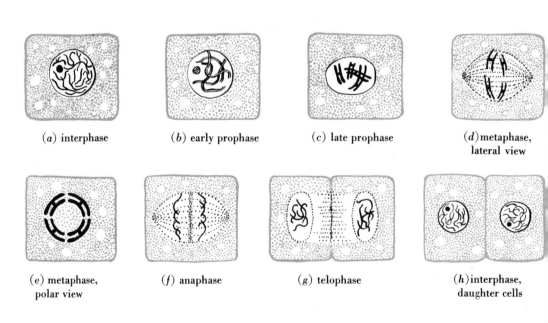

(*a*) interphase   (*b*) early prophase   (*c*) late prophase   (*d*) metaphase, lateral view

(*e*) metaphase, polar view   (*f*) anaphase   (*g*) telophase   (*h*) interphase, daughter cells

97 Cell division in a hypothetical plant whose cells possess four chromosomes. a, interphase. b, early prophase. c, late prophase. d, metaphase, lateral view. e, metaphase, polar view. f, anaphase. g, telophase. h, interphase, daughter cells.

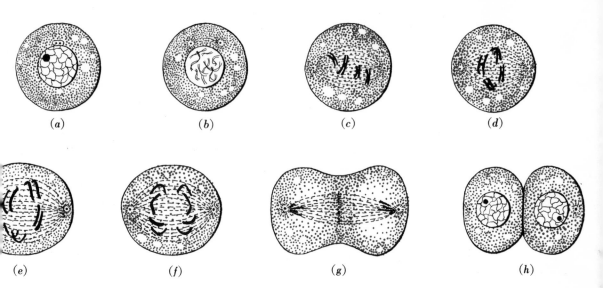

98 Cell division in a hypothetical animal whose cells possess four chromosomes. a, interphase. b, early prophase. c, late prophase. d, metaphase, lateral view. e, early anaphase. f, late anaphase. g, telophase. h, interphase, daughter cells.

logical partner; that is, the chromosomes exist in pairs, although paired chromosomes show no tendency to associate closely in the nucleus.[1] Hence, it is frequently said that an organism exhibits a certain number of chromosome pairs; onion has eight pairs, *Ascaris* has two pairs, and so on. As will be emphasized in a later chapter, the members of these pairs are the descendants of those contributed by the individual's two parents.

If the chromosomes are closely examined as they become visible at prophase, they will be seen to consist of two parallel halves called **chromatids,** which are connected by a **centromere** (Figs. 97, 98). Hence, this stage of mitosis reveals the presence of twice as many chromatids as there are chromosomes.

At some time during prophase, the nucleoli and nuclear membrane disappear. The full significance of this is not completely understood, but one immediate result is that the nucleoplasm is no longer separated from the cytoplasm. Consequently, beginning with late prophase, a cell does not really possess a nucleus during its division, even though we speak of "nuclear division."

[1] Paired chromosomes do become closely associated during a special type of nuclear division called meiosis, which we will discuss in a later chapter.

METAPHASE. Near the end of prophase, the chromosomes become oriented in such a way that a lateral view of the cell shows that the chromatids of a given chromosome are in position to move toward opposite poles of the cell; at the point when the centromeres of all the chromosomes are so oriented as to lie in an equatorial plane (Fig. 97*d*, 98*d*), metaphase is said to begin. In a polar view of the cell (Fig. 97*e*), a ring or plate of chromosomes is characteristically seen. Meanwhile, a **spindle,** so called because of its shape, appears in conjunction with the orientation of chromosomes, and some of the **fibers** which compose it attach to the centromeres of the chromosomes, while others simply run from pole to pole.

Perhaps the most significant event which occurs during metaphase is the division of chromosomal centromeres. This results in the possession of a centromere by each chromatid. Half the original number of chromatids (now called **daughter chromosomes**) are thus prepared for movement toward one pole and half toward the other, each set constituting the chromosomal complement of a daughter nucleus.

ANAPHASE. With the division of centromeres, which occurs simultaneously in all the chromosomes of a given nucleus in most cases, **anaphase** begins. There is a shortening of those spindle fibers that attach to the centromeres of daughter chromosomes, as though a pulling force were being exerted. Actually, the forces responsible for chromosomal movement in this situation are not clearly understood, but the attachment of spindle fibers to the centromeres is suggestive of some active role by the fibers in chromosomal migration. At late anaphase, chromosomes which are moving toward opposite poles of the cell are widely separated (Figs. 97*f*, 98*f*).

TELOPHASE. Telophase begins when chromosomal migration is complete, and it is somewhat the reverse of prophase. The chromosomes gradually lose their apparent individual identity and they collectively form the chromatin "network," or mass, typical of a nucleus that is not involved in division. Nucleoli and the nuclear membrane reappear, and telophase ends when the two daughter nuclei are identical to the original nondividing nucleus except in size.

A nucleus which is not undergoing mitosis is said to be in **interphase.** In actively dividing cells, this is a period of synthesis and growth on the part of the nucleus, which enables it to enter again into mitosis at a later time. During interphase the chromosomes lose their definite stainability, but it has been shown that their individual identity is retained. In other words, chromosomes are not dissolved and reformed at telophase and prophase respectively; they simply assume different morphological forms.

It should be recognized that the stages of mitosis are portions of a continuous division cycle and that there is no definite point between each; the phases are recognized by cytologists simply as convenient divisions for reference purposes. By observing the process closely with proper optical equipment, it can be seen that the nucleus moves smoothly from one phase to another.

Intimately associated with the process of mitosis in animal cells is the behavior of the centrosome and centrioles. During prophase, the centrosome divides and each half undergoes migration in such a way that the two centrioles lie opposite to each other. At metaphase, a centriole is thus situated at either side of the nucleus, and each serves as a center from which the spindle fibers and **astral rays** radiate (Fig. 98*d*). Plant cells, except for those of certain lower forms, do not exhibit centrioles. Nevertheless, a spindle is generally formed, although astral rays are not.

Division of the Cytoplasm—Cytokinesis

The process of cytokinesis is considerably less dramatic than that of mitosis, consisting in a given cell of some mechanism whereby the cytoplasm is separated into two more or less equal parts. Usually, cytoplasmic organelles or inclusions such as mitochondria or plastids are distributed more or less equally in the process.

In animal cells, cytokinesis is accomplished by **constriction,** the process generally being initiated at about the time of mitotic anaphase. By the end of telophase, when daughter nuclei are fully formed, constriction is complete (Fig. 98*h*). A variation of constriction is seen in the furrowing process characteristic of certain embryos and other cellular aggregates in which groups of cells divide simultaneously and remain in close contact with each other following cytokinesis.

As an accompaniment of their non-living cellulose walls, whose rigidity renders constriction impossible, plant cells exhibit a mode of cytoplasmic division different from that described above for animal cells. Cytokinesis begins in the plant cell by the formation of a **cell plate** in the middle of the cell at about the time mitotic anaphase ends (Fig. 97*f*). The cell plate continues to grow in circumference until it meets the outer walls of the cell. In the meantime, the nucleus has progressed from telophase to interphase, and division of the cell is completed by differentiation of a new cell wall on both surfaces of the cell plate.

In certain plants, cytokinesis is somewhat animal-like. For example, dividing cells of the green alga *Chlamydomonas,* a unicellular species, undergo constriction of the protoplast within the cell wall. Each division product may undergo subsequent divisions, but at any rate, daughter cells will have secreted new cell walls when the original wall breaks open and releases them (Fig. 99).

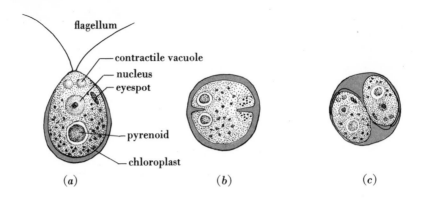

99 *Chlamydomonas eugametos.* a, vegetative cell. b, telophase of mitotic division within cell wall, cytokinesis of protoplast almost complete. c, two daughter cells within old cell wall.

In spite of certain minor variations that occur among organisms in regard to its details, cell division is a remarkably uniform phenomenon. This is highly significant, since it lends further support to the view that living forms are fundamentally similar. Whatever the physical and chemical factors involved, nature seems to have hit upon the mechanism of mitosis as a means for ensuring a qualitatively and quantitatively equal distribution of certain key nuclear substances to newly synthesized cytoplasm. As we shall see, the chromosomes are bearers of hereditary determiners (**genes**), and it is significant that each cell of an organism normally possesses exactly the same complement of these as any other cell. The process of mitosis makes this possible. Because it can produce more cells, a given multicellular organism is able to increase its own body mass, undergo histological specialization, and repair tissues through cell replacement. As a fundamental biological process, therefore, cell division ranks exceedingly high.

THE PHENOMENON OF DIFFERENTIATION

It will have occurred to the student by this time that protoplasm is an extremely versatile material. Although it exhibits basic characteristics which are found universally, variations exist in its chemical and physical constitution. Were this not the case, all cells, tissues, and organisms would be exactly alike.

For reasons that are not entirely clear (although some insight has been gained), cells and protoplasmic structures may become so organized as to perform specialized tasks that other cells or structures do not perform. The process by means of which such specialization is achieved is termed **differentiation.** The differentiation of cells is most clearly demonstrated by the changes which occur in embryonic tissues of plants and animals between the time they arise by division of a parent cell and the time when they become fully specialized.

Perhaps an analogy will serve to clarify these processes, at least in regard to their significance. In our society, we produce children who are destined to become specialized members of a complex social group. To a certain age, they are much alike except in potentiality and environment. They all attend school and study the same subjects, and at least until they finish their early education, they are not much different from each other as far as society and their roles in its behalf are concerned. They are merely students. Gradually, however, they are led into different fields of endeavor. By the time a given class of unspecialized twelve-year-olds has reached the age of thirty, great diversification has taken place. One person is a physician, another a teacher, still another an electrician, and so on.

In a metaphorical sense, such individuals are the "cells" of a societal organism, and their specialization parallels in certain ways that of cells which develop in an actual organism. Furthermore, as is the case with their societal analogues, the factors which contribute to the ultimate fate of a given cell or its progeny are quite complex. It is entirely beyond the scope of this book to attempt a detailed account of the mechanics of differentiation in various organisms, but perhaps mention of experimental approaches to the problem and some of the factors that have been discovered will be enlightening.

Generally speaking, there are two classes of factors which determine the fate of a given cell and its division products. Certain of these factors are **intrinsic,** being localized within the cells themselves, while others are **extrinsic,** depending upon influences external to the cells.

As an example of the experiments which show that normal development and differentiation of embryonic cells are dependent upon intrinsic factors, the work of certain investigators on embryos of the sea urchin, an echinoderm, may be cited. The fertilized egg of the sea urchin is so constituted that one half is much richer in yolk than the other. Normally, the first divisions are in such a plane as to produce cells that are similar in the amount of yolk they contain. If these cells are shaken apart under appropriate conditions, each will develop into a sea urchin larva. Thus, differentiation of cells does not begin in the sea urchin until divisions occur in such a plane as to produce cells with unequal amounts of yolk and other cytoplasmic inclusions. In fact, the sea urchin egg can be forced to divide at right angles to the normal plane at the first division by constricting it with a string. As a result, neither cell develops into a normal larva, because differential distribution of certain materials has been induced too early for normal development to occur (Fig. 100). Some animals, however, begin their divisions in such a way that distribution is initiated at the first cleavage.

The intrinsic factors which influence differentiation in the early divisional stages of the sea urchin or in the first division of some cells are thus cytoplasmic in nature since distribution of nuclear material in the mitotic process is equal. Because all cell divisions of this type involve an equal distribution of nuclear material to daughter cells, it might be thought that the nucleus has nothing to do with differentiation. Actually, it has a great deal to do with it, as certain experiments show. Again, using the sea urchin as an example, it is possible to cause double fertilization by introducing two sperm cells into the egg. This creates an abnormal nuclear situation in which early divisions produce cells some of which receive an abnormal set of chromosomes, and still others which manage to receive the normal complement. Upon separating these cells, it is found that only those with a normal chromosomal complement develop normally. Thus it is seen that development and differentiation are dependent upon a particular "set" of chromosomes.

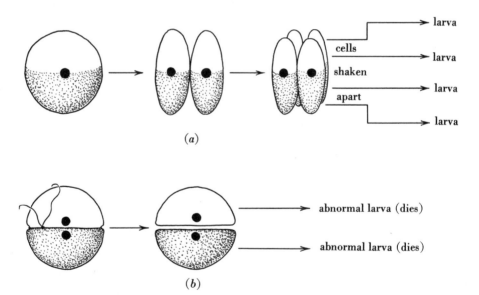

100 Diagram representing experiments with fertilized sea urchin eggs. a, division allowed to proceed to four-cell stage, at which time cells are shaken apart. Each undergoes subsequent normal development into a separate larva. b, abnormal constriction induced artificially with a string, resulting in unequal distribution of yolk. Each daughter cell may divide a few more times, and then dies.

As a matter of fact, the nucleus with its chromosomes and genes is by far the most important intrinsic factor in development. As we have seen, DNA of the nucleus (which operates as the units we call genes) controls protein synthesis in the microsomes. The genes interact with the immediate cytoplasm, which furnishes the substrates necessary for protein synthesis, and in this manner they dictate the specific nature of any given cell or the division products of a cell. At any level of development or differentiation, therefore, there is a chain of cause and effect which carries over to the next level. In a sense, each embryonic stage of a plant or an animal is a new organism, and the next stage is built on the shoulders of the preceding one. Obviously, the total picture is not complete without a consideration of extrinsic factors, but it should be kept in mind that the genic pattern and the substrate materials localized within the cell are the major controlling factors of development and differentiation. The processes associated with the phenomena of genic control and precise embryonic development are sufficiently intricate that we have only begun to understand them at all.

Less is known about extrinsic factors which influence differentiation than about intrinsic ones. Experimental studies indicate, however, that these play an important role. For example, the differences in oxygen availability and the opportunity for waste removal which exist between cells at the surface of an embryo and those that lie more deeply result in different metabolic and divisional rates. Furthermore, chemical influences from one cell group to another are known to prevail. In a vertebrate embryo, groups of cells develop as "organizers," which is the first stage in differentiation of cells to form specific organs. These organizers influence cells around them, which are as yet undifferentiated, to form certain tissues. That this influence is a chemical one is shown by the phenomenon that induction may be effected by the use of extracts from organizer cells. For instance, the first organizer to form in the frog embryo is a certain patch of tissue which influences, among other things, the development of the nervous system. If cells of this organizer are transplanted to a portion of the embryo far removed from the normal site of nervous system development, they induce a nervous system there. However, it is not necessary to transplant the cells themselves; if they are destroyed and extracts of their contents are injected just beneath the surface of an embryo at some point of its body, a nervous system will develop at that point. In other words, such experiments as this definitely establish the principle that substances from one cell group may pass into another cell group in the normal embryo with the result that the latter cells are influenced to differentiate along certain lines. Thus, any such chemical substances constitute extrinsic factors *as far as the influenced cells are concerned,* even though they are not extrinsic to the embryo itself. Much is yet to be learned about the exact chemical basis for such influence, but organization and induction are very important factors in differentiation.

Aside from the fundamental causes, or the *how* of cell differentiation, embryologists have gained much information about the actual processes, or the *what,* in several types of organisms. In animal embryos, for example, cells or groups of cells may be marked in various ways and their fates can thus be traced. It has been common to use harmless dyes, graphite or other such materials for marking cells. Similarly, methods for studying cellular differentiation have been developed in regard to plants. From such studies, a wealth of information has been gained regarding the ultimate fate of various embryonic plant and animal parts.

Thus far in our consideration of differentiation, we have thought only in terms of *histological specialization,* that is, the development of cells to form a part of some tissue which is known by its particular function. How can we account for the ability of unicellular organisms to exhibit within a single cell the many accomplishments necessary to the maintenance of life? It must be concluded that a cell such as *Amoeba* is obliged to be a jack-of-all-trades in its activities, and any differentiation within its protoplasm is of necessity based on *cytological* specialization of cell organelles. A great deal of research has been directed toward the identification of structure with function in such organisms, and much evidence for a high degree of specialization has accumulated. For example, removal of the nucleus from *Amoeba* by microdissection results in a cell which may live and carry on some activities for a time, but loss of the nucleus is accompanied by a loss of certain vital activities. These may be restored if a nucleus from another amoeba is pushed into the cell. Again, it has been shown by centrifuging mitochondria from cells and testing them for physiological properties that they serve as storehouses for enzymes without which the cell could not carry on respiration. Other organelles of the cell have been similarly shown to perform definite and specific functions.

Actually, all cells exhibit a high degree of cytological differentiation, as is shown by the well-nigh universal appearance of nuclei, mitochondria, microsomes, and certain other organelles. The organization of an endoplasmic reticulum, which was previously noted, indicates a high degree of structural organization. It will be recalled that the sea urchin egg is differentiated in such a way as to require early divisions in a certain plane for normal development to occur. Thus, it should not be thought that cells of multicellular organisms are specialized past all cytological differentiation; some, in fact, are hardly specialized at all histologically. The unicellular forms are the Robinson Crusoes of the cell world, and cells such as nerve cells of higher animal bodies are the physicians, teachers, and electricians of a complex society. The physician is, nevertheless, obliged to retain certain unspecialized abilities to at least a degree; he can still drive a nail or change an automobile tire, although he is neither a carpenter nor a mechanic. In the same way, even highly specialized cells retain some of their unspecialized abilities. For example, liver cells of higher animals are more active in metabolism than most cells, but all carry on metabolism to some degree. Nerve cells are specialized in the conduction of impulses, but all cells are capable of this to at least a certain extent.

One of the many outstanding biological principles which have come to be recognized as a result of such cell studies as those described above is that unicellular organisms are no less complex than their multicellular superiors except in a purely organizational sense. It is simply that their organization is completely *cytological* rather than being partially *histological*. This has resulted in a revised viewpoint toward the so-called "simple" organisms and has bred a profound respect for protoplasm and its complexities in all forms of life.

GROWTH AND DIFFERENTIATION IN ANIMALS

Early Embryogeny of Multicellular Animals

Although some of the lower multicellular animals reproduce by the development of new individuals from single, uniparental cells or aggregates of cells (asexual reproduction), by far the most common method is that in which a male reproductive cell (sperm) unites with a female reproductive cell (egg) to form a **zygote.** This new cell, which is made up of cellular materials from both parents, undergoes successive divisions to form an **embryo.**

Differentiation of cells occurs in such a way that sheets of cells, the **primary germ layers,** are soon formed. We have already learned that diploblastic embryos develop two such layers, the ectoderm and endoderm, and that triploblastic embryos develop a third, the mesoderm, in addition to these. It is as though the embryo were both a weaver and a tailor charged with the task of making a suit of clothes. Before attempting to start the actual construction of the garment, it first weaves its cells into two kinds of "cloth," if the end product is to be fairly simple in form, or three kinds, if more complexity is required. Thus, early embryogeny is concerned with cell division and differentiation to the extent that the primary germ layers are laid out and made available for more exact specialization of body parts. The details of this process differ some-

101 A group of amphioxus, natural size, arranged in rows. The dorsal surface is the more curved, while the ventral surface is marked by a series of gonads that appear light in color in this photograph. (Courtesy General Biological Supply House, Inc.)

what among the various species of animals and especially among members of phyla which are widely separated in the phylogenetic scale. However, it is significant that this general plan of primary germ layer formation is seen wherever sexual reproduction occurs in multicellular animals.

As an example of the actual process of germ layer formation, let us consider the early development of an animal whose common name is amphioxus (Fig. 101), a protochordate, which has been the subject of much study, and whose development is similar to that of both the vertebrates and many of the invertebrates. Amphioxus is a marine animal about two inches or less in length which spends most of its adult life buried in the sand of the shallow ocean floor with only the anterior end of its elongate body protruding into the water. Male and female individuals release their reproductive cells simultaneously in the same vicinity, and zygotes are soon formed as a result of sexual union of eggs and sperm.[2] Development of the zygotes and embryos then proceeds upon or near the surface of the water.

The egg of amphioxus is relatively small (about one-tenth of a millimeter in diameter) and contains very little stored food. Successive cleavages (Fig. 102) produce a ball of cells which gradually round up to enclose a cavity (Fig. 102*f*). At this point, the embryo is called a **blastula,** and the cavity is termed a **blastocoele** (Gr. *blastos,* sprout + *koilia,* cavity). When the blastula is fully formed, more than two hundred cells are arranged in a single thickness around the blastocoele.

[2] "Sperm" is both singular and plural.

It will be noticed that the cells at one side of the blastula are larger than the rest (Fig. 102*e*, *f*). This is a result of their being derived from that portion of the original cell which contained the most yolk, or stored food material. By the time blastulation is complete, these cells begin to lag behind the others in their divisions. This difference in division rates, plus certain other forces, causes an inpushing of these larger cells, much as though one were to push his finger into a soft, hollow rubber ball (Fig. 103*a–c*). This changes the single-walled blastula to a double-walled form called a **gastrula,** and the point where the inpushing occurred marks the site of an opening, the **blastopore,** which opens into a new cavity, the **archenteron** (the blastocoel having been obliterated by the inpushing of cells). Thus, the embryo at this point exhibits two layers of cells, the ectoderm and endoderm.

Further development results in an elongation of the embryo (Fig. 103*d*) and an overlapping of the blastopore by the ectoderm. The dorsal surface becomes flattened, and the central portion of the ectoderm of that region begins to sink inward, pushing that part of the endoderm which lies beneath it into the archenteron (Fig. 103*e*). This results in the formation of the **neural tube,** a structure which later gives rise to the entire nervous system from that portion of the ectoderm which sinks inward (Fig. 103*f–j*).

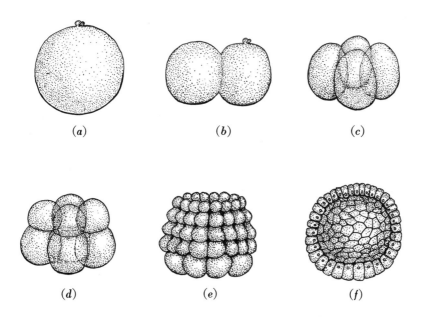

(*a*)   (*b*)   (*c*)

(*d*)   (*e*)   (*f*)

102 Early divisional stages of amphioxus. (By permission from GENERAL ZOOLOGY, 3rd ed., by Storer and Usinger. Copyright, 1957. McGraw-Hill Book Co., Inc.)

Endodermal cells,[3] affected by the movement of those cells which form the neural tube, give rise to the third germ layer, the mesoderm which immediately begins the formation of an **enterocoelic pouch** or **somite,** on each side (Fig. 103*f, g*). Each of these pouches elongates ventrally to encircle the gut, eventually meeting beneath it. Thus, a coelome is formed by an enlargement and fusion of the enterocoelic cavities on each side of the embryo, and the mesodermal cells involved form the peritoneal coelomic lining. Meanwhile, certain mesodermal cells form the notochord, which lies just ventral to the neural canal (Fig. 103*g–j*).

Since a full account of the development of amphioxus would take us farther into the field of specialized embryology than we can afford to go, we shall terminate our description of its development at this point. Suffice it to say that further differentiation of the primary germ layers and their derivatives results in the eventual development of body organs and systems. It is apparent, however, that early embryogeny proceeds in a definite and clear-cut manner to produce the three primary germ layers and to arrange them in such a way that later specialized tissue and organ formation can occur. Although development in other animals is varied in specific detail, with many individual differences being noted, that of amphioxus may be considered representative. To say the least, some pattern of germ layer formation is followed in the development of all multicellular animals, and perhaps the description of amphioxus embryogeny given above will at least serve to emphasize this point.

No doubt it would be of interest to the student to trace the development of the human embryo, but there are at least two factors which render such a study impracticable at this point, the first of which depends upon the fact that relatively little is known about early stages of human development, since it is extremely difficult to recover very early human embryos. Although a few have been studied closely, the field of human embryology has been obliged to rely heavily upon studies of monkey embryos and the like, establishing by inference the stages through which the developing human passes. A second difficulty lies in the complexity of human (and general mammalian) development. Unless one has engaged in a phylogenetic study of embryology leading up to the mammal through the other classes of vertebrates, he is in a poor position to understand the events which occur and their significance.

In the multicellular animals whose body systems are well developed, the primary germ layers give rise to certain definite organs and organ systems. The ectoderm develops into the outer layer of the skin and also gives rise to the nervous system. From the endoderm are derived

---

[3] Technically, the inner layer at this stage is not *endoderm*, but *mesendoderm*, since it later gives rise to both endoderm and mesoderm.

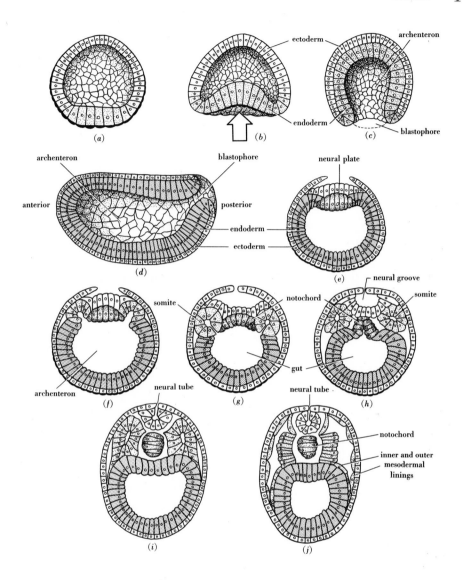

103 Later developmental stages of amphioxus. At (*c*), during the gastrula stage, the embryo begins to elongate (see (*d*), which is shown in sagittal section). Figures (*e*) through (*f*) represent transverse sections, hence their different appearance from (*d*). See text for further explanation. (From Sussman, after Villee: BIOLOGY. 3rd ed., 1957. Philadelphia. W. B. Saunders Company.)

the inner lining of the gastro-intestinal tract and its associated organs. The mesoderm proves to be the most versatile of the three layers; that portion which is associated with the embryonic gut forms the outer wall of the gastro-intestinal tract and the outer covering of organs which attach to it, while that part which lies next to the ectoderm gives rise to structures such as bones and muscles, and to the inner layer of the skin (Fig. 104).

Tissue Types of the Higher Animal Body

After development is well advanced and the many cells of the higher animal body have become in large part highly specialized, they tend to be associated together as tissues according to function. A tissue may be defined as a group of similar cells that are associated together in the performance of a particular function. Four types of animal tissues are generally recognized by histologists. These are termed **epithelial, nervous, muscular,** and **connective.** Nervous tissue is derived entirely from ectoderm, muscle and connective tissue generally arise from mesoderm, and epithelium may come from ectoderm, mesoderm, or endoderm, depending on its location in the body.

Epithelial tissue is essentially protective in its function, and it serves to cover or line surfaces. One is inclined to think only of the ex-

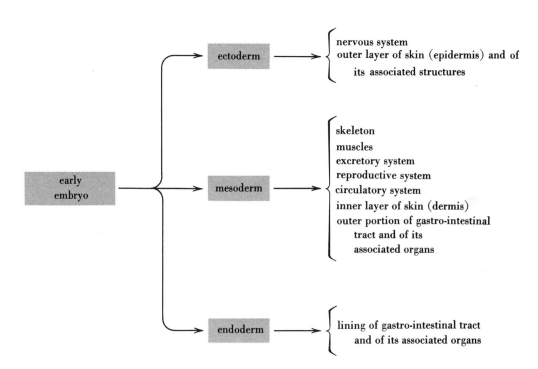

104 Important structures and organ systems of the vertebrate body according to germ layer derivation.

ternal body surface in this connection. The outermost layer or layers of cells are epithelial in multicellular animals, but a great many internal surfaces exist, and epithelium is also found as a protective tissue for these. The gastro-intestinal tract is lined in this fashion on its internal surface. The external surfaces of organs which lie within or adjacent to the body cavity of a given coelomate animal are covered by peritoneum, an epithelium of single-cell thickness. Blood vessels and tubules of various sorts exhibit this characteristic also. Because of its external location, epithelium frequently assumes other roles in addition to that of protection. One of these is that of **secretion,** in which certain epithelial cells produce some particular substance or substances; an aggregation of such specialized cells which perform a common secretory function is called a **gland.** Another secondary role played by epithelial cells is that of **absorption,** as is the case in cells which surround the lumen of the small intestine. We have already seen that in the movement of digested foods from the small intestine of man to the blood and lymph streams, they must be absorbed into the epithelium, a process which is, in a sense, somewhat the reverse of secretion. Figure 105 illustrates representative epithelia which are found in higher animals.

It is the specialized function of nervous tissue to transmit impulses throughout the animal body. In their organization, nerve cells form a coordinated system which allows for the reception of external or internal stimuli, the transmission of impulses arising from such stimuli, and an orderly distribution of these impulses to organs of action. The typical nerve cell (Fig. 106) is well adapted to this function, consisting as it does of a cell body whose cytoplasm may possibly extend for considerable distances in the form of **nerve fibers.** These fibers maintain connections with fibers of other nerve cells, and there is thus a systematic mechanism for reception, transmission, and action. It is significant that nervous tissues are found in all multicellular animals except sponges, and that the morphology of nerve cells is remarkably uniform among the animals that possess them. The function of nervous tissue in higher animals will be considered in a later chapter.

Like nervous tissue, muscle is found in all multicellular animals except sponges. It is specialized for contraction, and the animal possessing it thus is able to exhibit a considerable degree of motility. Muscle cells are somewhat elongate, and contraction occurs when a complex series of chemical reactions within a given cell cause it to become shortened and thickened. In all but the simplest animals, many muscle cells may be bound together to form a **muscle,** in which case their contraction is very highly coordinated for the performance of work. In the higher vertebrates, three types of muscle cells are recognized. There are those which are **striated,** so called because small bands or striations are

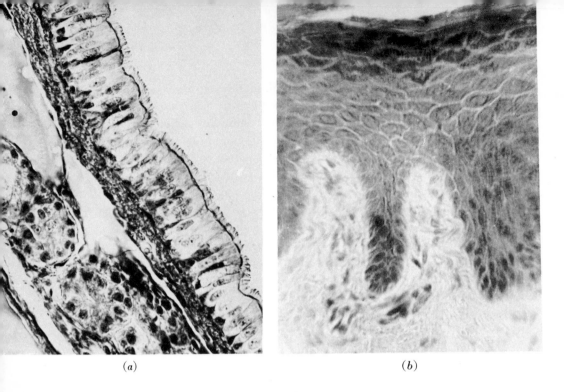

(a)   (b)

105 Two types of epithelial tissues. a, a section of human trachea, showing a row of columnar cells whose outer surfaces are covered with cilia. (Courtesy Carolina Biological Supply Company). b, stratified, or layered, epithelial tissue as seen in the human skin. The upper portion is the epidermis, which is epithelial, and the lower (light) portion is the dermis, which is composed of connective tissue.

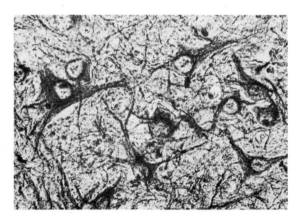

106 Several nerve cells. Note the fibers that extend from each cell, and the prominent nuclei. (Negative furnished by Bio-Foto, Nashville, Tennessee).

seen when the cell is highly magnified (Fig. 107*a*), those which are
smooth, lacking such striations (Fig. 107*b*), and a third type are known
as **cardiac** (Gr. *kardia,* heart) cells, which are found only in the heart
(Fig. 107*c*). Striated cells, or fibers, are usually fairly long and are
multinucleate. They are associated with the endoskeleton in vertebrates,
to which they attach in groups as muscles. Smooth muscle cells are found
in the internal organs, for example, in the wall of the gastro-intestinal
tract. They are uninucleate, and contract much more slowly, as a rule,
than do striated fibers. They may be grouped together in sheets or bands,
or they may exist as somewhat isolated units. Cardiac muscle presents a
rather complex, branching appearance, with individual cells lying along-
side and across each other in somewhat intimate contact. Muscle cells or
fibers are usually induced to contract through stimuli transmitted to them
by way of the nervous system.

As the name implies, connective tissues serve chiefly to bind
the other tissues together in the organism, although some are specialized
for other functions, as is described below. One characteristic which all
connective tissues share is that non-living **fibers** are closely associated
with cells, both of which are surrounded by a non-living **matrix.** Both
the fibers and the matrix are produced by the cells. Three general types
of connective tissues are recognized by histologists, namely, **binding,**
supporting, and **fluid** tissues. Binding tissue serves to connect the
outer epithelium (epidermis) to underlying tissues such as muscle; it ties

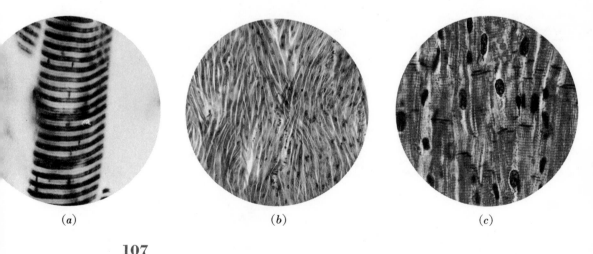

(*a*)   (*b*)   (*c*)

107

Types of muscular tissue. a, a portion of a striated muscle fiber. b, several smooth
muscle fibers closely packed together. c, cardiac muscle tissue; note branching of fibers
and light striations. (Photographs courtesy General Biological Supply House, Inc.)

nerve fibers into bundles, and so on. Ligaments and tendons of the higher vertebrates, which connect bones to each other and to muscles, respectively, represent a type of binding connective tissue in which fibers are sufficiently numerous to replace much of the matrix ordinarily present. Supporting tissue is represented in the higher vertebrates by bone in which the matrix becomes impregnated with calcium salts and is thus solid, and by cartilage, in which the matrix is less firm. It should be borne in mind that supporting tissues, although unusually compact, contain living cells which are continuously active in maintaining the fibers and matrix. In fluid connective tissues, of which the blood of vertebrates is most typical, the matrix exists as a liquid and fibers are only *potentially* present in the form of a blood protein called **fibrinogen.** Whenever blood is induced to clot through the initiation of certain complex reactions, fibrinogen is precipitated out of solution and fibers are formed. A blood clot consists of these fibers plus any blood cells that may become enmeshed in the fibrous network. The various types of blood cells represent the living portion of this fluid tissue. Representative connective tissues are shown in Figure 108.

The four types of tissue are bound together within the animal body in the formation of **organs,** which are structures composed of two or more tissues associated together in the performance of a common function. The stomach, for example, is an organ whose wall is composed of

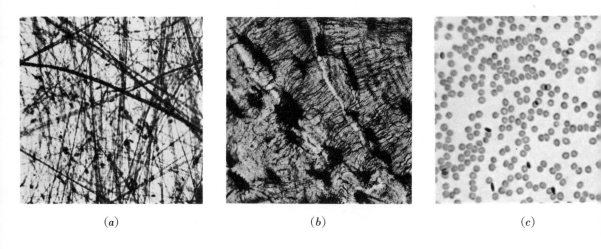

(a)   (b)   (c)

108 Various connective tissues. a, one type of binding connective tissue. Note fibers, among which are cells whose nuclei are stained darkly here. b, a thin section of human bone, showing characteristic circular arrangement of cells (very dark here) within the hard matrix. c, human blood in a stained preparation, showing several red cells. (Photographs courtesy Carolina Biological Supply Company)

two epithelial layers between which are situated smooth muscle fibers. These layers, along with blood vessels and nerves, are held together by connective tissue. Even in an organ such as a muscle, where one type of tissue predominates, other tissues are present. Binding connective tissue ties the muscle cells together in this case, and nerve fibers supply them with impulses. Whenever organs are associated together in the performance of a common function, we speak of a **system.** For example, the esophagus, stomach, intestines, and other organs associated with the function of digestion in higher animals may be referred to collectively as the **digestive system.** A group of related systems, of course, constitute an organism.

GROWTH AND DIFFERENTIATION IN PLANTS

Ontogeny of Higher Plant Tissues

It will have occurred to the student by this time that plants and animals, especially those whose bodies are somewhat complex, are vastly different in their over-all morphology. This is an accompaniment of their different modes of existence and simply reflects the principle that structure and function are closely related in organisms. Thus, the animal tissues that we have studied show adaptations to an actively motile type of organism whose body cells generally carry on a high rate of metabolism. A somewhat different picture presents itself when tissues of the complex plant are examined, however. These reflect the sedentary existence carried on by the plant, and adaptations to the structural and functional requirements of this mode of life become obvious with study.

Although certain non-vascular plants (for example, the giant kelps and the mushrooms) exhibit bodies of considerable size and complexity, as a general rule relatively little specialization is seen in their cells. It is particularly significant that they lack tissues which make possible the transport of fluids throughout the plant body. This necessitates a mode of existence for the plant which will enable some of its cells to receive vital materials from other cells by diffusion. Thus, it is no accident that the non-vascular plants, except for certain algae whose cells are all in relatively close contact with nourishing sea water, do not usually attain much size since they are limited by their lack of specialized conducting tissues. Because the non-vascular plants demonstrate a limited degree of cellular differentiation, therefore, little value is to be gained in studying their development in the hope of discovering any great degree of histological specialization.

The vascular plants offer an entirely different picture, however. Not only does a high degree of cellular differentiation result in the pres-

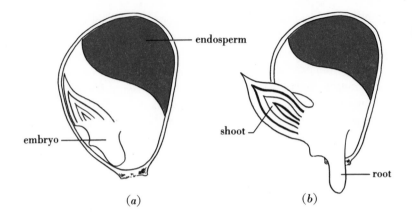

109 Germination of a seed, showing emergence of root and shoot.
a, dormant seed. b, germinating seed.

ence of tissues that conduct fluids, but there are adaptations for greater size and more varied habitats. As is the case in animals, there is a considerable degree of variation in the structure of higher plants, but there are tissue types which are common to all.

Embryogeny of typical vascular plants begins with early divisions of the zygote within the tissues of a parent plant. Although there is little or no histological specialization at this point, a pair of embryonic organs, the **root** and the **shoot,** soon become evident (Fig. 109). The root, which exhibits a positive response to gravity, ultimately gives rise to the root system of the plant, whereas the shoot, which is affected oppositely in its growth, serves as the forerunner of the **stem** and **leaves.** In the seed plants, the embryo usually stops growing just after these embryonic organs have developed and becomes surrounded by the tissues derived from the parent plant in the formation of the seed.[4] The seeds of many plants are obliged to undergo a period of dormancy, which seems to be an adaptation for propagation of the species. If seeds of a plant produced in the fall of the year in temperate climates were to germinate immediately, for example, they would all be killed by cold weather, and none would remain for spring germination. There are other species whose seeds remain dormant only until proper conditions of moisture, temperature, and oxygen supply are such as to initiate embryonic growth.

[4] Up to this point, the root and shoot are not influenced by gravity. It is after germination of the seed that their orientation in respect to this force begins.

After the root and shoot have grown for a short time, some of their cells differentiate to form the tissues characteristic of the mature plant. Cells generally remain at about the same level of the plant organ where they begin to specialize. New growth occurs at the tip, which makes it possible to study the changes that take place simply by proceeding from the younger to the older cells. If one starts at the tip of a young shoot and proceeds downward by examining both transverse and longitudinal sections, he finds that the first cells encountered are small, undifferentiated cells which are active in division. These constitute **meristematic** tissue, a term applied to any tissue in a plant that possesses the ability to undergo active division. As more cells are produced by division, those that are older remain at the same level at which they were produced and begin the process of differentiation. Thus, as one proceeds farther and farther down the stem in his sectioning and study, successive degrees of specialization are seen. Figure 110 shows the result of making sections in this manner, with various levels of increasing complexity being identified.

Tissue Types of the Higher Plant Body

As a consequence of gradual differentiation, certain tissues come to characterize the mature plant. For purposes of convenience, these may be classified as being either **simple** or **complex,** a distinction based on whether a tissue is composed of one cell type or several cell types. Near the growing tip of a given plant organ, one of the first simple tissues to become differentiated is **epidermis,** which persists as an external layer, usually one cell thick. It is essentially a protective tissue, and chloroplasts are often absent in all its cells except those which surround **stomata** (Fig. 111). The most common simple tissue to be found in higher plants is **parenchyma,** cells of which serve chiefly in synthesis or storage. They are rather thin-walled, usually exhibiting only slight elongation, and function in the living state (Figs. 112, 113). Another simple tissue is **collenchyma,** which is concentrated chiefly at sites in the plant where strength and support are required while the plant is still relatively young. These cells generally possess rather thick walls composed of cellulose and they tend to become somewhat elongate (Fig. 112). Like parenchyma, they function as living cells. A fourth type of simple tissue is **sclerenchyma,** cells of which assume two different forms. Some are isodiametric (such as the **stone cells** which lend a gritty aspect to the edible portion of a pear) and others may become extremely elongate, the latter being called **fibers** (Fig. 112). Unlike the preceding types of simple tissue, sclerenchymatous cells do not achieve their full potential function until after their protoplasts have disappeared, a process which leaves an extremely thick cell wall surrounding a small **lumen**

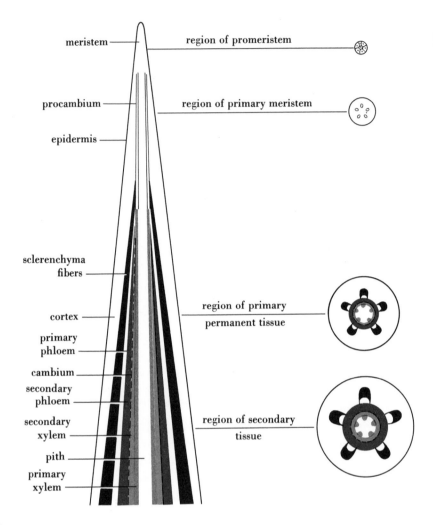

110 Diagrammatic representation of a stem tip, showing the development of tissues as a result of cellular differentiation.

formerly occupied by the protoplasmic contents. The walls of sclerenchymatous cells owe much of their strength to a material called **lignin,** which becomes associated with the cellulose of young cell walls as they gradually differentiate. This physical characteristic renders sclerenchyma, and especially fibers, very serviceable in lending strength to a given plant part. The fibers of some plants such as flax and sisal are commercially valuable since they can be used in the manufacture of such commodities as cloth and ropes. In addition to these four types of simple tissues, it should be remembered that meristem is always present at the growing

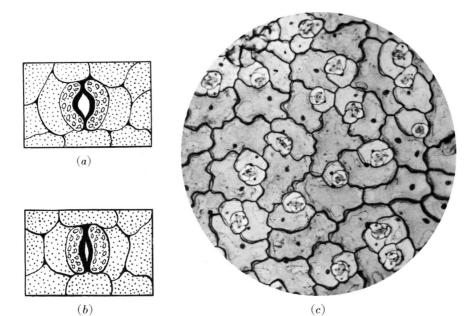

(a)

(b)

(c)

111 Guard cells and stomata. a, drawing of guard cells as seen in plant epidermis. A stoma forms whenever guard cells become sufficiently turgid that they pull apart. b, stoma partially closed due to loss of turgidity of guard cells. c, surface view of leaf epidermis, showing several guard cell pairs. (Courtesy General Biological Supply House, Inc.)

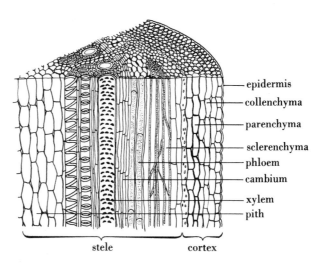

epidermis
collenchyma
parenchyma
sclerenchyma
phloem
cambium
xylem
pith

stele   cortex

112 Three-dimensional representation of a herbacious stem showing a portion of a vascular bundle.

tips of plant organs, as well as at various other locations in the plant, and it may be regarded as a fifth type.

Complex tissues are of two types, **xylem** and **phloem,** which are concerned with the movement of materials in vascular plants. The functional cells of xylem are either elongate, somewhat tapering units called **tracheids** (Fig. 64*d*), whose ends join in the function of conduction, or **vessel elements,** which are larger and more uniform, and which become fused together at their ends to form conducting tubes called **vessels** (Figs. 64*a–c,* 112, 113). The walls of tracheids and vessels, like those of sclerenchymatous cells, are characterized by the presence of lignin, which lends great strength to them. Lignin may be deposited in the walls of these cells according to a variety of patterns, namely, as rings, spirals, networks, and so on. These conducting cells of xylem lose their protoplasts upon reaching maturity, and the fluids which they conduct travel through the region of each cell originally occupied by living material. In addition to the tracheids and vessels that have been described, parenchyma cells and sclerenchymatous fibers often are present in xylem, the entire aggregation of cells associated together in the common function of fluid transport being regarded as a single tissue type. In general, xylem serves to transport water and dissolved materials upward in the plant. The functional units of phloem are called **sieve cells,** and they are somewhat analogous to the vessel elements of xylem; in many plants,

113 A portion of the stem of corn, a monocotyledonous plant, in cross sectional appearance. Note scattered vascular bundles, each of which resembles a face. In each "face," the eyes are large xylem vessels, the forehead is phloem, with companion cells appearing small and square in this view, seive tubes larger and more rounded. Between the vascular bundles are located large storage cells of parenchyma. (Courtesy General Biological Supply House, Inc.)

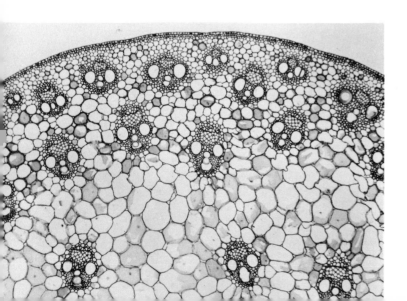

sieve cells are formed as multicellular tubes comparable to xylem vessels. Unlike the latter, however, they retain their protoplasm in the functional state, although nuclei disappear. Typically, sieve cells are very closely associated with other components of phloem called **companion cells** (Figs. 64-e, 113). Because there are perforations between companion cells and sieve cells, it has been suggested that the nuclei of the former may serve the cytoplasm of the latter. In addition to these two cell types, phloem is always characterized by the presence of **phloem parenchyma** and frequently by sclerenchymatous **phloem fibers.** In the transport of fluids, which are chiefly dissolved food materials manufactured in the upper parts of the plant and which are carried downward to other parts, the sieve tubes perform a similar function to that of tracheids and vessels in regard to the movement of materials upward in the plant.

Distribution of these tissues throughout roots, stems, and leaves varies greatly among plants, but there are some definite structural patterns that can be identified. Xylem and phloem tend to develop centrally in roots with absorption occurring only at the level of the root where epidermal **root hairs** are present (Fig. 114). Water and dissolved inorganic salts pass into the root hairs, and from cell to cell inward toward the xylem, by way of which these materials travel upward in the plant. Sectioning of the roots of flowering plants at the region where they join the stem reveals the phenomenon that xylem and phloem become dispersed from their central position and form isolated areas known as **vascular bundles.** These bundles are characteristically arranged in a circular pattern in dicotyledonous plant stems, whereas in many monocotyledonous stems they tend to occur randomly (Fig. 113). Roots and stems exhibit three general regions, called **epidermis, cortex,** and **stele.** The epidermis (which is a tissue as well as a region) is typically a single layer of cells, the cortex is that region extending from the epidermis to the beginning of vascular tissues, and the stele is composed of all cells which are thus surrounded by the cortex (Fig. 112). Because the stele of many roots forms a solid, central cylinder without pith, the cortex of the root is relatively more expansive than that of the stem (Fig. 114). Wherever a leaf grows from a stem, a vascular bundle gives off a **leaf trace** containing xylem and phloem, which serves the blade of the leaf by branching into **veins.** Figure 115 illustrates the appearance of a leaf in section showing the relationship of a vein to other tissues.

Thus far, we have spoken of meristem only in terms of its presence at the tips of growing plant organs, but wherever growth occurs in the plant, it must do so by virtue of cells which are functionally meristematic. Again, there is considerable variation among plants in this respect, and it is difficult to establish generalizations regarding plant growth. In tree-like and shrubby seed plants, areas of meristem called **cambium**

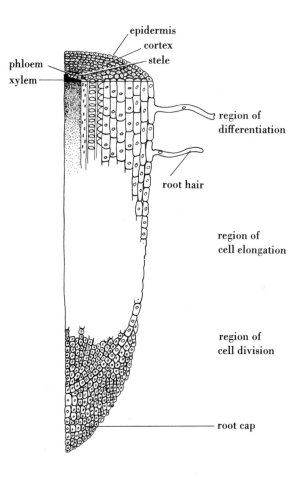

114 Three-dimensional representation of the tip of a young root, shown in longitudinal section. For purposes of illustration, the region of differentiation, where vascular tissues begin to form, is somewhat "telescoped."

develop between the xylem and phloem of stems and roots. In the stem of this plant type, for example, the xylem and phloem of each vascular bundle is separated by cambium (Fig. 112). Division of this layer results in more xylem and phloem, since cells produced by the cambium may become associated with either tissue. As the stem continues its development, the layer of cambium grows in such a way as to form a complete circular sheath, and thus an increase in stem diameter is made possible by constant division of the cambial cells. Stems of woody plants exhibit a cambium which adds zones of xylem and phloem annually. A plant stem of this type grows laterally in such a way that the original xylem is buried along with the pith. Just outward from the cambium, phloem continues to be produced, and this plus other tissues (the original epidermis, cortex, and a meristematic layer called **cork cambium** with its derivatives) compose the **bark** of the perennial dicotyledonous stem. Hence the cambium is the point of separation between the bark and the xylem, which is also called **wood** (Fig. 116).

THE PHENOMENON OF REGENERATION

Planarian worms (Fig. 23), which are commonly found on the surfaces of rocks in ponds or streams, may be used for a simple and extremely interesting experiment in animal growth. It is possible to cut a worm in a variety of ways in order to produce the effect described below, but let us suppose that three transverse cuts are made in such a manner that four pieces are produced (Fig. 117). This action not only fails to kill the worm, but if each piece is placed in a separate container of pond water, it grows into a new individual. This process of growth in the development of an entire organism from a part or in the re-growth of a lost or injured portion is termed **regeneration.** The growth and differentiation which are necessary in producing a new worm do not occur in a haphazard fashion; careful observation will reveal that an anterior end always develops from the portion of a given segment which lay nearest

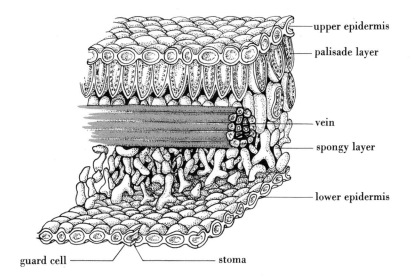

115 Three-dimensional representation of a portion of leaf blade.

116 A portion of a woody stem in its third year of growth, shown in cross sectional view. The upper area, much of which is made up of alternating light and dark bands as seen in this view, is the bark; it is separated from the wood (xylem), seen here as the inner light-colored portion, by the cambium. Note annual growth rings in the xylem. (Courtesy General Biological Supply House, Inc.)

the anterior end of the original worm (Fig. 117). This implies a certain organization for growth on the part of the animal, apparently built around its longitudinal axis.

In general, the power of regeneration is great among those animals whose bodies are relatively simple and becomes more and more limited

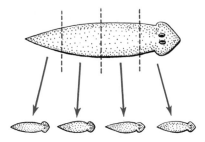

117 Regeneration in planaria, showing orientation along an axis,
so that a new anterior end develops from the anterior-most
portion of the piece as it was situated in the original worm.

with the increase of complexity. Among the vertebrates, it is virtually
limited to the healing of wounds, a process that is extremely complex and
not always completely successful, particularly when muscular and nervous
tissues are destroyed. This differential in regenerative powers is obviously
a reflection of the greater specialization seen in mature cells of the higher
animal body; cells such as those of planaria are considerably more unspecialized and versatile than are most cells of the adult human, for
example.

Although botanists usually prefer the expression "vegetative
growth" in speaking of regenerative processes, plants also demonstrate
the ability (in varying degrees) to replace and repair.[5] In fact, even some
very complex plants may be propagated by virtue of the tendency of their
stems, roots or leaves to develop into entire plants. Here again, as
in planaria, there is generally an orientation; a piece of willow stem, for
example, if placed in water, does not develop roots on the end which grew
uppermost in the original plant even if this end is placed downward in
the water. Instead, roots invariably grow at the lowermost end of the
piece, if they grow at all, while leaves develop at the opposite end.

Perhaps the most important biological principle to be gained
from experiments in regeneration is that plants and animals possess a certain organization above the cellular level which results in their being

[5] One reason the term regeneration is avoided by some botanists is that the
form of individual plants tends to vary much more within a species than does
that of animals. If a limb is broken from a tree, it is not replaced as such; the
leaves that appear in the spring on a deciduous tree do not grow in the same
positions occupied by the leaves which fell during the preceding autumn.
Hence, there is some justification for regarding plant regeneration as being
fundamentally different, at least in an organizational sense, to that occurring in
animals.

more than a mere sum of their parts, or cells. We have already seen that this is true in the development of animal embryos where the activities of cell groups called organizers have been clearly demonstrated in embryological research. To return to our former analogy, these organizers (both in embryos and in mature organisms) are comparable to civic clubs and other organizations within a society whose effects on that society supersede the influence of any one individual. Because of the extremely important principles and implications involved, both to biology and to philosophy, the area of research dealing with regeneration and organization is one of the most active and exciting fields of modern biological research.

CONCLUSION

The foregoing discussion of growth and certain processes which are related to it should serve to demonstrate further the highly complex nature of protoplasm and of organisms. Obviously, there are many problems to be solved in biology before a complete understanding of these phenomena can be gained, but it is gratifying that much progress has been and is being made. Perhaps no area of biological interest bears more directly on the very basis for and nature of life than this one, and it is highly probable that future research will reveal the operation of principles that will greatly influence or even revolutionize our present concepts. At any rate, the student should be aware by this time that organisms are truly unique in nature by virtue of their chemical activities and the growth effects produced thereby, a principle which will greatly enrich his understanding of the world of life.

QUESTIONS

Multiple Choice

1. An animal embryo may resemble a hollow ball at one stage of development. It is then called (a) a blastula, (b) a blastocoel, (c) a gastrula, (d) an archenteron, (e) an enterocoelic pouch.

2. Which of the following is first to break the proper sequence? (a) interphase, (b) prophase, (c) anaphase, (d) metaphase, (e) telophase.

3. In addition to its primary function of protection, epithelial tissue frequently becomes specialized as well for (a) division, (b) contraction, (c) impulse transmission, (d) conduction of fluids, (e) absorption.

4. That embryonic plant organ which exhibits a negative response to gravity is called the (a) root, (b) shoot, (c) stem, (d) meristem, (e) xylem.

5. Xylem in a woody plant may also be called (a) bark, (b) wood, (c) heartwood, (d) sapwood, (e) pith.

6. Which of the following organisms was used in this chapter to illustrate the principle of regeneration? (a) amphioxus, (b) sea urchin, (c) *Ascaris*, (d) *Chlamydomonas*, (e) planaria.

7. Which of the animals above was used to illustrate the process of early development in animals?

8. The term "mitosis" is used in biology to describe (a) differentiation in triploblastic animals, (b) cell division, (c) nuclear division, (d) cytoplasmic division, (e) one type of regeneration.

9. Which of the following is responsible for the growth in circumference of a stem or root? (a) xylem, (b) phloem, (c) cortex, (d) cambium, (e) epidermis.

10. In a cell, genes are closely associated with (a) mitochondria, (b) microsomes, (c) nucleoli, (d) chromosomes, (e) vacuoles.

11. Which of the following represents the parallel drawn by introducing an analogy regarding the vocational specialization of children in a society? (a) Children should be properly trained. (b) Cells exhibit the power to divide. (c) Cells may differentiate toward specialized functions. (d) Embryonic growth is influenced by intrinsic factors. (e) Living organisms have much more in common than superficial inspection might indicate.

12. Cardiac cells of the vertebrate animal are found only in the (a) skeletal muscles, (b) digestive system, (c) brain, (d) liver, (e) heart.

13. Plant fibers are one type of which of the following tissues? (a) xylem, (b) phloem, (c) parenchyma, (d) collenchyma, (e) sclerenchyma.

14. Companion cells are associated with which of the following? (a) tracheids, (b) vessels, (c) sieve tubes, (d) fibers, (e) root hairs.

15. Which of the following is, in a sense, a reverse process to prophase? (a) interphase, (b) telophase, (c) metaphase, (d) anaphase.

16. The two halves which make up a prophasic chromosome are called (a) centromeres, (b) centrioles, (c) centrosomes, (d) chromatids, (e) spindle fibers.

17. Which of the following groups includes structures *all* of which are derived from mesoderm in the higher animal body? (a) bone, muscle, brain; (b) outer layer of skin, muscle, lining of digestive tract; (c) inner layer of skin, brain, bone; (d) muscle, outer layer of digestive tract, bone; (e) liver, lungs, outer layer of skin.

18. Which of the following is capable of giving rise to any of the others? (a) xylem, (b) phloem, (c) meristem, (d) parenchyma, (e) collenchyma.

19. If a sea urchin egg is fertilized by two sperm, normal development does not usually occur. What does this prove? (a) that extrinsic factors are important to development, (b) that a normal chromosome "set" is necessary to normal development, (c) that sea urchin eggs are rather unique in the animal kingdom, (d) that differentiation begins at the first cleavage in the sea urchin zygote, (e) that organizers are very important factors in development.

20. Which of the following is innermost in a typical young root? (a) cortex, (b) stele, (c) epidermis, (d) vascular bundle, (e) pith.

True-false

1. Xylem is classified as a simple plant tissue.

2. If a piece of willow stem is placed in water, roots will appear on the end in the water, whether it was uppermost in the original plant or not.

3. Telophase is marked by the reappearance of nucleoli and nuclear membranes.

4. If the nucleus is removed from an amoeba, it dies immediately.

5. One important difference in typical plant and animal cells is that the former exhibit mitosis and the latter exhibit cytokinesis.

6. Specialization is such in the animal body that only nerve cells are able to carry on any impulse conduction.

7. When a sperm unites with an egg, the resulting product is called a zygote.

8. Cytokinesis begins in the animal cell with the formation of a cell plate.

9. One important difference between parenchyma and sclerenchyma is that cells of the former remain living during their functional period, whereas those of the latter do not.

10. Lignin is a material that is always associated with cells of collenchyma.

11. In general, the power of regeneration is greater in those animals that are more complex, whereas it is limited in simpler forms.

12. Of the three primary germ layers, mesoderm proves to be the most versatile in the higher animal body in that it gives rise to more varied types of tissues and organ systems than do either of the other two.

13. Among unicellular organisms, the term "growth" (defined in this case as increase in number of cells) is equivalent to the term "reproduction."

14. One very significant event which occurs during prophase is the division of chromosomal centromeres.

15. The notochord arises in amphioxus during the blastula stage.

16. Smooth muscle cells are generally multinucleate.

17. Blood is one type of connective tissue.

18. A system may be defined as a group of organs which are associated together in the performance of a common function.

19. The seeds of many plants will not germinate until they have undergone a period of dormancy.

20. Food materials manufactured in the upper parts of a vascular plant are transported downward chiefly in the xylem.

Questions for Consideration and Discussion

1. Describe the series of events involved in the early development of amphioxus.

2. Summarize the process of cell division, contrasting important differences between plant and animal cells in this respect.

3. Why do botanists generally avoid use of the term "regeneration" in regard to plants?

4. Why is an understanding of metabolism essential to a proper understanding of growth?

5. What do you understand to be the meaning of the terms "histological specialization" and "cytological specialization?"

6. Outline the types of animal and plant tissues which were discussed in this chapter.

7. Discuss the function of cambium in stems of woody plants.

8. What are "organizers?" Discuss some experiments that show their importance as factors in animal development.

9. Contrast the terms "growth" and "differentiation."

10. Do all organisms grow? Explain.

REFERENCES

GALSTON, A. W. *The Life of the Green Plant* (see reference at end of Chapter 5). Portions of the author's fourth and fifth chapters, entitled "Plant Growth" and "Differentiation and Morphogenesis," respectively, are related to the materials of this chapter.

HUETTNER, A. F. *Fundamentals of Comparative Embryology of the Vertebrates.* New York: The Macmillan Co., 1949. A reasonably simple presentation of vertebrate embryology; the account and illustrations having to do with the development of amphioxus are particularly recommended.

MAZIA, DANIEL. "Cell Division." *Scientific American,* Volume 189 (August, 1953), p. 53. A discussion of mitosis and related phenomena.

ROBBINS, W. W., T. E. WEIER and **C. R. STOCKING.** *Botany: An Introduction To Plant Science,* 2nd ed. New York: John Wiley & Sons, Inc., 1957. A textbook of elementary botany that is especially recommended for additional study of plant structures and their development.

STORER, T. I. and **R. L. USINGER.** *General Zoology* (see reference at end of Chapter 4). This textbook will be helpful in regard to the growth and development of animals.

SUSSMAN, MAURICE. *Animal Growth and Development.* Englewood Cliffs, N.J.: Prentice-Hall, Inc., 1960. This book, which is one of the FOUNDATIONS OF MODERN BIOLOGY series, is applicable in its entirety to this chapter.

SWANSON, C. P. *The Cell* (see reference at end of Chapter 3). Chapters 4 and 8 of this book, which are concerned with cell division and development respectively, will be helpful to the student at this point.

CHAPTER

Reproduction

Organisms are more or less short-lived, relatively speaking. When one considers that few animals present on the earth today live longer than one hundred and fifty years (certain tortoises are known to attain this age), this period of time seems small indeed when compared with the time that life has existed on our planet (possibly two billion years). Even the oldest living plants that are known, the bristle-cone pines (*Pinus aristata*), some of which are well over 4,000 years old, make a very slight impression upon the time scale. To draw a comparison, if the period of time that life may have occupied the earth were reduced to twenty-four hours, and the life span of the bristle-cone pine were reduced accordingly, the latter would be only about one-sixth of a second!

In view of the phenomenon that individual organisms do not live for a very long time, it is obvious that reproduction is the only mechanism whereby a species can maintain itself in time. As we have already observed (and this idea will be developed more fully in a later chapter), even species are subject to changes. Nevertheless, whatever stability nature is able to achieve depends upon the ability of organisms to produce other organisms whose characteristics are essentially like their own.

This is not to say that all individual organisms reproduce. Circumstances frequently dictate that plants or animals fail to survive to a reproductive age, or possessing the full potentiality, are somehow unable to fulfill it. A puff ball, for example, may produce several million spores, but if none of them lodges on a suitable substratum, the puff ball has failed to reproduce itself. A single willow tree, isolated from others of its species, may not form seeds because of its dependence upon other trees for pollen. A moment of reflection will lead one to the conclusion that many human beings live out their lives without producing offspring. Some organisms, for one reason or another, are sterile (lacking reproductive capacity) and therefore have no part in maintaining their species. Thus, when biologists speak of reproduction as a characteristic of living organisms, the concept is in terms of *species* and not necessarily of *individuals.*

In the over-all economy of nature, reproduction is most efficient. We have already seen that cells, tissues, and organisms, when young, tend to exhibit a high degree of versatility in regard to metabolism and growth. In time, this versatility generally becomes lowered. By virtue of reproduction, new organisms replace old ones in a continuous chain, thus keeping the characteristic biochemical and differential activities of a species "fresh."

SEXUAL AND ASEXUAL REPRODUCTION

The vast majority of organisms exhibit sexuality, a phenomenon which, in its most obvious form, becomes apparent in the existence of two sexually distinct "kinds" of individuals (male and female) within a species. For purposes of definition, male and female individuals are distinguished from one another on the basis of their production of specialized reproductive cells, or **gametes.** Typically, the two cells which meet and unite in sexual reproduction are morphologically dissimilar, one being relatively large and non-motile, the other being relatively small and motile (Fig. 118). When this is the case, the larger gamete is termed an **egg** or **ovum,** and the smaller one is called a **sperm.** Whenever an individual is capable of producing sperm it is designated a male; if it produces eggs, it is a female.

The major exceptions to this typical manifestation of sexuality are extremely interesting. Among several of the algae and fungi, there are two sexually distinct strains within a species which are morphologically indistinguishable in every detail. Sexual reproduction is carried on through the union of gametes, but there is no discernible structural difference between them. Because there is no basis for designating one of the strains "male" and the other "female," it is common to refer to one as the "plus" strain and the other as the "minus" strain in a completely arbi-

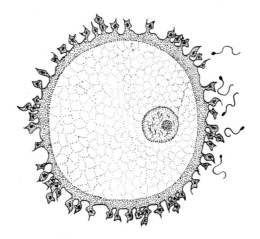

118 Human egg and sperm shown in relative size, enlarged about 500 times.

trary manner. Figure 119 illustrates this type of reproduction as it occurs in a common mold. Certain protozoa exhibit a phenomenon called **multiple sexuality,** in which there are various levels of sex rather than two contrasting forms or strains (Fig. 120). In multiple sexuality, the concepts of maleness and femaleness are, of course, entirely without meaning. Some animal species are composed of individuals which are functionally both males and females. Whenever an animal possesses this capacity, it is termed an **hermaphrodite** (Gr. *hermaphrodites,* from the myth of Hermaphroditus). The common earthworm is such an animal. It is interesting to note that among species whose members are definitely males or females, such as the human, there is the occasional appearance of an individual who manifests certain characteristics of both sexes. Such an individual is known as a **pseudohermaphrodite** since its appearance in the species is abnormal rather than natural. Furthermore, such an individual is not truly functional both as a male and a female as is a real hermaphrodite. Although certain plant species are made up of male and female individuals, this is not as widespread a condition as in the animal kingdom. Whereas the highest and most successful animal species tend to be **dioecious** (male and female individuals distinct), the vast majority of higher plants are not so ordered. In fact, sexuality in plants is generally obscured to such a degree as to render it virtually unknown to the casual observer. We shall defer explanation of it until later. Finally, some animal and plant species manage to reproduce without union of gametes, and reproduction is said to be **asexual.**

It should not be thought that sexual and asexual reproduction are necessarily exclusive in a given species. Although sexuality has never been observed in some species (for example, members of the blue-green algae apparently reproduce exclusively by asexual means), and in others reproduction is entirely sexual (as is the case with most animals), a great many species exhibit both sexual and asexual reproduction. *Hydra* (Figs. 20, 21), a common fresh-water coelenterate, is such an organism. In addition to egg and sperm formation, which is a manifestation of sexuality, **buds** are frequently formed, and these eventually develop into adult individuals. Many flowering plants may be propagated vegetatively from a root, stem, or leaf, which represents purely asexual reproduction, even when seeds are formed as a result of sexual reproduction.

We are now prepared to make a definitional distinction between sexual and asexual reproduction. **Sexual reproduction involves the union of gametes, the union of their nuclei and an association of their chromosomes. In general, asexual reproduction is to be defined as any process in which there is the production of new individuals without these accompaniments of sexual reproduction.** The essential difference in these two modes of reproduction, therefore, is that any new individual arising by asexual means is identical in chromosomal constitution with its sole parent, whereas the organism

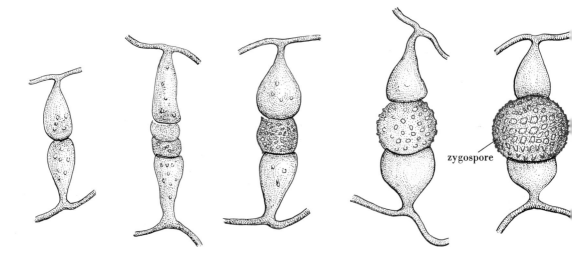

119 Sexual reproduction in a mold, *Rhizopus stolonifer* (see Figure 57). When "plus" and "minus" strains grow in the vicinity of each other, extensions of two filaments meet, an area of cytoplasm including several nuclei is delimited, and a thick-walled *zygospore* is formed. The **zygospore,** which is thus a product of sexual reproduction, may later germinate to form a new mycelium.

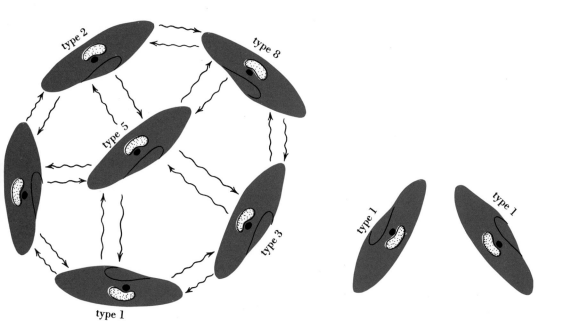

sexual attraction   sexual isolation

120   Multiple sexuality in *Paramecium bursaria*, one strain of which is known to consist of at least eight mating types. Each will conjugate with any other, but not with members of its own type.

originating as a zygote receives a chromosomal complement from two parents.[1]

Few species fail to exhibit sexuality in some form, but in spite of this, asexual reproduction is very widespread in the world of life. Many organisms reproduce most of the time in this manner, with sexual reproduction occurring rarely or occasionally. In general, asexual reproduction is limited in the animal kingdom to certain members of the lowest phyla in the scale of complexity, notably the Protozoa, Porifera, Coelenterata, and Platyhelminthes, of the phyla we have considered as major ones. In the plant kingdom, however, some of the most advanced plants reproduce in this fashion with regularity.

[1] It cannot be said that every individual produced through sexual reproduction must have two parents. Although few hermaphrodites practice self-fertilization, some forms such as tapeworms do. Many flowering plants are normally self-pollinating, which renders the embryonic plants within their seeds uniparental. Parthenogenesis (see p. 227) constitutes still another exception.

Fundamentally, there are two ways in which asexual reproduction may occur. The first method might be termed **vegetative reproduction,** the essence of which is the production of a new individual from a part of the parental body. The simplest form of this is seen in unicellular organisms such as protozoa, yeasts, bacteria, and certain algae whose cell division automatically results in their reproduction. We have mentioned previously that some organisms such as *Hydra* produce **buds** which ultimately develop into independent organisms. Certain of the free-living flatworms undergo a longitudinal division of the body, which results in the formation of two organisms from one. Among the higher plants, some species exhibit very elaborate modifications for vegetative reproduction, such as the tubers of Irish potatoes, the runners of strawberries, and the bulbs of tulips. As a second asexual method, some organisms exhibit the production of spores, which are single-celled units capable of growing into whole organisms. This method of reproduction is virtually limited to the plant kingdom, where it is demonstrated in some form by the vast majority of species.

Perhaps it will occur to the thoughtful student to wonder whether or not regeneration, which was discussed in the preceding chapter, constitutes a form of asexual reproduction. In consideration of this question, it must be remembered that we limited the definition of this phenomenon to situations where parts of an organism are lost and replaced, or to those in which an entire organism develops from a part. Replacement of structures certainly does not constitute reproduction, nor can regeneration be considered a natural means of reproduction among organisms. We can separate a planarian worm into several parts experimentally and *induce* the regeneration of new individuals, but the worm does not perform this task autonomously. Hence, it is best to regard the term regeneration as one describing a certain aspect of growth. To state the matter another way, *vegetative growth* and *vegetative reproduction* are two distinct phenomena.

Since we have done little more than introduce the idea that chromosomes with their genes play an important part as intrinsic developmental factors, perhaps the full significance of gametic union and chromosomal association will not occur immediately to the student. It should be apparent, however, that whatever part genes may play in the development and behavior of an organism, these effects must of necessity remain unchanged from parent to offspring in asexual reproduction. This principle has been exploited by man in the vegetative propagation of many plants such as fruit trees when it is desirable to ensure that all qualities of a parent plant are exactly reproduced in offspring. Although man has thus utilized asexual reproduction to some extent for his own purposes, and even though there are a great many organisms that have become adapted to it as a mode of reproduction,[2] it is significant that asexual reproduction is the exception rather than the rule in nature. However sexuality may have originated, it has become very widespread and must be recognized as a tremendously important biological phenomenon. Since it is the essence of typical sexual reproduction that the gametes of two separate individuals including their particular genes are brought together in the formation of a new individual, **variation** is made possible. We shall see later that sexual reproduction and variation have played important roles in the rise of new species in nature, a process directly responsible for the multiplicity of present-day living forms.

THE PROCESS OF MEIOSIS AND ITS SIGNIFICANCE

Inasmuch as sexual reproduction involves the union of gamete nuclei and an accompanying association of the chromosomes which come from each parent, it becomes important to understand certain phenomena that are involved in these processes. Let us suppose that a certain species is characterized by individuals all of whose cells, including gametes, possess ten chromosomes. This means that if gametes of male and female individuals unite, there are twenty chromosomes in the zygote nucleus, and it is not difficult to visualize that unless some mechanism were to reduce the number at one point or another, the chromosomal complement of these organisms would not remain numerically constant.

Fortunately for our understanding of biology, such a mechanism is operative in all organisms that reproduce sexually, except for a few unusual types. It involves a special type of nuclear division called **meiosis** (Gr. *meioun*, to make smaller), accomplished by two successive divisions with the production of four daughter nuclei each of whose chromosome number is exactly one-half that of the original cell nucleus. Hence, if meiosis occurs in gamete formation, as it does in animals and in a few plants, it results in eggs and sperm whose union merely restores the normal chromosome number of the species to the zygote, and subsequent mitotic divisions ensure that all cells of the individual possess this characteristic number.

In order to understand the events which take place in the meiotic process, let us review certain details of ordinary, or mitotic, nuclear division. It will be recalled that prophase is marked by the appearance of distinct chromosomes, each of which is composed of two chromatids

[2] The Irish potato, *Solanum tuberosum*, reproduces quite successfully by means of its tubers. In fact, it appears that its flowering process, which ordinarily fails to produce many viable seeds, has become virtually useless to the species as a means of survival.

connected by a centromere. At anaphase, chromatids become separated, and with the subsequent events of telophase and daughter cell formation, each new nucleus comes to possess a representative chromatid of each original chromosome. Thus, if the number of chromosomes appearing at prophase is ten, each new daughter nucleus receives ten chromatids (daughter chromosomes), which duplicate themselves before the onset of new prophases in actively dividing cells. By virtue of this mechanism, chromosome numbers remain constant, and in a quantitative sense, mitotic division is purely *equational.*

As is so often the case with difficult problems in biology, it must be admitted that the forces responsible for initiation of meiotic rather than mitotic division in a given cell are not entirely clear. At any rate, the nucleus of such a cell enters prophase as though it were going to divide mitotically, but the chromosomes behave quite differently than do those in a mitotic nucleus. The descendants of the parental chromosomes, brought together in the zygote that produced the individual and carefully duplicated by many mitoses, now exhibit a strong attraction for each other, and actually unite in a process called **synapsis.** In this union, **homologous** chromosomes (members of a pair) become intimately attached to each other, and because the four chromatids constitute a unit, they are sometimes referred to collectively as a **tetrad** (Fig. 121). During synapsis, opposing chromatids of homologous chromosomes frequently become coiled and twisted about each other, and they may even exchange portions, an event which has considerable genetic significance. Eventually, there is a meiotic metaphase, and the tetrads line up on a spindle. Characteristically, they separate in the plane of their original union, and the two original chromatids of a chromosome (except for any portions that may have been exchanged with homologous chromatids) move toward

121 Diagrammatic representation of meiosis in a hypothetical organism with ten chromosomes. The brown chromosomes came from one parent of the organism, the black chromosomes from the other parent. For the sake of simplicity, only nuclei are illustrated, and nuclear membranes are not shown as breaking down. A, prophase of nucleus just before synapsis of homologous chromosomes. B, synapsed chromosomes at metaphase of the first meiotic division, with parental chromosomes being oriented randomly. Note that portions of two non-sister chromatids of the J-shaped chromosomes have become crossed upon each other. C, anaphase of the first meiotic division; homologous chromosomes separate in the plane of their original union. Note that the portions of two non-sister chromatids of the J-shaped chromosomes, mentioned above, have become exchanged. D, end of first meiotic division; whole chromosomes located in separate nuclei. E, metaphase of second meiotic division; chromatids of each chromosome preparing to separate. F, anaphase of second meiotic division. G, end of meiosis. Four nuclei now share the twenty original chromatids (see nucleus at A). Note that each nucleus now possesses a chromosome representing each original chromosome *pair.*

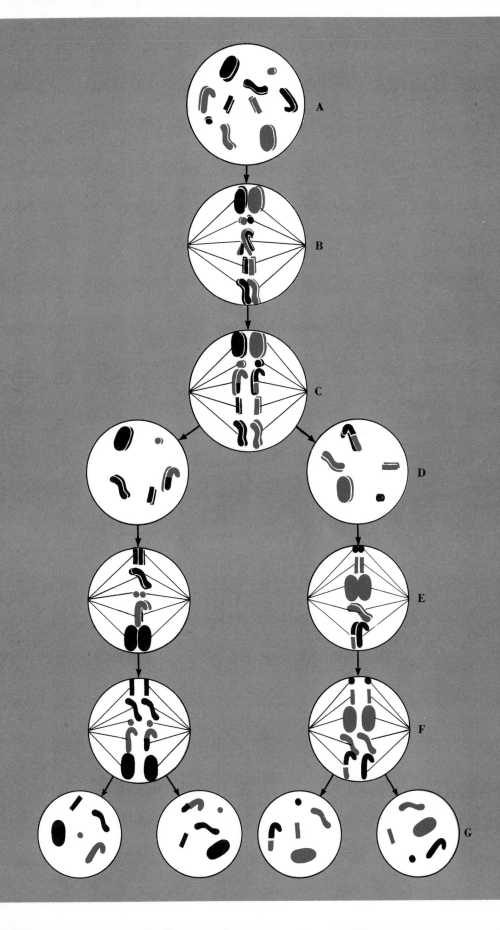

one pole in meiotic anaphase, while those of the homologous chromosome move toward the other (Fig. 121).

In regard to the number of original chromatids, this first meiotic division accomplishes precisely what a mitotic division does, that is, half of the prophase chromatids are delivered to each daughter nucleus. There is a considerable difference, however, in the distribution of these chromatids. In mitosis, one chromatid from each original chromosome becomes situated in a daughter nucleus. This is not the case in the first meiotic division; whole chromosomoes go into one daughter nucleus, and a second division is required in order to separate the chromatids. To state the matter differently, a mitotic daughter nucleus receives one chromatid of each *chromosome*, while a meiotic daughter nucleus receives one chromosome (consisting of two chromatids) of each chromosome *pair* characteristic of the species.

Following the separation of chromosomes in the manner described above, it would be expected that each nucleus should pass through telophase into interphase. Although nuclear membranes are characteristically formed, the chromosomes tend to retain their individual appearance, and interphase is thus greatly reduced. There is, of course, a great deal of individual variation among organisms and their cells in this respect. In many cells, the chromosomes remain in a prophase-like condition, with their individual identity and form being retained. Regardless of telophase-interphase details following the first meiotic division, each daughter nucleus enters second meiotic metaphase. This time, the chromosomes line up on the spindle in such a way that centromeres divide and sister chromatids separate as in mitosis. Since both daughter nuclei of the original cell undergo this second division, the result is four nuclei each of which receives a chromatid representing each chromosome *pair* of the original cell. Thus each nucleus resulting from meiotic division has *exactly one-half the number of chromatids* (which may be called chromosomes after they become separated from each other) *as the original cell had chromosomes* (Fig. 121).

Perhaps the full significance of meiosis will not immediately occur to the student since all its implications can hardly be appreciated at once. At least two things should be apparent at this point, however. One of these is that the process of meiosis is *reductional* in terms of chromosome number, resulting in nuclei which possess only one of each original chromosome pair. This is a result of the chromosomes having divided only *once* while the original nucleus divided *twice*. It might be pointed out here that a cell whose nucleus exhibits paired, or homologous, chromosomes is said to be **diploid** (Gr. *diploos*, double), and one whose nucleus possesses only one member of each chromosome pair is said to be **haploid** (Gr. *haploos*, single). It frequently becomes convenient to refer to the haploid nucleus, cell, or organism by the designation **n,** while the diploid condition is expressed as **2n.** In the formation of gametes, the reduction of the chromosome number from $2n$ to n solves the difficulty which would otherwise exist in maintaining a constant chromosome number for a species. A second significant feature of meiosis is that it provides opportunity for a random mixing of chromosomes in gametes. Whereas each haploid "set" ordinarily must include a representative chromosome of each homologous pair, the distribution of original parental chromosomes seems to be entirely fortuitous (Fig. 121). This particular aspect of meiosis and its importance will be developed more fully in a later topic.

Whenever meiosis occurs in the formation of gametes, as described above, it is said to be **gametic.** This is characteristic of animals, where eggs and sperm are normally the only haploid cells in otherwise diploid bodies. It is interesting to note that in typical gamete production in the male animal, the cell which undergoes meiosis produces four sperm cells, as we would predict, but in the production of eggs, the first meiotic division results in only one functional cell, the other (called a **polar body**) having sacrificed its cytoplasm in the divisional process. Although the polar body eventually degenerates and thus plays no further part in the reproductive process, it may undergo the second meiotic division. The functional cell undergoes its final meiotic division with the production of a second polar body, which also degenerates. The net result of this total process, therefore, is the production of only one functional egg instead of the four that would be expected theoretically. This egg, however, enjoys the advantage of possessing all the cytoplasm of the original cell, a feature which makes for considerable biological advantage, since the egg is thus equipped with stored food materials for early embryonic growth following its fertilization (Fig. 122).

Most plants exhibit **sporic** rather than gametic meiosis, with reduction of chromosome numbers occurring in the production of four haploid spores from a diploid **spore mother cell.** Pollen grains of flowering plants, for example, are such haploid spores (Fig. 136). In the life cycle of plants whose meiotic process is sporic, there is alternation of a haploid, gamete-producing generation which grows from a spore with a diploid, spore-producing one which arises from a zygote (Figs. 133, 135, 138). Although gametic and sporic meiosis are generally characteristic of animals and plants, respectively, certain algae and fungi display a third type, **zygotic** meiosis, where the zygote is the only diploid stage in the life cycle.[3] Meiosis occurs in such plants during first divisions of the zygote.

---

[3] It has already been pointed out that certain algae undergo gametic meiosis. Thus, all three types occur in the plant kingdom, with sporic meiosis being by far the most common.

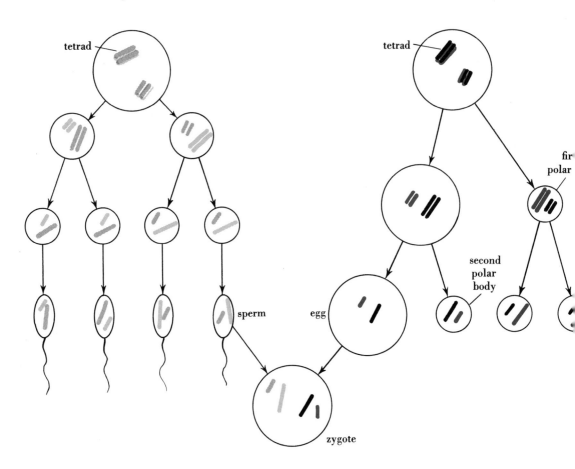

122 A comparison of sperm and egg development in animals.

SOME EXAMPLES OF SEXUAL REPRODUCTION AMONG ANIMALS

The foregoing portion of this chapter has been devoted to a discusion of terms and concepts that are necessary to an understanding of reproduction as it occurs among organisms. We are now in position to appreciate more fully the actual process as it occurs in representative animal types. A few selected examples will be presented at this point. It should be kept in mind, of course, that there is a great deal of individual variation in the several species of the animal kingdom, and these types which are discussed constitute only a scant survey. In general, however, they may be considered representative.

Paramecium

If one obtains a quart or so of water from any pond found in temperate climates and immerses a handful of hay or straw in it, large numbers of *Paramecium* (Figs. 16, 123) are almost certain to appear in this mixture after it has stood at room temperature for a few days. These protozoa do not arise spontaneously, of course; the hay provides food for a variety of microorganisms already present in the hay, forming a food chain for *Paramecium,* a few of which are present in the pond water. Thus provided with food, they are able to reproduce asexually by division. Microscopic examination reveals that these are relatively large protozoa, capable of rapid motion by virtue of their hair-like **cilia.** Each individual possesses a large **macronucleus,** which is not directly involved in sexual reproduction and a smaller diploid **micronucleus,** plus several other organelles.

Intensive study of this genus has revealed that certain species or varieties within species exhibit multiple sexuality. One variety of *Paramecium bursaria,* for example, has been found to include eight such mating strains (Fig. 120). As long as one given strain is maintained separately from any other, sexual reproduction does not occur. Upon being mixed with another strain, however, the phenomenon of **conjugation**

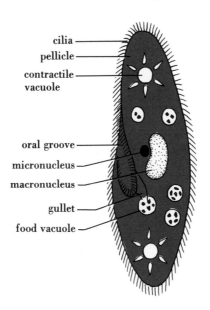

cilia
pellicle
contractile
vacuole

oral groove
micronucleus
macronucleus

gullet
food vacuole

123 A simplified drawing of *Paramecium* in typical view. Compare with Figures 16, 74.

occurs, in which cells from the two separate strains pair off. The macronucleus of each organism degenerates, and each micronucleus undergoes meiotic division to produce four haploid nuclei, three of which degenerate. At this point, definite nuclear material is present in each cell only in the form of one haploid micronucleus. Within each cell, the haploid micronucleus divides mitotically, and one of the two nuclei now seen in each cell moves into the other cell, that is, micronuclei are exchanged. Fusion of the two nuclei now occurs in each of the two cells, and the organisms separate, each possessing a new diploid micronucleus. Subsequent events result in the production of new cells, each with a macronucleus and a micronucleus (Fig. 124).

Since there is no actual gametic union, and because sexuality is hardly typical, it might be argued that conjugation in *Paramecium* does not constitute true sexual reproduction. Although it is obvious that the entire process does not fit our previous definition of sexual reproduction completely, it must be remembered that definitions almost always must be stretched somewhat to include exceptions. Although gametes as such are not produced, the process as a whole conforms to our definition. It is the essence of sexual reproduction that haploid chromosome sets from separate individuals become associated in the production of a zygote nucleus, and this certainly occurs in the conjugation of *Paramecium*.

Hydra

The several species belonging to this genus of coelenterates are common inhabitants of fresh-water ponds where they may be found attached to submerged leaves or other objects. They are generally less than a half-inch in length, even when the body is elongated to its limit, and it is easy for the inexperienced collector to miss them even when they are present in large numbers. Body structure is relatively simple, an outer **epidermis** having developed from the embryonic ectoderm, and with endoderm forming the inner **gastrodermis.** In addition to these definite layers, a few cells are found in the lifeless material between them. There is a network of nerve cells, and certain contractile fibers make limited muscular movement possible. Specialized epidermal cells, concentrated largely on the tentacles, contain bodies called **nematocysts,** each of which releases a coiled thread upon being properly stimulated. These threads serve *Hydra* in the capture of smaller animals which are utilized as food, since they carry a paralyzing chemical substance. It is enlightening to place a hydra (the generic name may also be used as the common name) in a dish, to guide a smaller animal toward it, and to watch the process of capture. If the victim is taken from the hydra and examined under the microscope, it will be seen to have been shot through

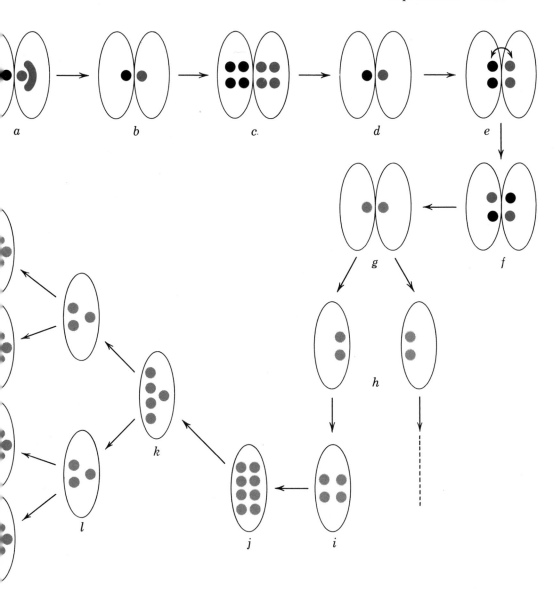

124 The process of conjugation as practiced by certain species of *Paramecium*. Note that micronuclei are exchanged at f, followed by nuclear fusion in each cell. The cells separate, each new fusion micronucleus undergoes mitotic division, and eight nuclei eventually are formed. Four of these become macronuclei, one remains a micronucleus, and three disintegrate (k). Two successive divisions of the cell produce four cells occupied by these macronuclei; the micronucleus divides mitotically during these divisions, with the result that four individuals are produced from each original conjugating cell. Each of these may become involved in asexual reproduction indefinitely.

by some threads and entangled by others. Unless interrupted, the hydra will guide the smaller paralyzed animal into its mouth by using its tentacles, and subsequent digestion occurs within the **gastrovascular cavity.** Structural details of a hydra are shown in Fig. 21.

We have already mentioned that asexual reproduction may occur in *Hydra* by the process of budding. Sexual reproduction occurs when **testes** (male reproductive organs) or **ovaries** (female reproductive organs) are formed from certain epidermal cells. Some species are **monoecious,** in which case one individual exhibits both types of reproductive organs, while others are **dioecious,** with individuals being definitely males or females. In monoecious species, testes and ovaries generally do not form at the same time, a mechanism which ensures cross-fertilization between different individuals. Several sperm form within a testis, with meiosis occurring in the process, and these eventually escape into the open water. Each is provided with a **flagellum,** or tail, by means of which it swims actively. Meanwhile, a single large egg forms within each ovary of a given animal, meiosis having occurred with the formation of polar bodies. The egg matures and is finally forced out of the ovary, apparently by a splitting of epidermal cells which were greatly stretched by growth of the egg. It remains attached to the surface of the parent animal, however, where it is eventually fertilized by a sperm (Fig. 125). Union of the haploid sperm and egg form a diploid zygote, and embryogeny of a new individual begins. A blastula is formed, at about which time a thick wall is secreted around the embryo. Gastrulation occurs, the wall becomes thicker, and the embryo drops at this stage from the parent body and undergoes a period of dormancy, the length of which depends upon several environmental factors. Eventually, the thick wall bursts and development continues with the formation of an adult animal with its specialized cells. It is obvious that further over-all development is quite limited from the histological standpoint since the fully formed hydra is little more than a gastrula with tentacles (which are merely out-pushings of the body proper.)

Earthworm

Perhaps few animals are more widely known and easily recognized than is the earthworm, *Lumbricus terrestris,* a member of the Phylum Annelida. A study of its over-all morphology reveals the presence of advanced structural organization, including well-developed nervous, muscular, and circulatory systems. In its life habits, the earthworm spends most of the time beneath the surface of the soil, where it forms burrows and tunnels by actually eating its way along, although if the dirt is quite soft, it may simply push its way through. The ingestion of dirt serves a

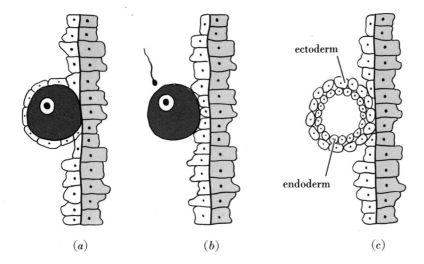

125 Sexual reproduction in *Hydra*. a, egg surrounded by epidermal cells. b, egg situated outside epidermis, sperm approaching. c, development to gastrula stage, embryo shown in section. It will shortly become separated from the parent animal. The thick wall surrounding embryo is not shown.

two-fold function; the worm is able to construct an elaborate system of tunnels, eventually depositing the castings on the surface of the soil, and it derives nutritive benefit from such organic materials as are digestible in the gastro-intestinal tract. For both of these reasons, the earthworm is of positive economic importance to the farmer. Air may penetrate the soil to greater depths by virtue of the tunnels, thus hastening decomposition of organic materials by aerobic microorganisms, and the digestive and metabolic activities of the earthworm contribute to soil fertility. It has been shown that greater crop yields are obtained from soil containing earthworms than from similar soil which is devoid of them.

As is characteristic of all but the lowest animals in the phylogenetic scale, the earthworm does not reproduce asexually. In its sexual reproduction, each individual possesses functional ovaries and testes (in which meiotic divisions produce haploid eggs and sperm) and is thus hermaphroditic. Self-fertilization does not occur, nor is any mechanism operative whereby sperm may travel freely from one individual to another, as is the case with *Hydra,* whose habitat is aquatic rather than terrestrial. Instead, two earthworms establish body contact in the act of **copulation,** or sexual union, during which the two individuals exchange sperm (Fig. 126). These are received by special receptacles in each worm where they are stored for a time. Eventually, eggs are formed in ovaries which

126 Earthworms in copulation. (Courtesy General Biological Supply House, Inc.)

lie behind the sperm receptacles and in front of the **clitellum,** an obvious band which encircles the worm beginning at the thirty-first or thirty-second segment from the anterior end (Fig. 28). At about the time of egg formation, the clitellum secretes a thick layer of mucous which gradually slips forward. As it passes the oviduct openings (located on the fourteenth segment), this mucous layer receives a number of eggs. Similarly, sperm are received at the openings of the receptacles (segments 9 through 11), and fertilization occurs. As the mucous layer finally slips off the anterior end and is deposited in the soil, its elasticity causes it to close, forming a pear-shaped **cocoon** whose greatest diameter is approximately that of a printed capital "O." There is a period of egg production by the worm, during which several cocoons may be produced in a similar manner. It has been reported that only one fertilized egg develops within each cocoon, even though several are present. Blastulation, gastrulation, germ layer formation, and further specialized embryogeny occur, and the young worm thus formed eventually breaks through the cocoon and begins an independent existence.

The Honey Bee

Most insects, including the honey bee (*Apis mellifica*), exhibit a life cycle in which more than one form of body structure is seen. Because bees are **social** insects, forming large hives wherein a complex division of labor and a high degree of organization are developed, they are not to be considered typical either in this respect or in their reproductive habits, but several interesting features regarding the latter are worthy of our attention at this point.

Ordinarily, only one reproducing female bee, the queen, is present in a hive. From a single mating early in her life, she receives a supply of sperm which she may store and use over a period of years. As she produces fertilized eggs, which she is able to lay in prodigious numbers, they are placed in special wax cells of the hive by worker bees. In about three days these eggs develop into **larvae,** which are small, worm-like forms that bear little resemblance to adult bees. Among the non-social insects, the larval form is generally free living (for example, the "caterpillar" of the butterfly life cycle), but honey bee larvae remain within their wax cells, which are not completely closed. They are fed by "nurse" workers for about five days, during which time they grow tremendously. Following this period, the larva spins a cocoon, and for about fifteen days it exists as a **pupa,** in which stage it undergoes drastic body changes. Finally, the adult bee emerges from the cocoon and chews its way out of the cell. It is now ready to take its place in the hive as a worker bee.

Individuals produced in the manner described above are all sterile females, incapable of reproduction, and it is obvious that the appearance of functional males and females at some point is necessary for the maintenance of the species. It has been found that fertilized eggs laid by the queen will develop into functional females (queens) if they are fed a special diet called "royal jelly" during the entire larval period.

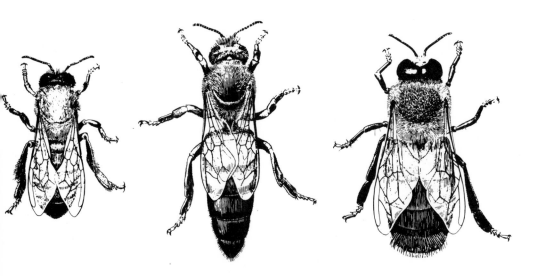

127   Worker, queen and drone bees, in that order, left to right. (Courtesy U. S. Department of Agriculture)

This is done occasionally in a hive, apparently upon some "decision" which is made when the hive has become sufficiently large to divide. At this time, a dozen or so larvae are given the special diet, and following their pupation (which requires only some eleven days, as compared with fifteen for workers) they emerge from their cells. If one queen hatches well ahead of the others, she may seek out the remaining queen pupae and sting them to death in their cells, or if all emerge within a short time of each other, a fight to the death occurs. At any rate, of the queens which develop, only one survives.

At a time previous to the development of queens, a number of functional males, called **drones,** were produced from eggs which the queen did not fertilize. In other words, unfertilized eggs actually develop into adult individuals, a phenomenon which will be discussed more fully later. The drones apparently serve no useful function in the society until the surviving new queen emerges from the hive for her "nuptial flight." At this point, she flies high into the air, and the drones follow her. The strongest of these is able to overtake and mate with her, while the others either die from exhaustion or return to the hive, where they are immediately stung to death by workers. The successful drone actually enjoys little advantage over the others, since the act of copulation proves fatal to him through the loss of reproductive organs and body parts to which they are attached. Following this experience, the queen returns to the hive, and either she or the old queen leave to establish a new colony, with the other remaining behind. The workers divide their numbers between the two queens, and a "swarm" is formed by the departing group. Actually, there are several possible variations of timing in regard to the production of new queens and the division of the hive. The account given above is a very general one.

Some interesting cytological factors are operative in the reproductive process of the honey bee. Cells of queens and workers are diploid, and meiosis occurs in egg production according to normal procedure. Fertilization of the haploid egg by a haploid sperm results in a diploid individual, as is the usual case in animal reproduction. Because the drone develops from a haploid cell, however, its body cells are haploid, and sperm production is not accompanied by meiosis. Although the honey bee is not the only animal to exhibit such a reproductive cycle, it is quite unusual for a sexually reproducing animal not to undergo meiosis in the production of gametes.

Because insects constitute a large and varied class of the Phylum Arthropoda, with many details of reproduction differing from group to group, the honey bee should not be considered typical in this characteristic. For one thing, it is a social species, which is not true of the vast majority of insects, and the life cycle with its various accompaniments is obviously a reflection of this mode of existence. In its cycle of egg-larva-pupa-adult, however, it resembles most insects. Certain orders, such as that including grasshoppers, are not characterized by the development of these body forms (called **complete metamorphosis**); rather, the egg hatches into a form which resembles the adult either very closely or to a considerable degree (**incomplete metamorphosis**). Changes which occur with growth to the adult stage, therefore, are much less dramatic than in forms which undergo complete metamorphosis.

The Frog

Inasmuch as the several species of frogs reproduce in essentially the same manner, the following description may be considered valid for the group. Like practically all vertebrates and most higher invertebrates, frogs are definitely either males or females, that is, species are dioecious. A mating season occurs in the spring, at which time eggs and sperm develop in mature individuals. In the mating process, the male frog clasps the female and may remain astride her back for several days. Eventually, her eggs are released into water from the vent,[4] at which time the male discharges sperm upon them. The eggs are thus fertilized and left in the water to develop, and the male releases the female. True copulation, which involves the introduction of sperm from one animal into another, does not occur here; the act of sexual union in frogs is sometimes called **pseudo-copulation.** It is interesting to note that copulation is not characteristic of the fishes, whereas it is of the land-dwelling vertebrates and aquatic mammals; thus frogs, which are amphibians, are in an intermediate position. This is only one of a great many structural and behavioral characteristics concerning which amphibians are intermediate between the two groups.

After fertilization, frog eggs undergo cleavage and eventually pass through blastula and gastrula stages. Further specialized development occurs, resulting in the formation of a **tadpole** within a few days after fertilization. The tadpole is equipped with gills which enable oxygen to diffuse from the water into the blood stream, and it remains aquatic for a period which varies considerably among frog species. Gradually, structural metamorphosis results in the growth of limbs, loss of the tail, disappearance of gills and appearance of lungs, plus a great many less obvious changes (Fig. 128). Thus, the frog is aquatic in its early life and

---

[4] Technically, the posterior opening of the frog is not an anus. Most vertebrates except mammals exhibit a common collecting reservoir, the **cloaca,** into which fecal, urinary, and genital products are emptied. Since an anus is the posterior opening of a gastro-intestinal tract, the term **vent** is accurate in describing the posterior cloacal opening.

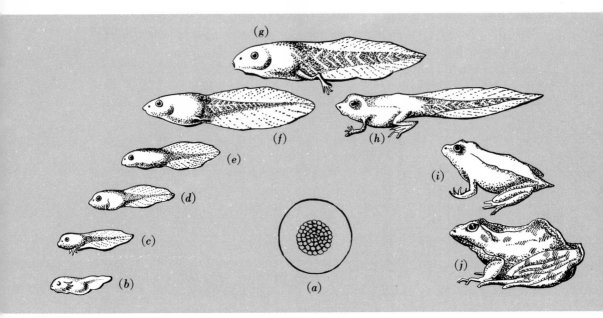

128 Development of the frog. a, embryo at blastula stage, surface view, surrounded by original gelatinous material of egg. b, young embryo equipped with gills. c–h, further development. Note the appearance of legs, disappearance of gills. i, tail becomes very short, individual spends most of its time on land. j, fully developed frog.

terrestrial at maturity. When testes and ovaries become functional in male and female frogs, respectively, meiosis results in the production of haploid reproductive cells. Union of sperm and egg, of course, restores the diploid condition characteristic of cells other than gametes.

The Human

As an example of reproduction in the most highly developed animals, the mammals, we shall consider the process as it occurs in the human species. Selection of the human as a representative mammal should not convey the idea that reproduction in man is ideally typical of the class to which he belongs; it is felt that an account of sexual reproduction in selected animal types would hardly be complete without some mention of our own species, and important deviations from more typical mammalian reproduction will be pointed out.

Although seasonal reproductive periods have been and still are important among certain primitive human groups, as is the case with various other mammals, civilized peoples of the present day are not so restricted. Sex drive remains fairly constant in a given human without regard to seasons or sexual cycles.[5] There is a restriction, however, on the time that a pregnancy can be established in the female. The human is one of a relatively small group of mammals (specifically, certain of the primates) the females of which exhibit a **menstrual cycle,** marked by a periodic build-up of tissue in an organ called the **uterus,** followed eventually by dissolution of this tissue and its passage to the outside of the body unless the cycle is interrupted by egg fertilization. In the human female, this cycle begins at **puberty** (the beginning of sexual maturity), which normally occurs at about twelve to fourteen years of age, and continues until **menopause** (the end of the reproductive span) some thirty or more years later. It repeats itself approximately every twenty-eight days, with an egg being released (**ovulation**) from one of the two ovaries at some time during each period. If the beginning of menstrual flow is counted as the first day of a cycle, ovulation generally occurs at about the tenth to the fourteenth day, although it may occur earlier or later. Upon being released from the ovary, an egg enters the open end of a **fallopian tube** and is conveyed toward the uterus. If sperm have been introduced into the vagina and travel upward through the uterus and Fallopian tubes, one of them may fertilize the egg if a sufficient number reach it while the egg is in about the upper one-third of the tube.[6] Thus, a pregnancy can be established only during a brief period following ovulation, the duration of which may be only twenty-four hours or less. At no other time during the cycle can fertilization occur.

In the event that the egg is fertilized, it continues to move toward the uterus, where it becomes imbedded within about ten days. Meanwhile, the zygote has undergone cleavage, and embryonic development is well under way by the time it reaches the uterus, the lining of which is kept intact by hormonal controls initiated by the embryo itself. Also by this time, the stored food material of the original egg has been exhausted by the embryo in its developmental activities, and it establishes a nutritive relationship with the lining of the uterus. At first, food materials and

[5] In a number of mammals, the female experiences sex urge only when eggs are released from the ovaries, a process which is under the control of hormones (internal glandular secretions), and which occurs at a certain time in a regulated cycle. In such species, of which most domesticated mammals are typical, the female will receive the male (whose sex drive remains constant) at no other time.

[6] The human egg (Fig. 118) is surrounded by a thick layer of material which cannot be penetrated by a single sperm. However, each sperm carries a small amount of an enzyme that is capable of digesting away this material, and after several thousand have contributed to this effect, one penetrates the cell membrane and fertilizes the egg. Immediately upon its entrance, a membrane is formed around the egg which prevents the entrance of other sperm.

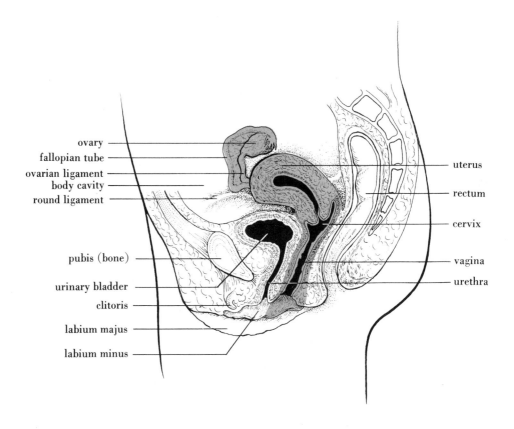

ovary
fallopian tube
ovarian ligament
body cavity
round ligament

uterus
rectum
cervix

pubis (bone)

vagina
urethra

urinary bladder
clitoris
labium majus
labium minus

129 Human female reproductive system, as seen in mid-sagittal section through the pelvic region.

oxygen diffuse into the embryo from the surrounding uterine tissue, and waste materials pass outward, but a special organ called the **placenta** is soon established between mother and embryo.

For several weeks, development proceeds with the formation of primary germ layers and subsequent growth of body organs. A heart and circulatory system appear rather early, and blood circulation begins. It should be pointed out that there is normally no actual mixing of maternal and embryonic blood, although they are brought into close proximity in the placenta.

During the first several weeks, the developing individual resembles a human being very little. In fact, stages are experienced during which pharyngeal pouches and a tail are evident, to mention only two of the many features which human embryos share in common with those of other vertebrates. At the end of about three months, however, it begins to resemble a post-natal human, and it is now termed a **fetus** instead of an embryo. Since most specialized development has already occurred at this stage, the remainder of time spent by the fetus inside the uterus is largely devoted to growth. After some nine calendar months of total development, a complex series of hormonal effects result in contraction of the uterus to expel the fully formed infant. Following a period of adjustment on the part of her reproductive system, the mother experiences resumption of the menstrual cycle. In the new individual thus formed, reproductive organs appear during embryonic development, and these remain generally inactive until puberty. At this time, mitotic and meiotic divisions are initiated among the **primordial germ cells,** and haploid gametes are formed.

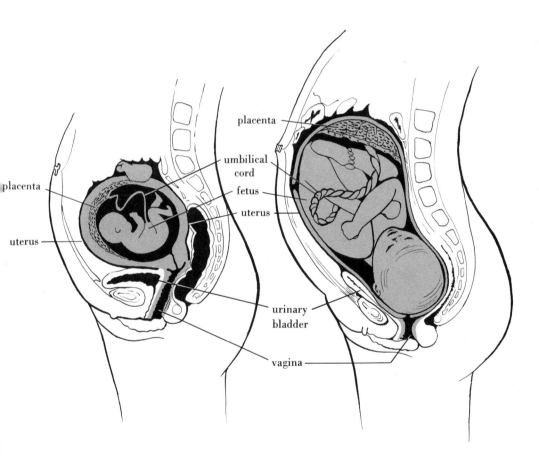

130 Female reproductive system of the human during pregnancy. (*a*) fetus at about four months of development. (*b*) fetus at full term. The developing individual is contained within a fluid-filled sac inside the uterus, and is connected with the placenta by means of the umbilical cord.

In a number of mammals, for example the pig, more than one egg is discharged during ovulation, with the result that several offspring may develop at one time within the uterus. In such animals, each embryo forms a separate placenta. In the human and other mammals which normally produce only one offspring at a time, multiple births are not at all rare. When they occur, one of two things must happen. Either the ovaries release more than one egg at a given ovulation, in which case human offspring do not resemble each other to any greater extent than do ordinary brothers and sisters, or abnormal division of the embryo during early cleavage results in two or more embryos, with the result that offspring are genetically identical.

Summary

As we have seen, numerous variations occur in the process of sexual reproduction among various animal groups. It is significant, however, that the life cycle is essentially the same in all (Fig. 131). Meiosis is gametic, with sperm and egg union resulting in a diploid zygote. The new individual produced by this means is diploid, and meiosis occurs in the formation of its gametes when it reaches sexual maturity. Thus, a fundamental similarity is seen in the sexual reproduction of the various animal species, which indicates a basic relationship between them all.

SOME EXAMPLES OF SEXUAL REPRODUCTION AMONG PLANTS

There is a tendency on the part of most people to regard sexual reproduction as being restricted to the animal kingdom, chiefly because the process occurs in plants in a far less obvious manner than in most animals, and it thus requires closer study in order to observe and to understand it. The plants discussed below are fairly representative of the plant kingdom as a whole with respect to sexual reproduction, and it is hoped that they will serve to impress upon the student that most plants, like the vast majority of animals, do exhibit sexuality.

Chlamydomonas

This organism is one of a large number of green algae which are very widespread in soil and fresh water. A great many species have been described as belonging to this genus; the description given below is generally valid for all members, but it applies specifically to *Chlamy-*

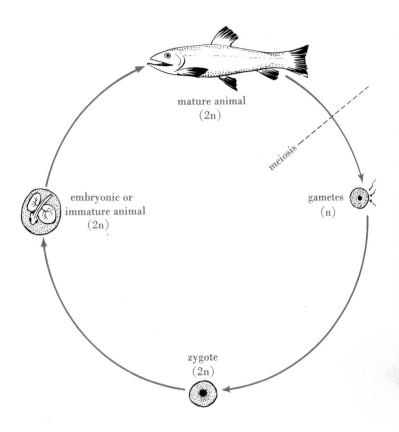

131 Generalized animal life cycle. Dotted line indicates point in the cycle at which meiosis occurs.

domonas eugametos, which has been one of the most widely studied species of the group. Individuals are unicellular, and each possesses a single **nucleus, chloroplast, eyespot,** and **pyrenoid,** the last-named organelle serving as a center of starch accumulation during photosynthesis. There are two (or sometimes more) contractile vacuoles at one end of the cell which function in osmotic regulation, and two whip-like **flagella** make it possible for the cell to achieve motility (Fig. 99a).

A given cell of *Chlamydomonas,* under ideal conditions, grows in size and undergoes mitotic nuclear division accompanied by cytokinesis, a process which repeats itself with each new cell thus produced. Therefore, continued cell division, as we learned to be the case in *Paramecium,* is equivalent to asexual reproduction. It was pointed out earlier (see page 157) that cytokinesis in *Chlamydomonas* is somewhat different from that occurring in either typical plant or animal cell division.

Sexuality has been studied quite extensively in a number of

species belonging to this genus, and it has been found that in *C. eugametos* and certain other species two strains, morphologically indistinguishable in regard to sex, exist. When these are mixed under proper conditions, there is an attraction between cells of the two strains, and these eventually pair off, with subsequent protoplasmic and nuclear fusion. Thus, the organisms (cells) themselves function as gametes, and a zygote is formed. It has been found that the zygote undergoes two successive meiotic divisions with the production of four individuals, which escape from the old zygote wall.[7] Hence, meiosis is zygotic, and the zygote is the only diploid structure in the cycle.

In its exhibition of zygotic meiosis and morphologically indistinguishable sexual strains, *C. eugametos* is typical of a great many algae and fungi. *Rhizopus stolonifer*, the bread mold (Figs. 57, 119), is one fungus of which this is true. Thus, sexuality in these "lower" plants is somewhat different from that observed in higher plants and animals, but it meets all the requirements of our previous definition.

Mosses

Although most people are vaguely familiar with the group of plants called mosses, it is doubtful that many students beginning a formal study of biology know very much about them. These plants are widespread in nature, occurring most abundantly in moist, shaded areas where they may cover the ground with a carpet-like growth. Close examination of a typical mossy area leads to the observation that many small, leafy plants make up the growth and that at certain seasons some of these plants may bear an elongated structure which resembles, more or less, a golf club.

The green, leafy plants are actually gamete-producing individuals (gametophytes), and in many species of mosses they are definitely either males or females. In others, one plant may produce both eggs and sperm, in which case there may appear male and female branches, or both types of sex organs may occur on the same branch. At any rate, sperm escape from the organ within which they are formed at a time when there is adequate moisture for them to achieve motility, and they reach female plants (or branches) and fertilize eggs, which develop individually within vase-like structures. Several eggs in the same plant may be fertilized, but only one zygote develops fully at the tip of a given female plant or branch. Repeated cell division results in the formation of the elongated structure

---

[7] In some species (including *C. eugametos*), the four products of meiosis may divide mitotically within the zygote wall to form more cells before escape is effected.

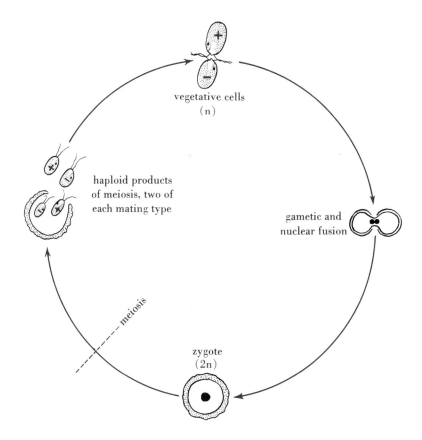

vegetative cells
(n)

haploid products
of meiosis, two of
each mating type

gametic and
nuclear fusion

meiosis

zygote
(2n)

132 Life cycle of *Chlamydomonas eugametos*, sexual phase.

referred to above, which bears a sporangium, or spore-producing organ, at its terminal end (Fig. 62). For this reason, the product of zygote development is called a sporophyte.

Botanists have learned that the gametophytes develop from spores produced in the sporangium and that both spores and the cells of these plants, including their gametes, are haploid. The sporophyte develops from a diploid zygote, and it is thus composed of diploid cells. Meiosis occurs in **spore mother cells** of the sporangium to produce four haploid spores from each. Hence, meiosis is sporic, as is typical of plants (Fig. 133).

Botanists regard the moss gametophyte and sporophyte of a given species as two distinct phases of a life cycle, since one is haploid in chromosomal constitution and produces gametes, and the other is diploid and spore-producing. Thus the moss is said to exhibit **alterna-**

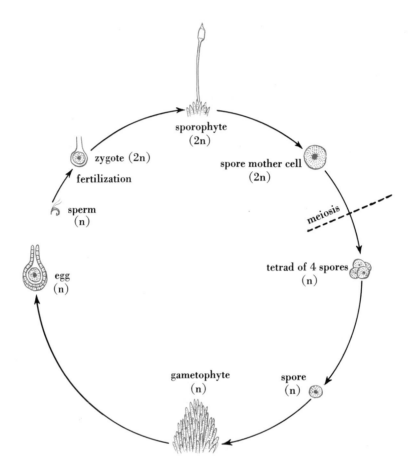

133 Life cycle of a moss.

tion of generations. Since the gametophyte is the more prominent and persistent generation in mosses, it is said to be the **dominant** phase of the life cycle in this group.

Ferns

It was pointed out in an earlier chapter that land plants characterized by vascular tissue may attain greater size than those without it, as a general rule, since they are able to conduct water and dissolved minerals to greater heights. In contrasting a typical fern with even the largest of the mosses, the difference in body size is immediately apparent. In addition to this difference, ferns demonstrate a considerable advance in complexity over mosses, exhibiting highly developed stems and roots, both of which typically grow beneath the soil surface, and leaves, which make up the visible part of the fern. The leaves are usually quite large, and at certain times they may bear sporangia (Fig. 134*b*) on their lower surfaces. The sporangia are generally concentrated into groups, each of

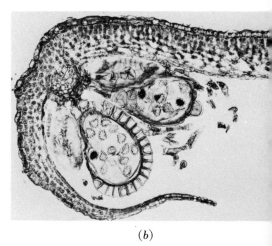

(*b*)

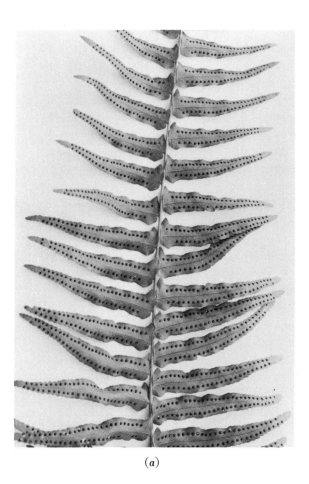

(*a*)

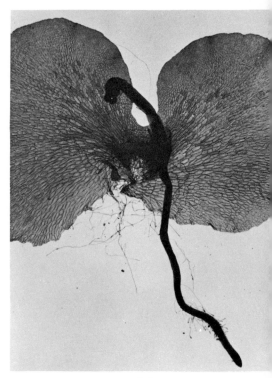

(*c*)

134 Some structures associated with reproduction in ferns. a, portion of fern leaf showing sori, or clusters of sporangia, on lower surface. b, section through a sorus showing two sporangia, each containing spores. (Courtesy Carolina Biological Supply Company) c, the lower surface of a fern gametophyte with young sporophyte (dark filament) beginning its growth. (Courtesy General Biological Supply House, Inc.)

which is visible to the eye as a small spot (Fig. 134*a*). It is not uncommon for people who keep ferns for ornamental purposes to be unaware of this habit of spore production, and to suspect that their plants have become infested with some animal parasite.

Cytological examination of developing fern sporangia reveals that meiosis occurs in spore mother cells, as it does in mosses, with the production of haploid spores. These are shed from the leaves in large numbers, and eventually germinate if they are subjected to proper environmental conditions. The plant which is thus produced from a spore (Fig. 134*c*) has very little in common with a fern in appearance; it is sufficiently flat and small (possibly one quarter of an inch in diameter in many ferns) as to escape detection by any but the practiced eye. This is the gametophytic stage of a cycle which is essentially similar to that of a moss, and it functions in the production of haploid gametes. In most ferns both male and female gametes are produced on the same gametophyte. Because they grow flat on the soil, sperm motility is readily effected through moisture accumulation, and eggs (which develop in vase-like structures similar to those of mosses) are fertilized to produce zygotes. As in mosses, only one zygote in a given gametophyte matures; it develops into an embryonic, diploid sporophyte, which eventually undergoes differentiation to form roots, leaves, and a stem. Thus the cycle is completed when this plant matures and produces spores (Fig. 135).

Although the life cycle of ferns is essentially like that of mosses, there is an outstanding difference in the relative duration and stature of gametophyte and sporophyte. In the moss, the sporophyte grows upon the gametophyte, which is the dominant phase of the cycle. In contrast it is the sporophyte of the fern that is the larger and more obvious plant, the gametophyte being small, insignificant, and short-lived. In fact, the gametophyte perishes and decays as soon as the sporophyte produced from it gains independence through root formation and chlorophyll development, whereas the sporophytic plant may persist for many years as a perennial.

Flowering Plants

By far the most numerous and successful plants on earth today are those which bear special organs of reproduction called flowers. It is a matter of simple observation that a great deal of variation exists in floral morphology among the different species of this group, but a close study of various flowers reveals a fundamental uniformity of structure.

Essentially, a flower is an aggregation of modified leaves, certain of which produce spores. In the typical flower, four types of structures are present: **sepals, petals, pistil(s), and stamens** (Fig. 136).

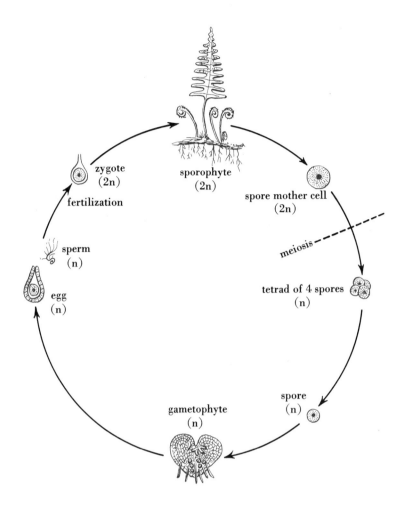

135 Life cycle of a fern.

Although the flowers of most plants exhibit these four parts, there are some which lack one or more of them. The flowers of grasses, for instance, are devoid of sepals and petals as such. In certain species, pistils and stamens are borne in separate flowers. Corn (*Zea mays*), for example, bears staminate flowers at the top of the plant and those which are pistillate at a lower point (the "ear") on the stalk. Some species, such as willow and mulberry, even bear staminate and pistillate flowers on separate plants.

The process of reproduction is initiated in flowers when certain cells of the **anthers** (sporangia), located at the tips of stamens, differentiate into spore mother cells and undergo meiosis in the formation of haploid

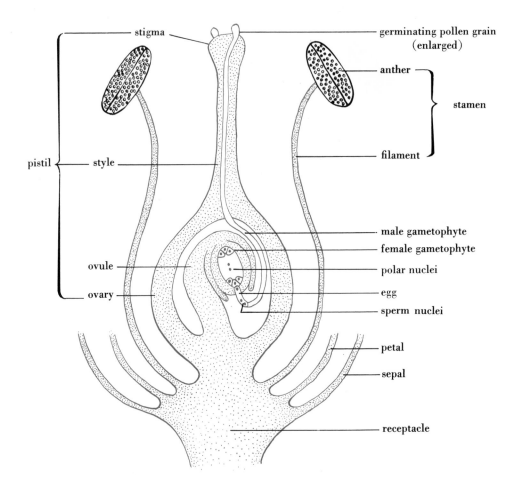

stigma

germinating pollen grain
(enlarged)

anther

stamen

pistil

style

filament

male gametophyte

female gametophyte

ovule

polar nuclei

ovary

egg

sperm nuclei

petal

sepal

receptacle

136 Diagrammatic representation of a typical flower at the time of fertilization. For purposes of simplicity, the ovary is shown as having only one ovule. In some species, such as peach or cherry, this is the case. It is more common to find a number of ovules within the ovary.

spores, which are called **pollen grains.** It is important at this point to realize that flowering plants (as well as the non-flowering seed plants), unlike most of the lower spore-producers, exhibit two kinds of spores which are different; one type, the pollen grain, is produced in the stamens, and the other type develops in the pistil. The pollen grains may be transferred to the tip of a pistil either of the same flower or to that of another flower belonging to the given species, depending upon circumstances. At this location, each pollen grain germinates to form a **pollen tube,** which begins to grow downward through the pistil. Meanwhile, the base of the pistil, called the ovary,[8] undergoes changes associated with production of the second type of spore. Depending on the species, one or more **ovules,** which ultimately develop into seeds, undergo changes resulting in the formation of a deep-lying spore mother cell in each. This cell undergoes meiotic division, three of the four haploid products degenerate, and the nucleus of the other divides mitotically to form eight nuclei. Cell walls form around six of these, one of which constitutes the egg cell. Two nuclei do not become enclosed by cell walls, and these are situated within the remaining cytoplasm. By this time, pollen tubes have grown down the pistil; one reaches each ovule, penetrates its tissues through a special passageway, the **micropyle,** and discharges two sperm nuclei in the vicinity of the egg. One of these unites with the egg, forming a diploid zygote, and the other fuses with the two free nuclei, forming a triploid ($3n$) nucleus (Fig. 137). The remaining five cells play no further important role in development.

From this point on, growth of the diploid embryo occurs with the formation of root and shoot. Meanwhile, the triploid nucleus has divided mitotically to form a nutritive tissue known as **endosperm.** The endosperm is ultimately utilized by the embryo, either before the latter enters the period of dormancy characteristic of seeds or after it renews its growth at germination. The outer tissues of the ovule form the **seed coats** which surround the embryo and endosperm (if any remains). A seed, therefore, is a special reproductive structure consisting of a dormant embryonic plant which is either surrounded by endosperm or filled with stored food and covered by the outer portions of the ovule. Under proper conditions of moisture, temperature, and oxygen supply, and in the case of certain types after a necessary period of dormancy, the seed germinates with further development of the embryo and its ultimate establishment as an independent plant.[9]

The ovary of the pistil with its enclosed seed or seeds matures into the **fruit.** It is popularly thought that a structure must be edible to be considered a fruit, but the ovaries of many flowers develop into fruits that cannot be used for food purposes. Furthermore, many fruits are considered to be vegetables; tomatoes, cucumbers, squashes, watermelons, and the pods of beans, for example, are all fruits by correct botanical definition. In consideration of edible plants, the question of whether or

---

[8] This term was ascribed to the structure by earlier botanists who did not fully understand its significance and who presumed it to correspond to the egg-producing organ of female animals. It is no longer regarded in this light, but the name still persists.

[9] The foregoing account represents typical seed production in flowering plants, but it should be pointed out that certain deviations from this particular pattern are seen in some species.

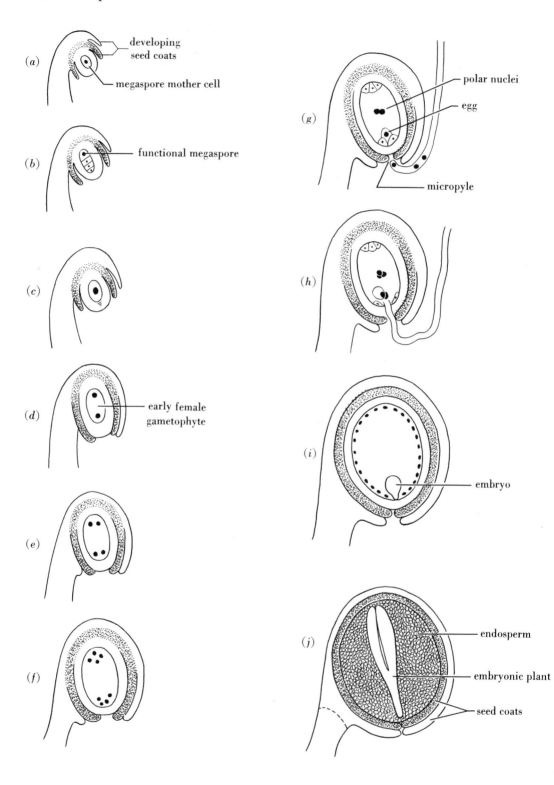

137 Typical development of female gametophyte within an ovule, with ultimate seed formation. a, young ovule with megaspore mother cell. b, end of meiotic division of spore mother cell. Three megaspores are undergoing degeneration. c, functional megaspore after a period of growth. d, end of first (mitotic) division of megaspore. e, four-nucleate stage. f, eight-nucleate stage. g, fully developed female gametophyte consisting of seven cells, the largest of which contains the two polar nuclei. Male gametophyte (pollen tube) now fully developed and approaching ovule. h, discharge of two sperm nuclei into female gametophyte, double fertilization about to occur. i, later development of ovule. Nuclear division has resulted in the presence of several endosperm nuclei, which have migrated outward. Embryo has begun its growth. j, fully developed seed containing embryo with root and shoot. Endosperm nuclei have become enclosed by cell walls, and these cells now surround the embryo. Two seed coats have completed their development and form the outer coverings for the seed.

not a given portion is a fruit or a vegetable must be decided on the basis of its origin on the plant. If it develops from a floral ovary it is a fruit, and if it represents some other plant organ, it is a vegetable.

In terms of the life cycles exhibited by such plants as mosses and ferns, the flowering plant body must be considered the sporophyte, with male and female gametophytes being formed by the spores produced in stamens and pistils, respectively. The male gametophyte begins its formation when the nucleus of the pollen grain divides. One of the two resulting nuclei divides once more to produce the sperm nuclei, and the fully developed male gametophyte is merely a pollen tube with three nuclei. The female gametophyte is only slightly more complex at maturity, consisting as it does of seven cells. Thus, the gametophytic phase of the life cycle is greatly reduced in flowering plants, with male and female gametophytes never becoming independently established apart from the sporophyte (Fig. 138).

An interesting question of sexuality arises in consideration of the two types of spores produced in flowering plants. It might seem logical to refer to pollen grains as male spores, and to consider those produced in ovules as being female since they give rise to male and female gametophytes, respectively. By the same reasoning, staminate flowers of corn might be considered male, and pistillate flowers would, of course, be female. To extend the concept further, species such as mulberry and willow would be made up of male and female trees. This application of sexuality is quite acceptable to some botanists, but it must be remembered that sporophytes are spore-producing plants, and that although spores are *potentially* male and female in flowering plants, they are still asexual in function, that is, with respect to the manner by which they produce the sexual phase. Although it is something of an academic question as to whether one can speak accurately of a male or female

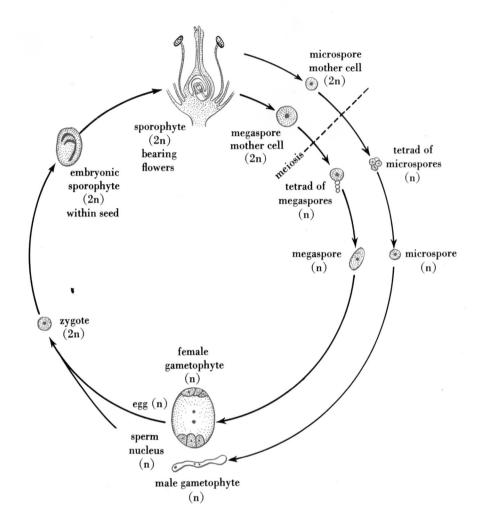

138 Life cycle of a flowering plant.

flower or plant, most botanists agree that sporophytic plants do not exhibit sexuality in the same sense that animals such as mammals do.

In reviewing the plant groups which have been considered, it will occur to the student that they are much alike in regard to their sexual reproduction. Among other similarities, the phenomenon that alternating sporophytic and gametophytic phases of a life cycle appear in most plant groups, with sporic meiosis, is significant in its suggestion of a fundamental relationship between them. Similarly, most animals have a great deal in common in regard to reproduction; the exhibition of gametic meiosis, flagellated sperm, and relatively large, non-motile eggs are a few of the features that indicate a basic similarity. Finally, sexuality and its accompaniments, so widespread in both kingdoms, add to the many other features which living forms generally share in common, allowing us to build toward some highly important generalizations which will be developed in a later chapter.

THE PHENOMENON OF PARTHENOGENESIS

It might be assumed from the principles and examples that have been introduced to this point that new individuals arise from gametes only after their union, although an exception was noted in the development of drone bees from unfertilized eggs. As a matter of fact, gametic union is the rule in sexual reproduction, but the development of eggs that have not been fertilized, a phenomenon called **parthenogenesis** (Gr. *parthenos*, virgin + *genesis*, to be born) sometimes occurs. From the viewpoint of the biologist, this phenomenon is either **natural** (occurring in nature) or **artificial** (induced under laboratory conditions).

Natural parthenogenesis occurs to a considerable degree among insects, where certain species are known that do not feature male individuals at all; instead, females develop regularly from unfertilized eggs. In other species, such as the honey bee, it is employed to a limited extent in the production of males. Parthenogenesis also is known among various other arthropods and in certain flatworms, as well as in a few algae such as *Ulva*, the sea lettuce, whose gametes develop without sexual union into new individuals. It undoubtedly occurs in a great many animal and plant species which have not been closely studied in this respect. Although there have been reports of natural parthenogenesis in humans, it is extremely doubtful that it ever occurs. Artificial parthenogenesis has been induced in a wide variety of animal forms including annelids, mollusks, echinoderms, amphibians, birds, and even mammals. For example, frog eggs may be stimulated to develop by pricking them slightly with a needle that has been dipped in frog blood. Studies of artificial parthenogenesis have been very rewarding, showing as they have that one function of normal fertilization is the activation of division-initiating forces within the egg. If these forces are set off by chemical or mechanical means rather than by sperm entrance, then development may proceed more or less normally, even though the diploid chromosome number has not been restored.[10]

[10] Artificial parthenogenesis seldom results in fully developed animals, which indicates that a normal chromosomal complement is necessary to normal development. In successful parthenogenetic development, apparently there is a chromosomal doubling during early cleavages to restore the diploid number.

It may occur to the student to wonder whether natural parthenogenesis is to be regarded as sexual reproduction inasmuch as there is no gametic union. Technically, of course, it is asexual, but since the individual arises from a cell that has undergone differentiation toward gametic union, many biologists regard parthenogenesis as being a highly unusual form of sexual reproduction. Certainly it fails to conform to our previous definition of sexual reproduction, but since one specialized sex cell is involved, it would be difficult to regard it in the same light as vegetative reproduction or spore germination. Actually, good arguments can be made for either viewpoint, and perhaps it is best to consider parthenogenesis a type of reproduction which involves both sexual and asexual features.

SOME ELEMENTARY PRINCIPLES OF GENETICS

When individuals are produced whose characteristics are essentially like those of the other members of their species, it is obvious that inheritance is manifested. The field of genetics has developed within biology through a study of the forces involved in the duplication of traits from parents to offspring, and a great deal has been discovered about the mechanisms which are responsible.

The Work of Gregor Mendel

Before about the middle of the nineteenth century, practically nothing was known about inheritance except that it occurred. At this time, an Austrian monk, Gregor Johann Mendel (1822–1884), began a series of experiments which served as the basis for a clarification of elementary genetic principles. Mendel was not a scientist by vocation, although he did teach various sciences for many years in the *Realschule* (comparable to the American high school) of what was then Brünn, Austria. He developed a great curiosity about inheritance and conducted experiments independently in a monastery garden. Following many years of experimentation involving a variety of cultivated plants, Mendel reported his results and conclusions in 1865, followed by their publication as a paper during the next year. Unfortunately, the biological world was not ready for Mendel's findings and did not fully appreciate them until the year 1900, when his paper was re-discovered and compared with cytological knowledge that had developed since Mendel's time. Thus it was never known to him or to his contemporaries that he had made one of the greatest scientific contributions of all time through the formulation of certain elementary genetic principles.

It was common in Mendel's day to regard inheritance as the result of a blending of traits since it was known that something of this sort occurred in the crossing of certain varieties within plant or animal species. In the four-o'-clock (*Mirabilis jalapa*), for example, red-flowered plants produce nothing but more red-flowered plants when crossed only among themselves, and white-flowered plants likewise breed "true" for white flowers. However, when pollen from either a red- or a white-flowered plant is transferred to the pistil of the other type of flower, the seeds which are formed by this cross produce pink-flowered plants. Thus a blending of traits could readily be seen. It disturbed Mendel that pink-flowered plants of this sort never bred true, as should be the case if a simple blending were responsible; this inept theory of inheritance failed entirely to explain why hybrids (offspring of parents which differ in a given trait) often revert back to parental types. For example, the offspring of two pink four-o'-clocks may be white, pink or red (Fig. 139). It was equally disturbing to him that this sort of reversion occurred in crosses where no blending was obvious but where a hidden trait kept cropping out.

The Monohybrid Cross

For his experimental work, Mendel relied chiefly upon the garden pea (*Pisum sativum*), which he knew to include several true-breeding varieties that could readily be crossed with each other. Some of these varieties were quite tall and had to be trained as vines, while others were extremely short. Other contrasting traits were seed colors (green or yellow), seed form (round or wrinkled), and flower positions (borne along the main stem or in a group at the top of the stem). In all, he worked with seven pairs of contrasting traits in this species. As it turned out, no blending of traits occurred; for example, seeds resulting from a cross between tall and short peas did not produce plants which were intermediate in height, but rather, all of them were tall. Mendel referred to that trait which appeared in the hybrid as being "dominant" and the one which did not appear as "recessive." Hence, tall proved to be the dominant trait in the cross just cited, and short was recessive to it.

At this point, Mendel took a very important step. He allowed hybrids for a given pair of traits to self-pollinate, and he analyzed the results of his seven separate experiments. In each case, individuals showing the recessive trait appeared and in definite numerical ratio to individuals exhibiting the dominant trait. **Without exception, in this second generation, a ratio of approximately three dominants to one recessive appeared.** For example, Mendel produced 1,064 plants in the tall-short experiment, of which 787 were tall and 277 were short. A still further extension of the general experiment revealed that in all seven

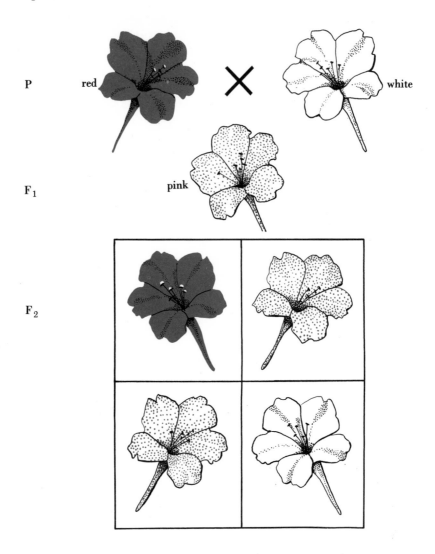

P   red   ×   white

F₁   pink

F₂

139 The "blending" of traits in four-o'-clocks. In this case, neither
gene is dominant over the other. P—parental types; F₁—first
filial generation; F₂—second filial generation, obtained by
crossing F₁ × F₁.

groups, the individuals showing recessive traits bred true for them, one-
third of the dominant individuals likewise bred true, and that the remaining
two-thirds of the dominants did not.[11]

      It seemed to Mendel that more was involved here than met the

      [11] Since it was a simple matter to ensure that the flowers were self-pollinated,
   it was relatively easy for Mendel to test the genetic "purity" of any given plant.

eye, and he postulated the existence of "characters" which were associated with the gametes of parent individuals. By allowing letters of the alphabet to represent these characters, he was able to manipulate them theoretically and thus to set up his crosses on paper. For the sake of convenience, capital letters were made to represent dominant characters, and small ones were used for recessives, a system which is still employed in genetics. On this basis, Mendel came to the conclusion that only if the genetic constitution of a parent plant were represented by two characters for a given trait, with one and only one of these being transmitted to a gamete, could his results be explained. Hence, in the crosses involving tall and short peas, where the contrasting parent plants were pure for their traits, the hybrids are mixed in regard to their genetic characters. A cross between two such hybrids, in which random combination of gametes occurs, results in one individual pure for the dominant characters, one pure for the recessive ones, and two which are mixed out of every four produced. Because of dominance, three of the four will exhibit the dominant trait (Fig. 140). It will be recalled that this agrees perfectly with Mendel's experimental results. Furthermore, it explains

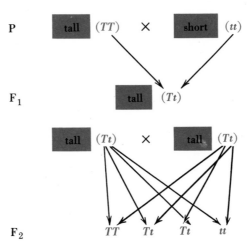

P   tall *(TT)* ✕ short *(tt)*

F₁   tall *(Tt)*

tall *(Tt)* ✕ tall *(Tt)*

F₂   *TT*   *Tt*   *Tt*   *tt*

140 A representation of theoretical results from two generations of crossing tall and short peas. It should be borne in mind that Mendel postulated the inclusion of one and only one character (gene) of a given pair within a gamete. The parental plants can produce only one type of gamete each; hence they produce only one type of offspring when crossed. The F₁ plants, however, can produce *two* types of gametes each, and they produce four classes of offspring, two of which are identical in type.

the situation in such cases of inheritance as that of four-o'-clocks, if it be assumed that neither of the characters involved is dominant over the other (Fig. 139).

The Nature of the Gene and Some Genetic Terminology

Since Mendel's time, the term "gene" has replaced his term "character," and it has been shown that genes are closely associated with chromosomes, being in some fashion a part of their chemical structure. Although the true nature of the gene is not yet fully understood, it is certain that it somehow operates as a discrete chemical unit or determiner of traits. It is now known that DNA is the actual genetic material of cells, and we have already seen (Chapter 5) how DNA controls synthesis in the cell. Apparently, a given gene (or DNA unit, in biochemical terms) is a certain fraction of a DNA molecule which serves as a master pattern, or template, from which RNA duplicates are made (Fig. 78). These duplicates travel from the nucleus to the microsomes, where they control protein synthesis, and it is the specificity of these proteins (which may function as structural components of new cells or as enzymes) that impart to the organism its characteristics. Thus, when we call attention to a difference between a given gene *A* and its recessive partner *a*, we are only giving meaningful expression to what is perhaps the ability of one gene to influence the production of some enzyme that is not produced under the influence of the other. Presence or absence of this enzyme in cells then possibly leads to some visible or functional difference in the organism. Besides serving as the template for the production of proteins, the gene is capable of producing still other templates, like itself. This occurs during the interphase preceding cell division.

Perhaps an example of genic action on the molecular level will serve to emphasize the principle that genes work through biochemical and physiological channels. The blood pigment hemoglobin, which is a protein, has a definite chemical structure; a molecule of hemoglobin is composed of about 8,000 atoms, with most of these being contained in some 600 amino acid molecules. An abnormality of the human called **sickle cell anemia** (Fig. 141), which is a so-called "genetic" disease, is actually a manifestation of abnormal hemoglobin. Biochemists are now certain that normal hemoglobin and sickle cell hemoglobin differ only in a *single amino acid* on each side of the molecule, which is a sort of "double" structure. The amino acid **glutamic acid** is present at a certain point in normal hemoglobin but is replaced by the amino acid **valine** in each half of the sickle cell hemoglobin molecule. Now this sort of substitution has extremely far-reaching implications for genetics, because it means that a change in a gene (from "normal" to "sickle cell,"

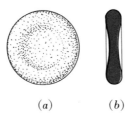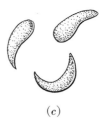

(a) (b) (c)

141 The effect upon human red blood cells of a gene which influences the production of "sickle cell" hemoglobin. a, normal red blood cell in "face" view. b, normal red blood cell in edge view. The depression in the center of the cell is caused by early extrusion of the nucleus. c, typical "sickle" red blood cells as they are seen in the blood of a victim of sickle cell anemia.

in this case), is accompanied by a change in sequence of amino acids within a particular protein molecule. When we consider that DNA units (genes) in the nucleus control protein synthesis in the microsomes through RNA "messengers" (see page 113), this is not at all surprising, but it has been only within recent years that this definite biochemical mode of "information transfer" from nucleus to cytoplasm has been known and appreciated. Even yet, many people (including some biologists) conceive of the gene as a mystical, almost magical, unit that somehow influences traits in organisms independently of physiological channels.

Complex organisms carry thousands of genes on their chromosomes whose effects upon development and behavior may be interwoven according to an intricate pattern. For example, one trait may be controlled by many genes, or one gene may play a part in the development of several traits. Furthermore, not all traits are obvious and visible; some genes are concerned with developmental characteristics, some with the production or regulation of chemical substances, and so on. We have reason to believe that even such abstract qualities as personality traits in humans and other higher animals are genetically influenced, although these are difficult to study because environmental factors can seldom if ever be controlled perfectly. For purposes of clarity in teaching genetics, it is necessary that obvious traits controlled by single genes be used to exemplify fundamental genetic principles, but it should not be thought that all situations of inheritance are that simple.

Although Mendel was not aware of the existence of genes located on chromosomes, he accurately predicted the discovery of meiosis through his **law of segregation.** Stated in precise terms, this generalization holds that **during gamete formation, each member of a pair of genes be-**

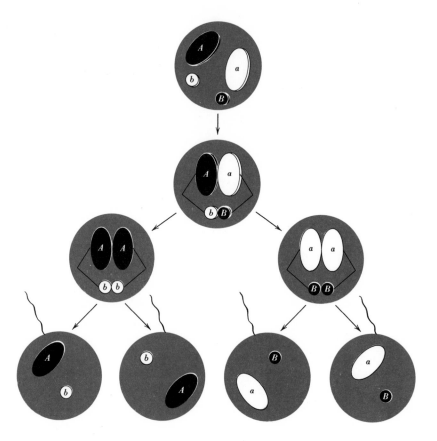

142 The cytological basis for the law of segregation. Notice that genes A and a *cannot* go into the same gamete at meiosis; the same holds true for genes B and b. In this illustration, genes A and b segregate together, as do genes a and B. There is an equal chance for genes A and B, a and b to segregate together. Compare with Figure 121.

comes associated with a different gamete. Let us note that this is exactly what happens to homologous chromosomes in the meiotic process of animals (Figs. 121, 122, 142).[12] Since chromosomes are segregated into different gametes, it follows that whatever genes they carry are also segregated, with equal numbers of gametes being formed for each gene type when members of a gene pair are not identical.

At this point, let us consider a few terms that are commonly used in genetics. In describing the genetic constitution of an organism

[12] When meiosis is either zygotic or sporic, as in most plants, the law of segregation still holds. Genes are merely segregated much earlier in terms of gamete formation than is the case in gametic meiosis.

for a given trait, the term **genotype** is used. Hence, the genotype for a pure-breeding tall pea is *TT,* that for a pure-breeding short one is *tt,* and the hybrid is *Tt.* The term **phenotype** is used to describe a genetically determined trait. Thus, a plant from the same example whose genotype is either *TT* or *Tt* is phenotypically tall. Whenever members of a gene pair are identical, as in the genotype *TT,* the individual is said to be **homozygous** in regard to these genes. If the members differ, as in the genotype *Tt,* it is said to be **heterozygous.** Members of the same gene pair which differ in their genetic expression, such as *T* and *t,* are called **allelic genes,** or simply **alleles.**

The Dihybrid Cross

On the basis of the law of segregation, let us predict what results could be expected if *two* pairs of contrasting factors were crossed. Again using the pea as an example, it will be recalled that Mendel found that round seed shape dominated wrinkled and that yellow color dominated green. If a pure-breeding plant which bears round, yellow seeds were crossed with one bearing wrinkled, green seeds, the situation might be symbolized as follows:

$$RRYY \times rryy$$

Because of genic segregation, the hybrid seeds should be *phenotypically* identical to those of the parent which was characterized by round, yellow seeds, but *genotypically* we would predict that they should be heterozygous for both gene pairs, as is shown in Fig. 143.

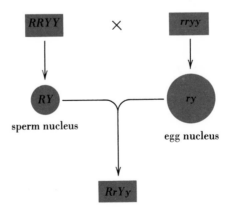

143

When two plants produced by such hybrid seeds are crossed (or one plant is allowed to self-pollinate), four types of sperm nuclei should be formed, as well as four types of egg nuclei, in regard to genotype as is shown in Fig. 144.

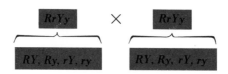

144

Let us illustrate the possible combinations that may occur when this cross is made:

SPERM NUCLEI	EGG NUCLEI			
	RY	*Ry*	*rY*	*ry*
RY	*RRYY*	*RRYy*	*RrYY*	*RrYy*
Ry	*RRYy*	*RRyy*	*RrYy*	*Rryy*
rY	*RrYY*	*RrYy*	*rrYY*	*rrYy*
ry	*RrYy*	*Rryy*	*rrYy*	*rryy*

145

Genotypically, several combinations would thus occur, but let us notice the theoretical *phenotypic* results. Of every sixteen seeds formed, we should observe the distribution shown in Fig. 146.

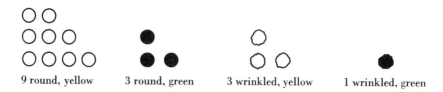

9 round, yellow   3 round, green   3 wrinkled, yellow   1 wrinkled, green

146

Mendel performed this very cross, and produced 556 F_2 seeds, as follows:

315 round, yellow
108 round, green
101 wrinkled, yellow
32 wrinkled, green

Since this is a $9:3:3:1$ ratio, allowing for some chance variation, it provided Mendel with very good evidence that his law of segregation was valid. Furthermore, he carried the experiment further by testing the F_2 seeds for genotype, which was accomplished by planting them and allowing the resulting plants to self-pollinate. His results substantiated, in general, the theoretical expectation.

From these and other experiments, Mendel was able to formulate a second important generalization, the **law of independent assortment,** which applies to genes of unlike pairs in their association within the same genotype. It should be obvious from the experiment discussed above that neither gene pair influences the other in any way. Taken separately, each produces a $3:1$ phenotypic ratio in the F_2 generation, even though the experiment involves both pairs. Stated more precisely, **the law of independent assortment holds that a gene pair is not influenced in its inheritance by association with other gene pairs located on other chromosomes.**[13] When we trace out the possible fates of genes and their chromosomes during meiosis, it is readily seen why this law is operative (Fig. 142). It should be remembered, however, that Mendel arrived at both his first and second laws through experimentation and statistical analysis and that it was many years before the cytological basis for their validity was known.

Linkage

By definition, the law of independent assortment can apply only when gene pairs are located on different chromosomes. Let us compare the inheritance of two hypothetical genes, A and B, when they are independent (located on different chromosome pairs) and when they are linked (located on the same chromosome pair).[14] It can be shown by

[13] This is the modern expression of the law of independent assortment. Mendel, of course, knew nothing of genes and chromosomes.

[14] Actually, some gametes are formed under these conditions which may carry *Ab* or *aB* chromosomes, since homologous chromosomes frequently exchange parts in synapsis, a phenomenon resulting in a *crossing over* of genes. Hence, a typical $3:1$ ratio is not usually realized in a linkage situation such as that illustrated in Fig. 147. Crossing over is an exception to linkage, just as linkage is an exception to independent assortment.

diagram that genes located on the same chromosome are obliged to become associated *together* in a gamete and that there is no independent
assortment (Fig. 147).

By chance, the gene pairs utilized by Mendel in his classic experiments with peas are located on different chromosome pairs, and he
found no exceptions to his law of independent assortment. Perhaps it is

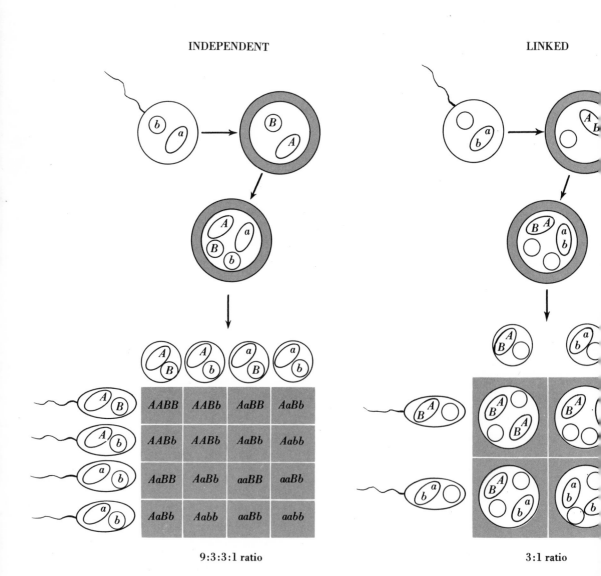

147 A comparison of independent assortment and linkage.

fortunate that this was the case, since the phenomenon of linkage would doubtless have been difficult for him to reconcile with his other data on a purely theoretical basis.

Sex Determination and Sex Linkage

Since Mendel's time, it has been found that in many animals, including the human, the sex of offspring is determined by the inheritance of a certain chromosomal complement. For example, there are normally twenty-three pairs of chromosomes in the body cells of the human, twenty-two of which consist of morphologically identical members. In the female, the other pair also consists of like chromosomes, but in the male the two members of this pair are both morphologically and genetically dissimilar. For purposes of distinction, biologists refer to members of the twenty-two pairs as **autosomes,** and to members of the twenty-third pair as **sex chromosomes.** The male, of course, possesses one sex chromosome which females do not carry, and because its shape in certain animals that were used in early work on this aspect of genetics is something like that of the letter *Y*, it is called the **Y-chromosome.** Its partner sex chromosome in the male is called an **X-chromosome;** the female, of course, possesses a pair of these. Hence, male and female individuals differ in regard to their sex chromosomes.

At the time of sperm formation in the testes of the male, the sex chromosomes undergo segregation as do the autosomes. Thus, it is a matter of chance as to whether the *X*-chromosome or the *Y*-chromosome go into a particular sperm, but it should be clear that both cannot be carried to the egg by a single sperm. The inheritance of sex depends upon whether an *X*-bearing sperm or a *Y*-bearing one fertilize the egg. The problem of sex determination actually is a complex one involving many factors, but the initial step in the process is the combination in the zygote of either two *X*-chromosomes (resulting in female sex) or of an *X* and a *Y* (resulting in male sex).

Now let us postulate that since the *X*- and *Y*-chromosomes differ morphologically, they might be expected to bear genes that are not homologous. As a matter of fact, although there are homologous sections of the human sex chromosomes, one portion of the *X*-chromosome does bear genes that have no counterpart on the *Y*, which means that inheritance of these genes is greatly affected. For example, a gene is known to reside on the *X*-chromosome of the human which controls normal color vision. Its recessive allele, when effective, interferes with the ability, characteristic of most people, to distinguish between certain colors. Possible genotypes and phenotypes of persons in regard to these genes are as follows, allowing the letter Y to represent the absence of any gene at all, since the Y-chromosome carries none for this trait:

> CC—normal (homozygous) female
> Cc—normal (heterozygous) female
> cc—color-blind female
> CY—normal male
> cY—color-blind male

Since the production of a color-blind female depends upon parents each of whom can contribute a recessive gene, females exhibiting the abnormality are somewhat rare. On the other hand, color-blind sons (but no color-blind daughters) can be produced by a normal man and a heterozygous woman as shown in Fig. 148.

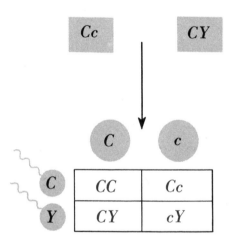

CC — normal (homozygous) female
Cc — normal (heterozygous) female
CY — normal male
cY — color-blind male

148

For this reason, most individuals who exhibit recessive traits dependent upon **sex-linked** (located on a sex chromosome) genes of this sort are men. Perhaps by a manipulation of genotypes, the student will be able to discover why such traits appear to skip characteristically from maternal grandfather to grandson.

Multiple Factor Inheritance

It was suggested earlier that many genes may contribute to the development of a single trait. Actually, it seems evident that most genes work in this fashion, and studies of such inheritance traits are of necessity more difficult to carry out. Although it is beyond the scope of our present study to investigate the more complex principles of genetics, perhaps an example of inheritance which involves the effects of several genes upon a single trait will serve to emphasize the principle that phenotypic characteristics that do not seem to depend upon elementary principles which we have learned nevertheless may be genetically controlled.

A few years after Mendel's paper was discovered, a Swedish investigator, H. Nilsson-Ehle, crossed two varieties of wheat, one of which produced very dark red kernels and the other white kernels. The F_1 generation all produced an intermediate shade, or medium red. Up to this point, it might be expected that this case is similar to that in four-o'-clocks and that an F_2 generation would consist of one very dark red, two medium reds, and one white out of every four individuals. Actually, Nilsson-Ehle found that in every sixty-four F_2 plants, one produced very dark red kernels, one produced white kernels, and the remainder were characterized by kernels whose color varied between these two extremes.

Clearly, this is similar to an ordinary cross involving three pairs of factors, because the appearance of individuals resembling the original parents occurs in the same ratio, that is, one out of sixty-four for each parent. It must be remembered, however, that only *one* trait is involved, not three, and some explanation must be given for the intermediate colors.

Experimental evidence indicates that there are indeed three pairs of genes here, each gene having a *quantitative* effect upon color of the kernel. Assuming that the parents whose kernels are very dark red is that of the genotype *AABBCC* and that the parent characterized by white kernels is *aabbcc,* then results might be interpreted as indicated in Fig. 149.

Obviously, the concepts of dominance and recessiveness are not involved here, at least in the usual sense. Rather, there are three pairs of independent genes, with each gene contributing to the determination of a single trait. This is characteristic of such **multiple factor inheritance,** as it is called. Since Nilsson-Ehle and others first clarified this principle, a great many traits in a variety of organisms have been shown to depend upon such a mechanism. Among these are milk yield in dairy cattle, fruit size of certain cultivated plants, yield of grains, height in some

P $AABBCC \times aabbcc$ (**very dark red** × **white**)

F_1 $AaBbCc$ (**medium red**)

F_2

	ABC	ABc	AbC	aBC	Abc	aBc	abC	abc
ABC	AABBCC	AABBCc	AABbCC	AaBBCC	AABbCc	AaBBCc	AaBbCC	AaBbCc
ABc	AABBCc	AABBcc	AABbCc	AaBBCc	AABbcc	AaBBcc	AaBbCc	AaBbcc
AbC	AABbCC	AABbCc	AAbbCC	AaBbCC	AAbbCc	AaBbCc	AabbCC	AabbCc
aBC	AaBBCC	AaBBCc	AaBbCC	aaBBCC	AaBbCc	aaBBCc	aaBbCC	aaBbCc
Abc	AABbCc	AABbcc	AAbbCc	AaBbCc	AAbbcc	AaBbcc	AabbCc	Aabbcc
aBc	AaBBCc	AaBBcc	AaBbCc	aaBBCc	AaBbcc	aaBBcc	aaBbCc	aaBbcc
abC	AaBbCC	AaBbCc	AabbCC	aaBbCC	AabbCc	aaBbCc	aabbCC	aabbCc
abc	AaBbCc	AaBbcc	AabbCc	aaBbCc	Aabbcc	aaBbcc	aabbCc	aabbcc

149 The inheritance of seed color in wheat, when a certain strain whose seeds are very dark red and one whose seeds are white are crossed. Three pairs of genes, all influencing a single trait, are involved. How many phenotypic classes are there in the F_2 generation, assuming that a total of five capitals results in dark red, four capitals in medium dark red, and so on? What ratio is to be expected in the F_2?

plants, and body weight of some animals. In man, it is certain that genes for height, longevity, and certain types of intelligence or aptitude are inherited in this manner, to mention a few traits that have been studied. In most cases of multiple factor inheritance, large numbers of genes are apparently involved.

Summary

Since the time that Mendel's work became recognized and appreciated, geneticists have studied thousands of hereditary traits in a variety of organisms and have found a general conformity to the laws and principles which he set forth. Even where inheritance mechanisms differ from the relatively simple pattern of Mendel's experimental materials, they are usually more complex variations of the basic principles. Thus, it has been possible to manipulate and even change genes in such a way as to allow for both theoretical and practical studies in genetics, and this field of biology continues to be a highly active one. Such agricultural triumphs as hybrid corn, disease-resistant grains, and higher quality livestock are the direct result of Mendelian genetics as applied to problems concerning the welfare of mankind. The genetics of man himself has been the subject of much study, with the result that many human traits and abnormalities are now understood on this basis. It is not without reason, therefore, that Mendel is accorded a place of high honor among scientists as one whose contribution has exerted a profound influence upon human affairs.

In our consideration of genetics within the framework of the characteristic of reproduction, we have not meant to imply that it is of no concern or importance to the other characteristics discussed in this book. As the student will recall, we relied heavily upon genetic concepts in discussing growth and development, and as we shall see, the characteristic of adaptation is closely allied with genetics. It is only for organizational reasons that we discuss it in connection with reproduction. As we shall emphasize more and more, it is the whole organism that the biologist seeks to view, and any method of organization for teaching purposes is of necessity highly artificial.

CONCLUSION

Although some variation appears among organisms in regard to their reproductive habits, it is significant that certain definite principles can be formulated. Thus, in regard to the phenomenon of reproduction, there is remarkable uniformity. Even the principles of heredity that have been presented are valid in their application to virtually all organisms that reproduce by sexual means. A study of reproductive principles sheds a great deal of light on the fundamental nature of life, and it is hoped that further understanding of biology on the part of the student has been encouraged through a consideration of this topic.

QUESTIONS

Multiple Choice

1. Meiosis in animals is (a) gametic, (b) sporic, (c) zygotic, (d) none of these, (e) possibly any of these.

2. Which of the following is capable of asexual reproduction? (a) frog, (b) honey bee, (c) earthworm, (d) hydra, (e) man.

3. In which of the animals above is the phenomenon of parthenogenesis exhibited?

4. The oldest living organisms known to man are about (a) 150 years old, (b) 350 years old, (c) 1,000 years old, (d) 4,000 years old, (e) 1,000,000 years old.

5. Which of the following structures ultimately develops into a seed in the reproduction of flowering plants? (a) ovary (b) ovule, (c) pistil, (d) spore, (e) egg.

6. In its development toward the adult form, the honey bee exhibits (a) complete metamorphosis, (b) incomplete metamorphosis, (c) no metamorphosis, (d) gradual metamorphosis, (e) either complete or incomplete metamorphosis, depending upon diet.

7. In which of the following plants are the gametes so similar that they are not referred to as eggs and sperm? (a) ferns, (b) seed plants, (c) mosses, (d) liverworts, (e) *Chlamydomonas.*

8. In the human, a special organ develops during pregnancy by means of which the mother and embryo may exchange certain materials. This organ is called the (a) fetus, (b) uterus, (c) placenta, (d) clitellum, (e) ovule.

9. In typical gamete production in the male animal, the cell which undergoes meiosis eventually produces how many functional sperm? (a) one, (b) two, (c) four, (d) sixteen, (e) possibly hundreds.

10. In typical gamete production in the female animal, the cell which undergoes meiosis eventually produces how many functional eggs? (Select from the choices above.)

11. Which of the following is another term for the female gametophyte in the flowering plant? (a) ovule, (b) seed, (c) pistil, (d) flower, (e) none of these.

12. Which of the following is composed of triploid ($3n$) cells? (a) male gametophyte of flowering plant, (b) drone bee, (c) spore mother cell, (d) endosperm of seed, (e) zygote of an animal.

13. How many nuclei are present in a fully developed male gametophyte of flowering plants? (a) one, (b) two, (c) three, (d) four (e) eight.

14. How many autosomes are present in the body cells of the human? (a) 22, (b) 35, (c) 44, (d) 64, (e) no definite number.

15. A male of the genotype *AaBbCC* would produce how many different kinds of sperm in regard to possible genic combinations? (a) one, (b) two, (c) three, (d) four, (e) eight.

16. In the cross *AaBb* × *AABb*, how many squares would need to be constructed if the possible offspring genotypes were plotted on a "checkerboard?" (a) two, (b) four, (c) six, (d) eight, (e) sixteen.

17. In man, let us assume that brown eyes are dominant over blue eyes, and that a single gene pair is involved. A brown-eyed man and a blue-eyed woman produce a blue-eyed child. One thing is certain: (a) one of the woman's parents had to be blue eyed; (b) one of the man's parents had to be blue eyed; (c) the child is heterozygous in genotype; (d) the man is heterozygous in genotype; (e) the next child of this couple will have brown eyes.

18. Long radishes crossed with short radishes produce oval radishes. When two ovals are crossed, the offspring prove to be one long, one short and two oval out of every four. What is the proper explanation? (a) long is dominant over short; (b) short is dominant over long; (c) neither is dominant over the other; (d) the trait is sex-linked; (e) two pairs of factors are involved.

19. In the human, color blindness is dependent upon a recessive sex-linked gene *c*. Normal vision is represented by *C*. A color-blind man marries a woman with normal vision. Which of the following can be said *with certainty?* (a) they can have no color-blind sons; (b) none of this man's daughters can be free of a color blind gene; (c) The man's father was color blind; (d) the man's mother was color blind; (e) the man's mother was heterozygous in respect to color blindness.

20. In guinea pigs, rough coat is dominant over smooth, and black is dominant over white. A rough, black male is mated to several smooth, white females. Out of a number of litters, offspring are as follows: 18 rough, black; 21 rough, white; 16 smooth, black; 24 smooth, white. If this male had been mated to another guinea pig of identical genotype to his own, what proportion of their offspring would have been rough, white? (a) 1 out of 4, (b) 1 out of 16, (c) 3 out of 16, (d) 6 out of 16, (e) 9 out of 16.

True-false

1. Pollen grains are actually the sperm cells of flowering plants.

2. Because they are hermaphrodites, earthworms do not practice copulation.

3. Worker bees require a longer time to develop into adults than do queen bees.

4. The highest and most successful animal species tend to be dioecious.

5. A given gene is a certain fraction of an RNA molecule.

6. During gamete formation, each member of a pair of genes becomes associated with a different gamete.

7. According to correct definition, a cucumber is a fruit.

8. In the human, multiple births always occur as a result of multiple egg release.

9. *Paramecium* does not reproduce asexually.

10. The body cells of the human are diploid in chromosome number.

11. The mammals as a group are characterized by females which exhibit a menstrual cycle.

12. By means of the placenta, blood of the mother and embryo are mixed together during human pregnancy.

13. Crossing over is an exception to linkage, just as linkage is an exception to independent assortment.

14. When a tetrad of chromatids separate in the first meiotic anaphase, they characteristically do so in the plane of their original union.

15. The vast majority of plants exhibit gametic meiosis.

Questions For Consideration and Discussion

1. Define the following terms: copulation, monoecious, fetus, spore mother cell, parthenogenesis, phenotype, synapsis, gametophytic phase, fruit, genetic linkage.

2. By means of diagrams, contrast mitosis and meiosis.

3. Explain the following: A drone bee had a grandfather, but no father.

4. In what ways are earthworms of economic value to the farmer?

5. Define and compare the law of segregation and the law of independent assortment.

6. In what ways is sexual reproduction in *Paramecium* somewhat atypical? In *Chlamydomonas*?

7. In what ways does human reproduction differ from that of most domesticated mammals?

8. Distinguish properly between sexual and asexual reproduction.

9. Discuss reproduction in flowering plants.

10. Why did Gregor Mendel not receive just recognition during his lifetime?

11. Discuss the mechanism of sex determination in the human.

12. In the human, assume that brown eyes (*B*) are dominant over blue eyes (*b*). A certain brown-eyed man married three times. His first wife was blue-eyed, and they had a brown-eyed son. His second wife was also blue-eyed, and they had a blue-eyed daughter. His third wife was brown-eyed, and they had one brown-eyed son and one blue-eyed daughter. Write the genotypes of all these individuals. There is one individual in the group concerning whose genotype you cannot be certain. Which one is it?

13. In guinea pigs, black coat (*B*) is dominant over white coat (*b*), and rough coat (*R*) is dominant over smooth coat (*r*). A black, rough guinea pig is mated to a white, rough one. Out of several litters totaling twenty-two individuals, eight are black and rough, five are black and smooth, seven are white and rough, and two are white and smooth. What are the genotypes of the parents?

14. Color blindness in the human is due to a recessive sex-linked gene. A man with normal vision marries a woman with normal vision. Her father was color blind. What are the genotypes of these three individuals? What genotypes and phenotypes *may* appear among the children of this couple?

15. A certain squash plant produces fruits which are all about six pounds in weight. Another squash plant produces fruits which weigh about three pounds each. When these two plants are crossed, the resulting plants produce fruits which weigh about four and one-half pounds each. An F_1 plant is then allowed to self-pollinate, and fruits produced by F_2 plants show considerable variation in size, ranging from three to six pounds. Assuming that multiple factor inheritance is involved here with three pairs of genes, diagram a hypothetical explanation of these results.

REFERENCES

BOLD, H. C. *The Plant Kingdom* (see reference at end of Chapter 4). This book will be helpful in regard to reproduction among plants.

BONNER, D. M. *Heredity*. Englewood Cliffs, N.J.: Prentice-Hall, Inc., 1961. This book, which is one of the FOUNDATIONS OF MODERN BIOLOGY series, is recommended in connection with the portion of this chapter that is devoted to genetics.

INGRAM, V. M. "How Do Genes Act?" *Scientific American*, Volume 198 (January, 1958), p. 68. A discussion of the principle that genes operate through physiological channels; the example of sickle-cell anemia, presented in this chapter, is used to demonstrate this principle.

PETERS, J. A. (editor), *Classic Papers in Genetics.* Englewood Cliffs, N.J.: Prentice-Hall, Inc., 1959. Gregor Mendel's original paper, translated into English by William Bateson and entitled "Experiments in Plant-Hybridisation," is reprinted in full in this book.

SNYDER, L. H. and **P. R. DAVID.** *The Principles of Heredity.* Boston: D. C. Heath and Company, 1957. A well-written, understandable textbook of genetics.

STORER, T. I. and **R. L. USINGER.** *General Zoology* (see reference at end of Chapter 4). Reproduction among animals, including the reproductive habits of various forms, is given considerable attention in this book.

SWANSON, C. P. *The Cell* (see reference at end of Chapter 3). For an account of meiosis, see Chapter 5 of this book. Chapters 6 and 7, which deal with reproduction in plants and animals, are also recommended.

Responsiveness

It is a matter of common knowledge that higher animals possess senses that enable them to respond to stimuli. Man, for example, is able to see objects, hear sounds, feel pain, and so on. This ability to respond to such stimuli is not limited to the higher animals, however. If an amoeba is brought into contact with light, heat, or the tip of a pointed object, it will withdraw from the source of irritation. Indeed, plants are sensitive to many stimuli, although in the case of forms that do not exhibit motility, this may not be immediately apparent. The capacity to respond to stimuli is called **responsiveness,** and it is characteristic of all organisms to at least some extent.

Of course, non-living substances or materials may exhibit responsiveness to a certain degree, just as chemical activity and increase in total mass are not limited to organisms in their characteristics of metabolism and growth. Here again, however, there is a considerable difference in the degree to which this may occur. The element mercury, for example, is highly responsive to changes in temperature, and for this reason it is utilized in thermometers, thermostats, and similar instruments. The art of photography is made possible through the sensitivity of certain chemicals to light. However, such physical and chemical changes are relatively simple and easy of explanation, whereas responsiveness in even the least complex of living organisms is a vastly complicated phenomenon.

RESPONSIVENESS OF PROTOPLASM

Since an amoeba is unicellular, it is obvious that the mechanisms involved in its responses to stimuli are contained within its protoplasm. In fact, single muscle cells or nerve fibers can be isolated from a higher animal and used to demonstrate responsiveness. Although such cells are highly coordinated with other cells in the performance of their normal functions in the animal body, it is clear from experiments involving single cells (whether of amoeba or of a highly differentiated tissue) that responsiveness is not dependent upon cellular relationships. Rather, it is a fundamental property of protoplasm, as are metabolism, growth, and reproduction. Like these characteristics, it reaches its most pronounced form of expression in highly complex organisms, but it should be remembered that *protoplasm itself is responsive to stimuli.*

Let us analyze the events that occur when protoplasm exhibits the characteristic of responsiveness. If an amoeba is touched lightly with a fine-pointed glass rod or needle, its fluid protoplasm begins moving in a direction away from the point of contact. In the entire sequence of events, three phases are evident: **reception** of the stimulus, **conduction** of the resulting impulse throughout the cell, and **response** on the part of the protoplasm. This series of events also occurs in higher animals, where specialized cells or parts of cells serve as receptors, conductors, and effectors in the accomplishment of responsiveness. Since we are accustomed by this time to thinking in terms of histological specialization, we can readily accept and partially understand reception, conduction, and response on that level. However, an amoeba is not equipped with nerves or muscles, and responsiveness must be accounted for on a cytological, not a histological, basis. Actually, biologists do not have a very satisfactory explanation at present for the events that transpire in protoplasmic responsiveness since the physical and chemical factors involved are extremely complex. However, it is clear that individual cells are highly organized (a point which must be emphasized repeatedly in the study and teaching of biology), and some of the same forces that are responsible for metabolism, growth, and reproduction make possible the phenomenon of responsiveness also. In the case of unicellular organisms, the entire surface of the cell is apparently capable of responding to certain stimuli, for example, touch. From the point of contact, it may be assumed that a wave of reactivity spreads throughout the cell, setting in motion forces which determine a response. Some unicellular forms possess specialized organelles that are sensitive to light (for example, the "eye spots" of many unicellular algae), and conduction must of necessity begin there in its effect on the organism. Response in unicellular plants and animals is most readily observed when motility is exhibited. This may be accomplished by means of cilia, flagella, or flowing action of protoplasm (as in amoeba). Regardless of the details involved, any consideration of protoplasmic responsiveness must take into account the phases of reception, conduction, and response.

Whenever a motile unicellular organism responds to a stimulus in such a way that movement is effected, the response is called a **taxis** (Gr. *taxis*, arrangement). For example, if a jar containing pond water is placed under conditions which allow a moderate amount of light to fall upon it from one side only, there is an accumulation of any motile algae that may be present on the lighted side of the jar. Such response to light is called **positive phototaxis.** In contrast, any amoebas present withdraw from the light and tend to collect toward the darker side of the jar. Hence, they are said to exhibit **negative phototaxis.** Various types of stimuli may be used to demonstrate tactic responses, and studies involving protoplasmic activity of this sort have contributed much to an understanding of animal behavior.[1]

RESPONSIVENESS IN ANIMALS

Although tactic responses are exhibited by *Amoeba* and other protozoans, animals higher in the scale of complexity than sponges possess more elaborate and coordinated systems which constitute a basis for responsiveness. This is made possible by the differentiation of cells to form nervous tissue, which is specialized for reception of stimuli and conduction of impulses. Muscle tissue is also a product of differentiation and serves as the chief type of effector in response. In the vertebrates, and especially in mammals, coordination of nervous, muscular, and glandular tissues makes possible a vastly complex system responsible for reception, conduction, and response within the body.

Typical nerve cells are so constituted that from two to several protoplasmic **fibers** extend outward for some distance from the **cell body** (Fig. 106). Experiments have been conducted showing that it is along these fibers that impulses travel, once initiated, and that they set off responses through a relay to effector structures. Receptors in the

---

[1] The term "taxis" is also applied to movements of multicellular animals in response to stimuli. Many insects, for example, are described as being positively phototactic. Since the behavior of multicellular animals is dependent upon the interaction of many specialized cells, it is doubtful that the same term should be used at all levels of complexity. However, possibly for want of a better term, "taxis" is applied more widely than at the level of protoplasmic responsiveness.

higher animal body are specialized nerve cells or endings of nerve fibers. Many types of these exist; those which are sensitive to certain wave lengths of light are localized in the eye, receptors are found in the inner ear which are sensitive to various pitches of sound, and the senses of taste and smell depend upon receptors located in the oral cavity and pharynx, respectively. The skin contains different types of receptors for touch, pressure, pain, heat, and cold. In addition to these, there are receptors that lie *within* the body, and these make possible the senses of internal pain, equilibrium, motion awareness, and a variety of others.

Let us consider a typical nerve fiber ending of the skin, a **Meissner's corpuscle** (Fig. 150), which is sensitive to touch. The fiber leading to the corpuscle is normally in a state of **polarization;** that is, ions carrying negative electrical charges are present *inside* the plasma membrane of the fiber, and ions carrying positive electrical charges are

150 A Meissner's corpuscle shown lying within epithelial cells of the skin.

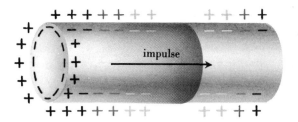

151 Diagrammatic representation of impulse flow along a nerve fiber. At any given moment, only a fraction of the total fiber membrane is depolarized. Thus, a band of depolarization, represented here by shading, moves along the fiber away from the source of stimulus.

present on the *outside* surface. These maintain their respective positions because the membrane, although generally semi-permeable, prevents their passage. The corpuscle serves the function of upsetting polarization, or the separation of ions, temporarily when it is stimulated by a sufficient amount of touch pressure to "fire" the membrane. In other words, the membrane loses its impermeability for a short time, and opposite ions join each other. By way of comparison, the corpuscle bears somewhat the same relationship to the fiber as a "cap" does to a stick of dynamite; it responds to a much lower degree of stimulation (called a **threshold stimulus**) than does the fiber itself, and it serves to upset normal polarization in the fiber membrane adjacent to it. Consequently, a wave of membrane disruption spreads along the fiber, each section upsetting the next as the ions come together (Fig. 151). The fiber quickly recovers its normal polarized condition, and stands ready to transmit another impulse, which explains the phenomenon that receptors, of which Meissner's corpuscles are one example, can receive separate stimuli at a very rapid rate.

It should be pointed out that the nerve impulse, while bearing certain similarities to the current of electricity which flows along a wire, is not merely an electrical phenomenon. For one thing, a wire only *conducts* a current of energy which must be supplied by the stimulating agent, while the *nerve fiber itself* supplies the energy required by impulse transmission. It thus constitutes an **electrochemical** system rather than a simple **electrical** one. Another difference lies in the relative rates of travel, that of an electrical current along a wire being something over 100,000 miles per second under most conditions. The speed of nervous impulses varies considerably, depending on (among other factors) size of the fiber and the type of animal involved, but it rarely exceeds one hundred meters per second. It may be as slow as five meters per second, especially in the fibers of certain lower invertebrates. It is also interesting to note that strength of stimulus has nothing to do with rate of impulse in nerve fibers, just as a powder fuse burns at the same rate whether it is lighted with a spark or with a blowtorch. This principle, which applies to all responsive tissues of animals, including both nerve and muscle fibers, is termed the **all-or-none law.**

Following its initiation at a receptor, an impulse travels along the fiber, whose cell body generally lies near the brain or spinal cord in vertebrate animals. Upon reaching the cell body, the impulse is relayed along a fiber or fibers which are also a part of this same cell. For purposes of representation, this is illustrated in Fig. 152 in a cell which possesses only two fibers, one of which ends in the spinal cord. As the impulse reaches the end of this second fiber, it is relayed to any other fibers whose branched endings may lie in close proximity to it. There is no direct protoplasmic continuity between such fibers (although the cell membranes of the fibers involved apparently touch each other), and the impulse "jumps" from one to another. This point of contact between nerve fiber endings which makes possible the transfer of an impulse from one to another is called a **synapse.**

Although only one synapse may be involved in the travel of an

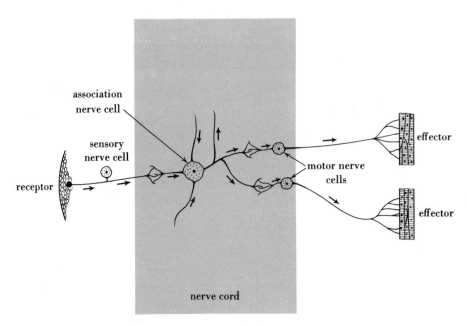

152 Simple reflex pathways along which impulses may be carried from a receptor to effectors in an animal possessing a nerve cord. The fiber extending from the receptor to the sensory nerve cell body and the fibers extending from the motor nerve cell body to the muscle cells are greatly reduced in length here.

impulse from a receptor to an effector in certain of the invertebrates, the higher animals exhibit nerve cells which reside, along with their fibers, entirely within the brain or spinal cord. These perform the function of connecting fibers which bring impulses from receptors with fibers that travel outward to effectors, and they are referred to as **association nerve cells.** As an impulse travels through an association nerve cell, it is relayed through synapses to fibers of nerve cells which in turn activate effectors such as muscle fibers (Fig. 152). From the point of impulse initiation to an effector, therefore, five important units are involved in this simple type of relay: receptor, first (or **sensory**) nerve cell with its fibers, second (association) nerve cell, third (or **motor**) nerve cell, and effector. Such a pathway by means of which an impulse is transmitted from receptor to effector is called a **reflex arc.**

Actually, the description above represents a very simple example of responsiveness in animals. It would be extremely difficult, except under special experimental circumstances, to stimulate only *one* receptor; furthermore, only one muscle fiber (or even several) would ordinarily have very little effect in initiating a response since muscles are usually composed of many thousands of muscle fibers. When the skin of a complex animal is touched, for instance, a great number of impulses are initiated. Several of these may travel to effector structures, while others lead to areas of the brain that are concerned with consciousness. Responsiveness in the higher animals is dependent upon a system of nerve cells, fibers, synapses, and effectors of sufficient complexity as to be almost beyond comprehension. Nevertheless, considerable is known about certain reflex patterns, and a functional basis for understanding the sum total of responsiveness, or the **behavior** of an animal, has been developed as a result of knowledge gained in regard to the nature of impulse transmission and the reflex arc.

To this point, we have said more about reception and conduction of stimuli than about the responses they produce. In the higher animals, the muscle fiber is the chief type of effector structure. As was emphasized previously, it is a type of cell specialized for contraction, thus making possible the movement of those animals which possess them. A great many complex factors are involved in the contraction of a muscle fiber, but energy derived from the breakdown of ATP to ADP is responsible for the work that is accomplished. Each muscle fiber is caused to contract when an impulse reaches it by way of a motor nerve cell fiber (Fig. 152); apparently, a series of reactions are set in motion by the impulse, the net result of which is a shortening of the fiber. Now the muscle fiber itself is subject to the all-or-none law and contracts to the full extent of which it is capable, but it must be remembered that a great many fibers constitute a muscle. Fibers usually contract in groups, and it depends upon how many groups are activated at one time as to how much total work a given muscle may perform. Hence, the entire muscle is not subject to the all-or-none principle; only its individual fibers are.

Another important point regarding muscle contraction involves the principle that it is a one-way process, that is, once having acted, the muscle fibers must be extended back to their original lengthened position. In other words, they work only by contracting, not by extending. In the skeletal muscular system of vertebrates, there are usually **antagonistic** muscles (Fig. 153) which work oppositely to each other; the contraction of one extends the other, thus putting it into position to contract when it is stimulated by a volley of nerve impulses. Although the muscle fibers of the internal organs and heart are not organized into definite muscles, groups of fibers serve as antagonists to others, and the same effect is realized.

In addition to muscle fibers, there are other types of effectors in multicellular animals. It was mentioned earlier that energy expenditure may take the form of electricity and light in certain organisms. The structures responsible for such energy release obviously constitute effectors, and it is known that reflex arcs are involved in their action. In all vertebrates and some higher invertebrates, groups of cells function as glands in the secretion of a particular chemical product. Although some of these are under the influence of nerve impulses, others respond to cer-

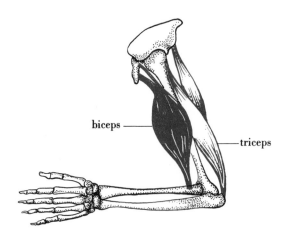

153 Muscular antagonism in the human arm. In its contraction, the biceps pulls the forearm upward, and at the same time the triceps is extended. Contraction of the triceps then pulls the forearm downward and extends the biceps.

tain chemical influences such as a high or low concentration of some particular substance present in their environment. Hence, gland cells of the latter sort constitute a *chemical* type of factor in responsiveness, as contrasted to the electrochemical nature of the reflex arc.

BEHAVIOR OF ANIMALS

The sum total of all the mechanisms of responsiveness that are operative in a given animal constitutes its behavior. Since no two animals receive exactly the same kinds or amounts of stimuli, there is a great deal of individual variation in the behavior of even two members of the same species. In fact, the same animal exhibits different behavior under differing conditions, and in at least many vertebrates and higher invertebrates, it is frequently difficult to predict exact behavior from a certain set of stimuli.

Theoretically, at least in terms of the reflex arc, a given stimulus should always produce a specific effect. In animals such as coelenterates, and in isolated situations among higher animals, this proves to be the case. Behavior can be predicted when a stimulus always produces the same response in a given animal; the organism in such cases is entirely under the influence of its reflexes. For example, if a crystal of carbolic acid is brought into close proximity with the oral end of a hydra, it will invariably contract its body. This type of behavior is termed **unconditioned behavior** because it depends upon a particular kind of synaptic relay called an **unconditioned reflex.** It is not limited merely to those animals that are lowest in the phylogenetic scale. Man exhibits quite a number of such reflexes; for instance, a tap made just below the knee normally causes certain muscles of the leg to contract, thus producing a "kick." Every multicellular animal above the level of sponges develops a number of such reflexes, most of which are adaptive in some way for its protection or well-being. Thus, the unconditioned reflex is actually established in an animal during its development and is therefore under genetic control.

Only in the very lowest animals are reflexes completely unconditioned, or as they are sometimes designated, **unlearned.** With an increase in complexity of nervous systems, and in almost direct proportion to such an increase, animals are seen to exhibit the ability for **learning.** Apparently, the capacity for learning is a biological "luxury" and exists only where sufficient reflex pathways exist for the animal to utilize some of them in developing responses to stimuli that it was not "born" to make. These new responses are termed **conditioned** or **learned** reflexes.[2] In most invertebrates, the capacity for learning is quite limited, although animals as low in the scale of complexity as flatworms may be taught to respond to stimuli. Even the lower vertebrates exhibit relatively little adaptability in this respect, although it seems certain that many responses are learned by trial and error on their part. With the increase in relative size of that portion of the brain known as the **cerebrum,** however, animals are seen to learn much more readily (Fig. 154). If we knew no more than this about the relation between structure and function in nervous systems, we could assume that the cerebrum is directly involved in learning. Actually, experimental evidence has accumulated which shows that although this portion of the brain is responsible for other functions than the facilitation of learned responses, increase in size of the cerebrum (phylogenetically speaking) makes possible the development of more association nerve cells. This, in turn, provides for more reflex pathways, and thus a greater degree of learning is made possible.

Although most animals can learn, which means that their behavior is at least partially determined by conditioned reflexes, the vast majority are governed almost entirely by unconditioned pathways of stimulus and response. Whenever a set of unconditioned responses are coordinated in such a way as to result in a particular act or set of acts directed toward the accomplishment of a specific end, we call such behavior an **instinct.** It is extremely difficult to determine with certainty that all instincts are *purely* innate, especially in higher animals where experience may have suppressed or modified the original inborn set of reflexes involved. There are instances, however, where it becomes clear that some instincts are not affected at all by learning. Females of a group of non-social insects known as digger wasps demonstrate this point very well in certain of their habits. After she has mated, a female digs a burrow in the ground, and goes off in search of a certain type of caterpillar. Upon locating her prey, she paralyzes it with her sting and carries it to the burrow, within which it is deposited. She then proceeds to lay an egg and to attach it to the outer surface of the caterpillar, whereupon she leaves the burrow, seals it over, and never returns to it. This process may be repeated many times by a given female. Under these conditions, the egg hatches into a larva, which utilizes the paralyzed caterpillar for food. Ultimately, it spins a cocoon, undergoes pupation,

---

[2] It should be pointed out that there is no actual movement, or switching, of nerve fibers to form new or different synapses in the process of learning. The conditioned reflex is functionally, not structurally, new to the animal. New functional pathways are probably accomplished chemically through an alteration of the thresholds of certain synaptic connections. This, in turn, makes certain pathways more likely to "fire" than others.

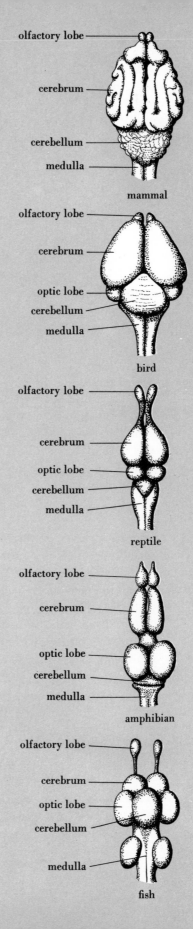

olfactory lobe

cerebrum

cerebellum

medulla

mammal

olfactory lobe

cerebrum

optic lobe

cerebellum

medulla

bird

olfactory lobe

cerebrum

optic lobe

cerebellum

medulla

reptile

olfactory lobe

cerebrum

optic lobe

cerebellum

medulla

amphibian

olfactory lobe

cerebrum

optic lobe

cerebellum

medulla

fish

154 The comparative structure of vertebrate brains. Each is adjusted in size so that they would appear this way in comparison if they were all of approximately the same weight. Even with this adjustment, note the difference in size of the cerebrum among these vertebrates.

and develops into an adult wasp. An adult female produced in such a manner ordinarily would never even see its mother, and certainly it receives no instruction from her as to how the reproductive process should be carried on. Nevertheless, as soon as she has mated, the new female will repeat the process exactly as it has been done by thousands of generations of her female ancestors. Clearly, her reproductive behavior is a matter of instinct.

It is certain, then, that some of the higher invertebrates possess specialized sets of instincts which make it possible for them to exhibit unusual coordination of activities. This is particularly obvious among social insects such as bees and ants where complex colonies are maintained with a minimum of confusion. Perhaps most people labor under the impression that these animals are very nearly as intelligent as human beings and that in their behavior they demonstrate great learning ability. Actually, some learning does occur in such forms, but it is definitely at a minimum *in determining total patterns of behavior.* By and large, conditioning merely serves the instincts. For example, a honey bee learns how to orient herself in relation to the hive, and she is thus able to travel a considerable distance from it and still find her way back. However, her behavior within and away from the hive is almost wholly instinctive. In using the term "intelligence," most students of behavior prefer to define it in terms of capacity for learning. In the light of this concept, social insects are still among the most intelligent of invertebrate animals, but they are, nevertheless, quite limited. Only in the higher vertebrates do we find any great degree of real intelligence, and even there instincts are involved in behavior to a considerable degree.

As we have observed, learning is essentially a matter of developing conditioned reflexes. When a group of such reflexes become coordinated in such a way as to determine a given act or set of acts in behvior, a **habit** is formed. In other words, a habit is a particular learned response which is made to a given stimulus or groups of stimuli. Thus, at least within certain limits, a habit bears much the same relationship to conditioned reflexes as an instinct does to unconditioned ones. Although it is true that conditioning and response may occur without habit formation, just as isolated responses of an unconditioned nature do not necessarily constitute instincts, most learning does eventually contribute to certain patterns of behavior that can be called habits. Perhaps this statement could be justly challenged were it not for the principle that many habits are developed in the higher animal, and particularly in the human, that are not always recognized as such. If a person will reflect for a moment, it will occur to him that most of his actions come under this definition. We grow so accustomed to doing certain things, that we perhaps unconsciously assume that they are accomplished instinctively. Actually, once a habit is formed in the human nervous system, it usually may be performed with a minimum of conscious effort on the part of the individual. The many separate acts involved in walking, speaking, driving an automobile, and so on, had to be learned at some time. In a sense, habits are nature's provision for freeing the conscious mind of responsibility for most acts of behavior that an individual is obliged to perform.

Thus far, we have only considered behavior which results in some way from sensory stimuli. It should be pointed out that, at least in the higher animals, activity may be initiated within the nervous system itself. For example, a person may decide to contract the biceps muscle of his arm, or to kick a ball. The primary signal for initiating such action arises somewhere within the nervous system itself. Now this is not to say that there was no **motivation,** or basic reason for the action, but it certainly did not come about as a result of external stimulation. Whatever stimulus may have been provided arose within the individual's own conscious mind. As a matter of fact, the ability of the higher animal, and particularly the human, to manipulate ideas is responsible for a great deal of the total behavior exhibited. Other abilities, including memory and imagination, also play an important part in behavior at this level of intelligence.

We have already mentioned that in the higher animals behavior is affected by glandular secretions and other chemical influences within the body. In the vertebrates, at least, that group of secretory organs known as the **endocrine glands** are perhaps more directly responsible for behavior than are any tissues other than the nerve cells themselves. These glands are distinguished by the ability of their cells to secrete **hormones,** which are chemical substances that are taken up by the blood stream and carried to some part of the body where they initiate a specific response. Some endocrine glands produce only one hormone, and others produce two or more. The major endocrine structures in man are shown in Fig. 155.

Hormones are highly specific in their action; that is, they are limited in their effects to those cells which are responsive to their particular chemical influences. For instance, a hormone called **secretin** is produced in the cells that line the internal surface of the duodenum when hydrochloric acid from the stomach comes into contact with them. This hormone passes into the blood stream and is carried throughout the body, but it apparently exerts no influence on body cells generally. Its specific "targets" are the cells of the pancreas which secrete pancreatic juice. These, in turn, are stimulated by action of the hormone, and their secretory product is carried directly to the duodenum by the pancreatic duct (Fig. 88). This mechanism ensures that those enzymes which are necessary at this stage of digestion are present at exactly the right time.

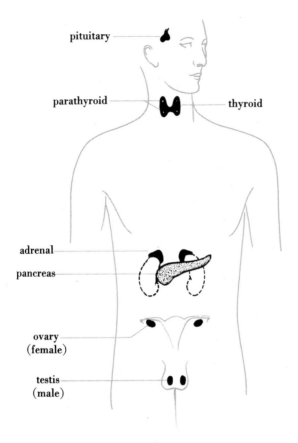

pituitary

parathyroid

thyroid

adrenal

pancreas

ovary
(female)

testis
(male)

155 The major endocrine glands of the human. For purposes
of representation, both ovaries and testes are shown as they
would appear in the female and male, respectively.

It might seem at first thought that such hormonal action as this
has little to do with behavior, but it is actually a very important aspect
of it. Stimulus and response are certainly involved, and the total behavior
of the individual is very definitely affected. In fact, proper hormonal
balance is so necessary to normal behavior that a slight malfunction of
an endocrine gland may exert profound effects upon the individual. As in
the case of so many other mechanisms that contribute to behavior, we
take normal hormonal balance so much for granted that it becomes difficult to realize how important these secretions really are. Some of
the more important hormones and their specific activities within the
human body are presented in Table I.

A great many complex factors are operative in the behavior of

TABLE I. MAJOR ENDOCRINE TISSUES AND HORMONES OF THE HUMAN.

Gland or Tissue	*Hormones*	*Major Function of Hormone*
Anterior lobe of pituitary	Growth-promoting	Stimulates growth.
	Thyrotropic	Stimulates thyroid gland.
	Gonadotropic	Stimulates gonads.
	Lactogenic	Stimulates mammary glands.
Posterior lobe of pituitary	Pitressin	Controls blood pressure.
	Pitocin	Stimulates uterine contraction.
	Antidiuretic	Controls urine concentration.
Thyroid	Thyroxin	Stimulates rate of metabolism.
Parathyroid	Parathormone	Controls phosphorus and calcium concentrations in body fluids.
Adrenal cortex	Cortisone and related hormones	Control sodium concentration, carbohydrate metabolism; various other functions.
Adrenal medulla	Epinephrine (Adrenalin)	Various "emergency" effects on blood, muscle, temperature.
Testis	Testosterone and related hormones	Influence development of sex organs and male characteristics.
Ovary (follicle)	Estrogenic hormones	Influence development of sex organs and female characteristics.
Ovary (corpus luteum)	Progesterone	Influences menstrual cycle, prepares uterus for pregnancy, maintains pregnancy.
Placenta (temporary)	Estrogens and Progesterone	These hormones function in the maintenance of pregnancy.
Pancreas (Islets of Langerhans)	Insulin	Influences cellular absorption of carbohydrates, regulates fat storage.
Duodenal mucosa	Secretin	Stimulates non-endocrine portion of pancreas.

higher animals other than those discussed here, but since most of them are of more direct concern to psychology, the science of behavior, than to biology, we shall make no attempt at this point to enter further into this highly specialized field. Suffice it to say that psychologists have contributed greatly to our understanding of behavior in the human especially, and the student will find it exceedingly profitable to delve more deeply into the subject matter of this field.

RESPONSIVENESS IN PLANTS AND THEIR BEHAVIOR

Perhaps the majority of people are not aware that plants exhibit any sort of activity that might be called "behavior." Indeed, there is a fundamental difference between most plants and animals in this respect,

156 *Dionaea*, the Venus fly-trap. This is an insectivorous flowering plant of bright green color. Shown in natural size. (Courtesy Carolina Biological Supply Company)

but it should be remembered that behavior is the sum total of the responses to stimuli which an organism is capable of making. Since plant cells contain protoplasm just as animal cells do, it is reasonable to suppose that the fundamental capacity which protoplasm shows for responsiveness should manifest itself in some way.

It is true that plants do not exhibit nervous or muscular tissues as animals do, nor are there any plant cells that even remotely approach these in their respective capacities for conduction and contraction. As a result, behavior is much less marked in plants than in animals. In general, reception, conduction, and response are limited to the protoplasm of plant cells themselves. In a very few forms among the higher plants, however, there is a type of coordinated behavior which resembles that of animals to a degree. A flowering plant, the Venus fly-trap (Fig. 156), bears certain leaves whose marginal hairs are sensitive to touch. Movement of an insect upon the inner surface of the leaf is a sufficient stimulus to bring about the closing response. Leaves of the sensitive plant, *Mimosa* (Fig. 157), respond very quickly to touch by drooping as though they had become wilted. At first appearance, it is tempting to postulate the existence of nervous tissue or something like it in these plants, but investigation has shown that in all such cases, there are mechanisms whereby turgor pressure is greatly lowered in certain cells. In *Mimosa*, for example, there are cell groups at the base of each leaf stalk and at the bases of the individual leaflets. The cells making up these groups are extremely thin-walled and lose water rapidly when the leaf is shaken.

(a)   (b)

157 *Mimosa*, the sensitive plant. a, plant whose leaves are in natural position. b, the same plant after leaves have been touched. (Courtesy General Biological Supply House, Inc.)

The result is that each plant part bends when its supporting cell group loses turgidity.

Most plant behavior is influenced by the production of **plant hormones** which, like animal hormones, may be produced in one part of the plant and transported to another part, where specific effects are produced. Of the several types of hormones recognized by plant physiologists, the **auxins,** a group of substances that affect growth, have been studied most extensively. Although it is known that different auxins exist, it appears that **indole-3-acetic acid** is the principal one produced by plant cells. The formula for this substance is known, and it has been used extensively in experimental work.

Wherever auxins produce their effects, it seems that they influence cellular elongation. In general, the degree to which a cell elongates is proportional to the amount of auxin present; however, there are many exceptions to this principle because tissues of different plant organs do not all respond similarly to given concentrations of auxin. The production of auxin occurs principally in meristematic cells at the tips of aerial shoots such as stems, young leaves, and flower buds. It appears to be produced only in extremely small amounts at root tips. From these sites of production, it may pass by diffusion to older cells.

A number of experiments have been devised to demonstrate the effects of auxins. One of the simplest to perform involves cutting off the tip of a germinating oat seedling[3] and observing the effect. It is seen that when this is accomplished, the remainder of the shoot virtually stops growing. If the tip of another shoot is placed on this stump, however, growth immediately resumes at a normal rate. If a block of agar (a material used in culturing bacteria) is placed beneath a cut tip for an hour or two and is then laid upon the stump of a shoot, growth also resumes.[4] Apparently, auxins have moved into the agar block from the tip, and will in turn move from the block to the stump, where they produce the characteristic effects. Again, if an auxin-laden block is placed on *one half* of the stump, growth occurs only on that side. These experiments are illustrated in Fig. 158.

Experiments such as these have led plant physiologists to the conclusion that auxins are responsible for many growth phenomena in plants and that these phenomena are influenced in a number of ways. One of the most important environmental factors to which auxins are sensitive is light. If a potted plant is set on a window sill in such a way as to receive light chiefly from one direction, it grows toward the source of light. Such a response is called a **tropism** (Gr. *trope,* a turning), and since the factor initiating the response in this case is light, it is termed **phototropism.** The influence of light is not always such as to cause a plant organ to grow in the direction of its source; it may grow away from it. Hence, phototropism (as well as other tropisms) may be **positive** or **negative.** The growth of a plant stem toward light is, of course, an example of positive phototropism. Evidence has accumulated showing that, under conditions where a stem receives light principally from one direction, there is a migration of auxins from the lighted side of the tip to the shaded side (Fig. 160). This means that cells of the stem on the shaded side receive more auxins and thus exhibit a greater degree of elongation,

---

[3] Auxins were first studied in the oat (*Avena sativa*), whose germinating shoot lends itself especially well to such growth studies. Actually, this experiment could be conducted on any number of higher plants.

[4] As a control, an agar block which has not been in contact with a tip may be placed upon the stump of a shoot. Under these conditions, there is no resumption of normal growth.

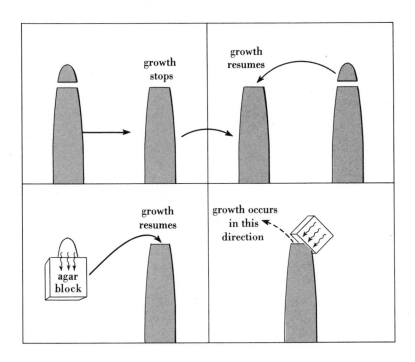

158 Various growth effects exhibited by oat seedlings under different experimental conditions. See text for amplification.

159 A demonstration of positive phototropism. These two *Coleus* plants were potted when they were quite small, and were allowed to remain on a window sill for several days. The left-hand plant was turned 180 degrees daily, while the right-hand plant was not disturbed.

the net result of which is a bending toward the light. It appears that there is also a certain amount of auxin destruction or inactivation by light. This is indicated in a negative way by the tendency of a shoot to elongate greatly when grown in the dark.

Another important environmental factor that influences growth through an effect upon auxins is gravity. In response to this force, a plant organ may exhibit positive or negative **geotropism.** In a germinating

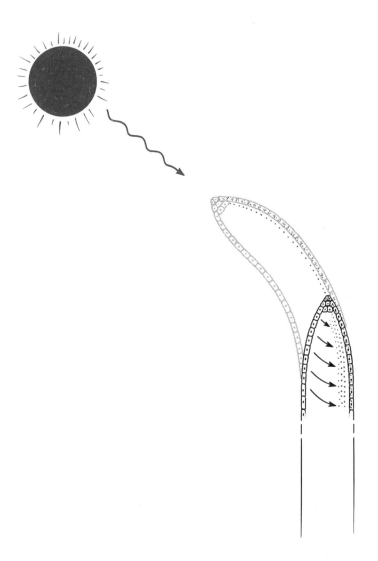

160 Auxin destruction and migration under the influence of light, resulting in positive phototropism. Cells on the shaded side of the stem tip elongate more rapidly than those on the illuminated side, causing a bending toward the light source.

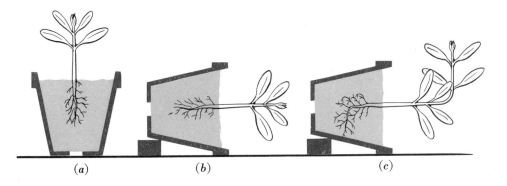

161 Positive and negative geotropism. a, potted seedling in normal position of growth. b, the same plant turned 90 degrees. c, the responses shown by root and shoot, respectively, to the influence of gravity.

seedling, the root is positively geotropic (tending to grow toward the center of the earth), and the shoot is negatively geotropic (Fig. 161*a*). If growth of the embryonic plant is allowed to proceed sufficiently far that these responses become evident, and then the plant is turned so that both root and shoot are horizontally rather than vertically oriented, within a few hours these organs begin to bend in their respective responses to gravity (Fig. 161*c*). The explanation here seems to be that in the shoot auxins gravitate to the lower side which causes elongation of the cells there. Hence, there will be a turning upward of the stem and leaves. In the root, there is also an accumulation of auxins on the lower side, but instead of being stimulated by the heavier concentration, root cells are so constituted that elongation is inhibited by amounts of auxin that are sufficient to stimulate cellular growth in the stem. Within certain limits, therefore, auxins produce opposite effects in the young root and shoot. Actually, there are many important factors involved here, and secondary roots or stems may respond to gravity in an entirely different manner to that described. Many roots, for example, grow horizontally within the soil. Nevertheless, early growth in most plants is readily explained on the basis of auxin influence on elongation of cells as described above.

Many other types of tropic responses besides those discussed here are operative in plant behavior, but perhaps these examples are sufficient to demonstrate the principle that definite mechanisms have been discovered that account for growth phenomena and other activities exhibited by plants. A consideration of these as well as that of such interesting topics as changes in the colors of leaves, leaf fall, and ecological adaptation must be left to those specialized fields of botany whose particular interest they are.

PHILOSOPHICAL CONSIDERATIONS
ASSOCIATED WITH RESPONSIVENESS

Perhaps we are justified by this time in considering the impact that certain biological principles have had upon the thinking of man in regard to problems of ultimate reality. Although Chapter 10 is devoted in part to such considerations, it seems appropriate at this point to suggest that many of the principles that biologists have clarified pertaining to the general phenomenon of responsiveness have an extremely important bearing upon questions which are often considered to be philosophical, not biological, in nature.

Anthropomorphism

One important change in thinking which has come about as a result of an improved knowledge of responsiveness and its mechanisms is in regard to a long-standing (and still existent) tendency of man to interpret nature **anthropomorphically** (Gr. *anthropos,* man + *morphos,* form). This rather long word simply represents a viewpoint that interprets the actions of any given organism or the condition of an object as arising from an intelligence similar to that of man. For example, if a child bumps into a door, he may blame the door for having been in his way, and "punish" it with a kick. Of course, the door is in no way responsible for the incident. On a somewhat higher level, the bending of a plant toward light may be interpreted (and often is) according to an anthropomorphic view. According to such a concept, it might be said that the plant "likes" the light because it thrives under its influence and thus "tries" to grow toward it. Now biologists have absolutely no reason to suspect that plants are equipped with the capacity for awareness, and we feel quite safe in saying that the particular plant under consideration does not like or dislike anything; its actions are simply the result of auxin influence. In other words, plants do not *try* to do things, but they do *act.*

As long as we are dealing with non-living objects and with plants whose lack of consciousness may readily be accepted, we have little difficulty with anthropomorphism, but where, in the animal kingdom, do we stop dealing with completely mechanistic, or determined, behavior and enter into a realm of such complexity that we are obliged to ascribe awareness and purpose? Actually, this becomes quite a problem, and we shall consider some of its more important ramifications later. For the time being, it may simply be mentioned that good reason exists for believing that lower animals whose behavior is entirely dependent upon unconditioned reflexes are no more "aware" than are plants. They are nothing more nor less than machines, albeit extremely complex ones, and their behavior is entirely explicable on the basis of the stimulus-response mechanism. Apparently, the quality of awareness comes into being in those animals whose nervous systems are sufficiently complex as to allow for some degree of learning, but just where it begins is a very difficult matter to determine. Certainly we feel justified in ascribing it to vertebrates and to some of the higher invertebrates. Even so, it is possible to interpret behavior on this higher level anthropomorphically. For example, a household pet may displease us by some action, and whether it obeyed an instinct or forgot a habit does not really matter much if we ascribe to it a degree of guilt or responsibility normally reserved for human beings.

Free Will and Determinism

Although it should be evident that behavior on the part of organisms other than man is not justly subject to consideration in terms of human values, to what extent is one person justified in evaluating the actions of another? This problem, which has been one of considerable importance in all areas of human affairs, including such widely divergent fields as religion and political science, is fundamentally a biological one. Basically, there are two views of man's behavior, namely, the concepts of **free will** and **determinism.**

According to the deterministic viewpoint, man is simply the most complex expression of a material universe, where every effect is preceded by a cause. That causes may not be known or understood in no way violates the principle, and since determinism is accepted as a way of investigation in all the sciences, human behavior should not constitute an exception to the cause-and-effect principle. Furthermore, since a great many aspects of man's behavior have been explained deterministically (for example, the reflex arc), it may be assumed that total behavior is thus controlled. Hence, according to this viewpoint, man is as bound by his instincts, conditioned reflexes, and hormonal secretions as any other animal, and since an individual cannot act differently than he does, he should not be held morally accountable for his actions. What might *seem* to be a free choice on his part is actually influenced by past experience and instinct. Determinism is not to be confused, however, with **fatalism;** it does not say that a person is obliged to do such-and-such a thing because of some cosmic pattern. It only says that a "choice" between alternatives is determined according to factors that are fundamentally biological ones.

In its literal form, the concept of free will holds that man's actions are *not* biologically determined in the final analysis but that he has within himself the power to act independently of causative factors. Thus, he is a "free moral agent" and is subject to judgement for his choices between the good and the bad. In its modern expression, this viewpoint concedes that man is not completely free, since many deterministic factors must of necessity be recognized. Furthermore, freedom may be greater in one individual than in another. However, man as an organism is capable of rising above the forces that restrict him, and he has at least some power to make choices.

The significance of the difference in viewpoint between free will and determinism may not be immediately apparent to most people because there is a human tendency to suppose that a given person enjoys considerable freedom to make choices. Let us consider a case in point. Suppose a person is taking a walk for exercise, and he comes to a fork in the road. There is no particular reason for him to choose either of the two branches, because he is walking rather aimlessly anyhow. Somehow, he makes a decision however. Even though this decision may seem quite arbitrary to him, there are factors of past experience, of imagination, and of his subconscious mind that influence whatever conclusion he reaches. These are all biologically determined by conditioned reflexes, and without knowing it, he may never have really had a choice at all! Of course, he *could* have decided differently, but had he done so, this choice would also have been determined. If this line of reasoning seems to be sheer nonsense, it should be remembered that the question of the freedom of human will has troubled the minds of mankind's best thinkers for many centuries and that it has extremely serious implications for man and his place in nature.

Actually, there are serious difficulties in both the concepts of free will and determinism. At present, neither viewpoint is completely subject to experimentation, and perhaps the factors in question will never be known with certainty on purely scientific grounds. For a time, determinists were encouraged because their viewpoint was upheld by experimental evidence to a considerable degree. Hence, during a period when experimental psychology and human physiology were making their greatest gains, it was not uncommon to hear such expressions as, "You are exactly what your glands make you," or, "Man is just a complex bundle of nerve fibers, reflex arcs, and genes." Determinists, however, have been obliged to concede that a whole may be more than a mere sum of its parts, and, at the same time, exponents of freedom of the will have generally accepted the principle that at least many factors in human behavior are determined. As a result of less dogmatic attitudes, each viewpoint has been able to accept the more valid points of the other. This is not to say that the problem has been solved. The question of just how free human beings really are continues to have a very important bearing upon many problems that are constantly before society. For this reason, it behooves the informed person at least to be aware of the biological factors that underlie the controversy.

CONCLUSION

There are a great many important principles governing responsiveness and behavior that have not been treated in this chapter. If those which have been presented are comprehended, however, they will provide a basis for a considerable degree of understanding in regard to these biological phenomena. The reflex arc and its application to animal behavior are so widely known in our society that ignorance of these principles virtually constitutes an intellectual misdemeanor. The same can be said for hormones, both plant and animal, as they relate to behavior in their respective groups. Finally, the relationship between causal factors of behavior and certain philosophical considerations should not be lost upon the student. The more one understands *why* organisms (including man) behave as they do, the better equipped he becomes to comprehend his world and adjust to it. In the process, his personal philosophy becomes more certain and meaningful, and this, after all, is one of the major goals of all education.

QUESTIONS

Multiple Choice

1. Which of the following is first to break the proper sequence? (a) receptor, (b) motor nerve cell, (c) association nerve cell, (d) sensory nerve cell, (e) effector.

2. Which of the following bears much the same relationship to conditioned reflexes as instincts do to unconditioned reflexes? (a) auxins, (b) synapses, (c) hormones, (d) habits, (e) value judgements.

3. Which of the terms above is *always* associated with plant behavior?

4. The shoot of a seedling turns upward immediately upon germination. We call this response (a) positive geotropism, (b) negative geotropism, (c) positive phototropism, (d) negative phototropism, (e) none of these.

5. The concept that man's actions are biologically controlled in their entirety is called (a) anthropomorphism, (b) determinism, (c) free will, (d) fatalism, (e) none of these.

6. The energy required in impulse transmission is furnished by the (a) stimulating agent, (b) brain, (c) muscles, (d) liver, (e) nerve fiber itself.

7. The all-or-none law holds that (a) nerve fibers are electrically polarized; (b) a threshold stimulus is one which is just sufficient to "fire" a receptor; (c) a responsive unit is stimulated to its full capacity if it responds at all; (d) a reflex arc depends upon five interconnecting structures; (e) a muscle either contracts to its full capacity or not at all.

8. Leaves of the sensitive plant, *Mimosa*, droop when touched because (a) auxins travel quickly from tip to base of the leaf; (b) nerve impulses reach effectors which rapidly contract; (c) cell walls in this plant lose their rigidity when stimulated by touch; (d) the plant tries to withdraw from irritation; (e) turgor pressure in certain cells is reduced.

9. A geranium plant that was placed on a window sill grew toward its source of light. Which of the following statements explains this action? (a) Auxins become more concentrated on the shaded side of the stem. (b) Auxins become more concentrated on the illuminated side of the stem. (c) Auxins inhibit cell division in the roots causing one-sided growth of the stem. (d) Auxins are not involved; turgor pressure becomes greater on the shaded side of the stem.

10. The rate of impulse transmission along nerve fibers rarely exceeds (a) 1 meter per second, (b) 100 meters per second, (c) 1 meter per minute, (d) 100 meters per minute, (e) 100,000 miles per second.

11. Which of the following organs secretes more different types of hormones than any other structure in the human body? (a) liver, (b) pancreas, (c) duodenum, (d) ovary, (e) pituitary.

12. The hormone insulin is produced in which of the organs above?

13. The functional connection between two nerve fibers is called a (a) taxis, (b) tropism, (c) synapse, (d) reflex, (e) receptor.

14. Which portion of the vertebrate brain is most directly concerned with the capacity to learn? (a) cerebrum, (b) cerebellum, (c) medulla, (d) pituitary, (e) optic lobes.

15. The field of psychology is primarily concerned with (a) cell studies, (b) body function, (c) behavior, (d) hormones, (e) anthropomorphism.

True-false

1. When a jar of pond water is placed so that it receives a moderate amount of light from one direction, motile algae exhibit positive phototropism.

2. When two nerve fibers synapse, cell membranes of the two fibers may touch each other, but there is no protoplasmic continuity.

3. In higher animals, it is necessary that all nerve impulses eventually reach the brain.

4. The digger wasp was used in this chapter to illustrate the establishment of conditioned reflexes.

5. In very young roots, auxin accumulation inhibits cell elongation, whereas it stimulates cell elongation in very young stems.

6. Only man can be said to be "aware" or "conscious."

7. Since plants do not possess nervous systems, it is meaningless to say that they "act" or "behave" in certain ways.

8. Secretin is produced in the duodenum of the higher animal when hydrochloric acid comes into contact with the cells that line the internal surface of that organ.

9. Protoplasm itself is not responsive to stimuli; responsiveness is a manifestation of cellular coordination.

10. In man and other higher animals, motor structures may be thrown into action by impulses that do not originate in sensory structures.

11. If an auxin-laden block of agar is placed on one side of a cut tip of an oat seedling, growth occurs in the direction of the agar block.

12. After a nerve fiber has conducted an impulse, it is not capable of conducting a second one for several seconds.

13. All receptors in the human body are located either at or very near to the surface of the body.

14. Although most animals can learn, the vast majority are governed almost entirely by unconditioned reflexes.

15. A plant grown in darkness tends to elongate greatly.

Questions for Consideration and Discussion

1. Identify or define: taxis, tropism, polarization, threshold stimulus, antagonistic muscles, habit, hormone, anthropomorphism.

2. Is responsiveness an exclusive characteristic of living matter? Explain.

3. Describe the working of the reflex arc.

4. What is the principal means by which plants exhibit behavior?

5. Why is the nerve fiber said to represent an *electrochemical* system of responsive activity?

6. Compare the honey bee and the dog according to intelligence.

7. Criticize this statement: "Plants grow toward a source of light because they like the light."

8. List the endocrine glands of the human body, the hormones they produce, and the functions of these hormones.

9. What conclusions can be drawn from the experiments involving oat seedlings and agar blocks?

10. What is the fundamental difference between the philosophies of free will and determinism? Do you feel that man is a "free moral agent?"

REFERENCES

CARLSON, A. J., VICTOR JOHNSON and **H. M. CAVERT.** *The Machinery of the Body.* (See reference at end of Chapter 5.) For an account of the human nervous system and its functioning, see appropriate sections of this book.

DETHIER, VINCENT and **ELIOT STELLAR.** *Animal Behavior.* Englewood Cliffs, N.J.: Prentice-Hall, Inc., 1961. This book, which is one of the FOUNDATIONS IN MODERN BIOLOGY series, is recommended for that portion of this chapter dealing with animal behavior.

GALSTON, A. W. *The Life of the Green Plant.* (See reference at end of Chapter 5.) Portions of the author's Chapter 4, entitled "Plant Growth," are appropriate to that part of this chapter that deals with plant behavior.

LEWIS, D. J. *The Science of Psychology.* Englewood Cliffs, N.J.: Prentice-Hall, Inc., 1962. A good general reference for the student who wishes to read further in psychology.

SCHMIDT-NIELSON, KNUT. *Animal Physiology.* (See reference at end of Chapter 5.) The author's Chapters 5, 6, and 7, entitled "Movements," "Information" and "Integration," respectively, are related to the topic of animal behavior discussed in this chapter.

University of California Associates. "The Freedom of the Will," in **HERBERT FEIGL** and **WILFRED SELLARS** (editors). *Readings in Philosophical Analysis.* New York: Appleton-Century-Crofts, 1949, pp. 594–615. For the student who wishes to read further and more deeply concerning free will and determinism, this excellent discussion of these subjects should prove very enlightening.

Adaptation

As we have observed, the characteristics of metabolism, growth, reproduction, and responsiveness are fundamental properties of protoplasm
that find their highest and most closely coordinated expressions in the
organism as a whole. Although the characteristic of **adaptation** very
definitely has its roots in protoplasmic mechanisms, it is a term which
applies fundamentally to the species in its adjustment for survival and
reproduction within the limits of a particular environment. Because the
four characteristics that we have studied to this point are concerned with
basic activities of individual organisms, there has been little opportunity
to view the world of life as a coordinated unit. In this chapter we shall
take this approach to the study of biology through a consideration of
adaptation as a biological process. To state the matter another way, we
are now ready to leave the "trees" and devote ourselves for a time to the
"forest."

A DEFINITION OF ADAPTATION

By way of more exact definition, let us distinguish between adaptation and **adaptability,** which are often confused. The latter term is
used in biology to describe that characteristic of a given organism which

enables it to orient itself to some new environmental condition. We often say that man is very adaptable to climatic conditions, for instance, since he can adjust from a warm climate to a very cold one. A more clear-cut example of adaptability is seen in the case of simpler organisms, such as protozoa, where certain chemical substances may be added to their aqueous environment by degrees until concentrations are reached that would have killed them if such a quantity of chemical were added all at one time. Evidently, such adjustment is possible through chemical and physical changes in the protoplasm, whose capacity for such adjustment is, of course, limited. However, the very occurrence of such adjustments is further evidence of the tremendous versatility of protoplasm, and this within itself is by no means an unimportant characteristic of living forms. All organisms exhibit the capacity for at least some adaptability to various environmental conditions.

However, this is not what is meant by adaptation. **This term describes the characteristic of living forms to develop, over a period of time, certain structural and functional features which enable them to survive and reproduce within the limits of a particular environment.** Hence, when a biologist says that adaptation is a characteristic of living forms, he has in mind a *process,* and one that has gone on throughout past ages, the result of which is the variety of present-day organisms. However, any structural or functional feature of an organism that has been developed by this process may be called *an adaptation,* and so the same term is at once used to describe an over-all process in nature and any given result of that process. For example, the stem and leaves of a cactus plant constitute adaptations to a physical environment whose nature is such that plants with typical stems and leaves would be at an extreme disadvantage. The leaves of cactus are greatly modified as spines, and these have very little surface area from which water might evaporate. Actually, they are of little use to the plant except that they prevent desert animals from eating it for the water that it contains. Reduction of exposed surface and loss of photosynthetic ability by these modified leaves have been accompanied in the over-all modification of the plant by an emphasis on the stem as a photosynthetic organ. These structural *adaptations* (spines, photosynthetic stem, and so on) relate the plant to its environment, but they developed over time by the over-all process.

TYPES OF ADAPTATIONS

In general, any characteristics exhibited by an organism which are of benefit to it in relation to a given environment are either **structural** or **functional** in nature. Structural adaptations are the more obvious, and it would be difficult for even an amateur biologist to miss the direct connection between the morphological features of almost any organism and its environment. We have already called attention to the spines and stems of cacti; these plants exhibit many other structures which make it possible for them to exist successfully where most other plants cannot. To cite another specific example of structural adaptations in plants, many flowers are so constituted as to attract insects which transport pollen from one to another, thus ensuring cross-pollination in the species. In the animal kingdom, structural adaptations are perhaps even more obvious. If one examines the beaks and feet of birds, a direct relationship can be seen between form in these structures and the life habits of the birds. Thus, a duck has webbed feet, and a hawk has grasping claws. In each case, it is not difficult to determine how these adaptations equip their respective owners for different modes of existence. It is most instructive to study the mouth parts of different insects, comparing them according to structure. One is thus able to determine rather accurately, without any previous knowledge, to just what type of environment a given insect is related. There are animals whose protective coloration or body form is of definite advantage to them; the striped coat of a tiger, for instance, makes it possible for this animal to move through vegetation in search of prey without being readily detected. An almost infinite number of such examples might be cited, but perhaps these will serve to emphasize the obvious phenomenon of structural adaptation in nature.

162 Hen mallard on nest. Notice how her markings blend with the immediate surroundings, providing a protective camouflage. (Photograph by George Purvis, courtesy Arkansas Game and Fish Commission)

Although functional adaptations are perhaps less obvious than structural ones, they are equally essential to an animal or plant in its organization for survival and reproduction within the limits of its environment. Bacteria, for example, are capable of producing digestive enzymes that pass out into the medium around them. As a result, food materials in the medium may be degraded to a diffusible state, whereupon they are made available to bacterial populations by passing into their cells. Termites, which are insects, possess the rare ability of existing upon a diet of wood by virtue of the phenomenon that certain protozoa existing in their digestive tracts produce enzymes that hydrolyze cellulose to utilizable sugars. In the vertebrate body, the vastly complex and coordinated enzyme system of the gastro-intestinal tract is the result of many adaptations to various food types. These are, of course, only a few of the many functional, or physiological, adaptations that might be cited.

In reality, it is impossible to separate structure completely from function in considering a given adaptation, and the distinction made between these two types is merely one of convenience for the sake of discussion. Actually, many adaptations, both structural and functional, work so closely in relating an organism to its environment that the entire phenomenon must be analyzed from the viewpoint of over-all behavior, not as a single adaptation. For instance, the courting behavior of many male animals is quite elaborate, possibly consisting of several gestures and acts carried out in a definite sequence. Such behavior is doubtless adaptive for a given animal and plays an important part in the process of reproduction. One can hardly consider courting behavior as a single adaptation; a great many factors, some structural and others functional, make their contribution. There are hormones, unconditioned reflexes, and various effector structures involved, all of which constitute a large number of *coordinated* adaptations. It is obvious, therefore, that the phenomena of responsiveness and adaptation are very closely associated since it is only through mechanisms of the former that the latter is made possible for an organism.

ORGANISMS AND ENVIRONMENT

The study of organisms in relation to their environments is known as **ecology.** Since the various adaptations exhibited by organisms are important to them in terms of their surroundings, it is essential that the student of biology understand something of ecological principles which have been formulated and which lend meaning to the over-all phenomenon of adaptation.

The environment of an organism not only includes its physical surroundings, but also such other organisms as may be present, which means that any influences they exert upon each other must be taken into consideration. For purposes of discussion, therefore, we shall distinguish between environmental factors that are **physical** in nature, those that are **biogeochemical,** and those that are **biotic.**

The Physical Environment

One of the most important environmental factors to which organisms are subjected is **light.** This should be obvious in the case of green plants since they are dependent upon sunlight as an energy source in the photosynthetic process. The leaves of higher plants are adapted in various ways to sunlight; in many cases, they are arranged on the plant in such a way that maximum exposure to sunlight is realized. However, the influence of light is not limited to photosynthetic effects; the flowering process in many plants is rigidly controlled by the amount of light received. This is one example of **photoperiodicity,** or the response of an organism to the length of time it is exposed to light. The principle of photoperiodicity is exploited by commercial nurserymen in producing blooms out of season. By supplying artificial light or by subjecting plants to periods of darkness, as the case may be, it is possible to regulate the time of flowering. For example, chrysanthemums may be grown under photoperiodic conditions that result in their blooming at seasons when demand for them is great. Some species are termed **long-day** plants, because they normally bloom only when days are long, whereas others are called **short-day** plants, since they respond in their flowering processes to shorter periods of light. As might be expected, there are species which are intermediate in their light requirements for the development of flowers, and there are some whose flowering process is not influenced at all by length of light exposure. In addition to the regulation of flowering, a great many other light-controlled processes are known in plants, some of which are seed germination, leaf fall, the development of color in leaves, and growth rates of plant organs. A number of adaptations to light are also seen in the animal kingdom, among the most obvious of which are the eyes of higher animals. The extent to which certain wave lengths of light may be received varies somewhat, which partly accounts for the different habits of animals regarding day and night activities. In addition, important aspects of animal behavior such as mass movements, reproductive activity, and feeding habits are influenced tremendously by photoperiodicity.

Another important factor of the physical environment is **temperature.** If a survey is made of plants and animals that exist at various temperature zones of the earth, it is found that there is a direct correlation between this factor and those features which adapt organisms to their respective habitats. Thus, there are plants that grow only in the tropics and others that are fairly well restricted to the far north. The same holds for animals, where adaptations for cold or hot climates limit these respective forms greatly. In addition to its influence upon animal and plant distribution, temperature is of considerable ecological significance in other ways. Seeds of most plants do not germinate until the temperature is fairly warm; some will not germinate even at the proper temperature unless they have previously been exposed to a period of cold. One rather unusual adaptation to temperature is seen in the case of seed cones of the jack-pine (*Pinus banksiana*), which do not open readily to release the seeds until they have been scorched by fire. Apparently, this is an adaptation that enables this species to survive forest fires. Among animals, temperature is an important factor in reproduction, rate of embryonic development, migratory activities, and a great many behavioral characteristics. As an example of temperature adaptations in animals, the birds and mammals are able to maintain constant body temperatures by virtue of a feature of the nervous system which is absent in "cold-blooded" animals. This is the **temperature-regulating center** of the brain, a kind of built-in "thermostat." This feature, plus accompanying heat-regulating adaptations such as the feathers and hair exhibited by these two groups of animals, respectively, makes it possible for them to exist under a wide range of temperature conditions.

Water is another factor that is ecologically important. Some organisms possess adaptations that make it possible for them to live entirely within an aqueous environment, whereas others are adapted to land. Structural features for existence in these respective environments are frequently quite obvious; gills of fishes and lungs of land vertebrates are among those that are better known. We have mentioned the contractile vacuoles featured by many unicellular fresh-water organisms which are adaptations to osmotic pressure. In oceans, it has been observed that certain species are characteristic of the various depth zones, indicating that there are adaptations for withstanding pressures that exist at different levels of the sea. Organisms that live on land are adapted variously to water; some plants and animals are restricted to moist environments, while others inhabit only dry areas. Cacti are typical of plants that possess features making possible their existence in desert areas, and among animals, the camel and the desert rat have become almost proverbial for their capacity to withstand dry conditions.

In addition to these physical factors, a number of others assume great importance. Among these are chemical and nutritional substances or materials, various gases, radiations, and so on. In general, however, light, temperature, and water may be considered the most important physical factors of the environment.

It should be pointed out that these environmental factors are merely separate parts of a total situation, and they frequently exert effects together. For instance, it was mentioned that seeds of a given species will not germinate below a certain threshold temperature. However, even if an ideal temperature is provided, there will be no germination unless enough moisture is present to activate enzymes and to enter into reactions within cells of the embryonic plant. In this case, neither temperature nor water are independent of each other; a seed is adapted to germinate only when certain conditions of both factors are met. Similarly, the temperature of an environment may be ideal for some animal to exist successfully, but if its water needs are not met, it cannot survive. This important principle is called the **law of the minimum,** and stated more precisely, it holds that regardless of how satisfactory one or more requirements of an organism may be, it cannot survive or flourish unless all requirements are met. As a further example of this law and its application, let us suppose that a certain plant is supplied with all physical and chemical requirements in adequate amounts except one essential element (for example, manganese). Regardless of how adequate other environmental conditions may be, the *minimum* requirements of the plant have not been met, and it cannot survive.

Biogeochemical Factors of the Environment

In a very real sense, the world is a coordinated whole in which matter and energy undergo cycles wherein they are changed but not destroyed. Hence, it is important to understand that plants serve the needs of animals, and vice-versa, with all the interrelations among organisms and their environments having an important bearing on the total situation. In order to comprehend at least some of the factors involved on this over-all scale, let us consider what happens to some of the elements that figure prominantly in life processes. Since the atoms of these elements may be used over and over, we say that they travel through **cycles.** Because certain phases of a given elemental cycle may involve other factors than purely biological ones, we refer to the entire pathway as a **biogeochemical cycle,** a term which tells us that biological, geological and chemical factors are all involved.

As we have observed repeatedly, carbon is one of the most important elements to living forms since it figures so prominently in organic compounds as an energy carrier. A carbon cycle is shown in Fig. 163, where it will be seen that atmospheric carbon dioxide serves as the carbon source for the synthesis of organic compounds in autotrophic plants. Animals, in turn, are ultimately dependent upon plants for their organic compounds. Further anabolic and even catabolic changes may occur which keep carbon "trapped" within organic compounds, and some may

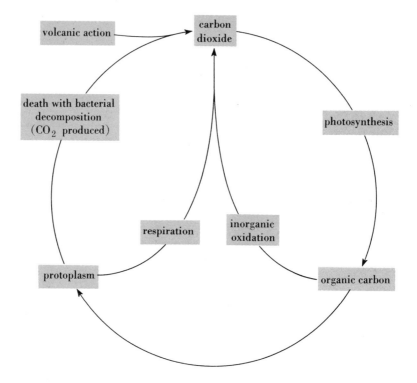

163 The carbon cycle.

be lost to the cycle for long periods of time. Coal and oil deposits, for instance, were formed many millions of years ago from plant and animal bodies, and the carbon involved is of necessity not available until these materials are burned. Eventually, however, the trapped carbon may be returned to the atmosphere by this means in the form of carbon dioxide. Ordinarily, of course, carbon gets back into circulation within a relatively short period of time through respiration of plants and animals and through processes of decomposition. Although of limited importance in a quantitative sense, volcanic eruptions contribute carbon dioxide to the atmosphere. Through the interaction of these various processes, which we have illustrated as a cycle, carbon is used over time and time again by living forms.

Another important element is nitrogen, which is found in quantity within all plant and animal bodies. It is not present as elemental nitrogen, of course, which is a gas; rather, it is an essential part of proteins and certain other types of organic molecules. A nitrogen cycle is shown in Fig. 164, where it will be seen that plants and animals, along with their waste products, eventually undergo decomposition. Of course, just as carbon may be trapped in organic molecules for long periods of time, nitrogen may become temporarily unavailable at some point of the cycle. At any rate, the nitrogen of waste products and dead bodies eventually appears in the form of ammonia (NH_3). Further bacterial action makes possible the formation of nitrites ($-NO_2$ compounds) and then nitrates ($-NO_3$ compounds). In the latter form, nitrogen becomes available to green plants, which combine it with photosynthetic products in the synthesis of plant proteins. It should be noted that a lesser cycle occurs between nitrates and atmospheric nitrogen; nitrates may be decomposed by certain bacteria in soil and water to release gaseous nitrogen to the atmosphere, which is something of a "loss" to the main cycle. However, this loss is compensated for by the phenomenon that lightning con-

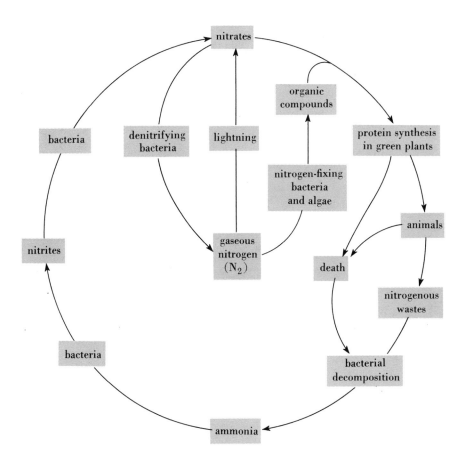

164 The nitrogen cycle.

verts gaseous nitrogen to nitric acid (HNO_3) which becomes deposited in the soil, and by the ability of certain bacteria and algae to "fix" gaseous nitrogen in the form of organic compounds. As Fig. 164 shows, nitrate nitrogen may become incorporated into plant proteins and thus complete the cycle as we have described it.

Carbon and nitrogen are only two of the many elements that undergo cycles of this sort, and the changes in form which they experience may be considered typical of others. Because these cycles function as they do, there is made possible a constant re-use of matter. In this sense, therefore, nature is tremendously economical; energy may be lost, organisms die, and species undergo changes, but the fundamental units of matter travel their cycles in unending fashion.

Biotic Factors of the Environment

A given organism may be influenced by two other groups of organisms: those that are members of its own species, and those that are not. There is at least one essential relationship which must exist among members of most sexually reproducing species, namely, that of reproduction. A great many adaptations are seen in both the animal and plant kingdoms which allow for bi-parental reproduction. Some of these are highly specialized. For example, as we have mentioned, certain animal species are characterized by highly complex courting rituals that are concerned with mate selection and subsequent production of offspring. In regard to essential requirements such as food (in the case of animals) and sunlight (which is necessary for food synthesis in green plants), members of the same species are frequently found to be in **competition** with each other. One of the most fundamental of all ecological principles is that the reproductive potential of a species tends to run far ahead of its food supply or available space, and it is inevitable that some members survive at the expense of others. As we shall see, this principle plays a very important part in the establishment of new adaptations in species. Some species are so organized that **cooperation,** rather than individual competition, is exhibited. For instance, wolves sometimes form packs that may successfully attack large animals whose size prevents their capture by any one individual. This type of cooperative group is called an **aggregation.** A much more closely unified arrangement for cooperation is the **society,** which achieves its highest form of development in certain insect species.

In consideration of relationships that exist between members of different species, competition is of great ecological importance. Plants of different species compete in nature for sunlight and root space; animals whose food or shelter requirements are similar may be in keen competition, especially when food or space become scarce. Perhaps the most important ecological consideration of inter-specific relationships, however, is the principle of the **food chain.** Essentially, a food chain is a series that begins with a chemical medium, either soil or water, within or upon which photosynthetic **producers** provide food for varying numbers of animal **consumers.** For example, in a typical fresh-water pond, the producers are various algae and perhaps some aquatic seed plants. These support certain microscopic animals which, along with the algae, constitute a mass of small, living forms collectively known as **plankton.** Certain fishes, especially small forms, are adapted to live upon plankton by virtue of mechanisms which strain these organisms out of the water as it passes into the mouth and over the gills. Eventually, these fishes are eaten by larger forms which may, in turn, be eaten by others, and so on. Hence, there is a chain beginning with the nutritive medium and ending with the ultimate consumers.

By careful study, ecologists have learned that a food chain results in a **pyramid of numbers,** wherein both numbers of individuals and their total mass decrease at each consumer level (Fig. 165). This means, of course, that the longer the chain, the less there is to show for the energy stored by the producers. Although this is of limited practical concern to man as long as it merely goes on in nature, the principle is extremely important in its bearing on human nutrition. After all, man is the ultimate consumer in a number of possible food chains, and the pyramid of numbers is important in an economic sense. For example, everything else being equal, it is far cheaper to exist upon vegetables than upon meat because there are no intermediate consumers when man himself feeds upon products of photosynthesis. Another important consideration lies in the principle that, as the human population expands, the food problem increases. Hence, there is great interest in the development of methods whereby man can utilize more producers (such as algae) directly, and it may be largely through studies of fundamental ecology that future problems of human nutrition will be partially solved.

Food chains necessarily involve **predation,** or the feeding of certain forms on others. Except for a few species of plants such as the Venus fly-trap, which we have mentioned, predators are all animals. Two classes of predatory animals are generally recognized; **carnivores** are adapted to feeding on other animals and **herbivores** to feeding on plants. Some species exist on a mixed diet, however, and thus a third group, the **omnivores,** may be recognized. Predation is frequently thought of as a somewhat unpleasant side of nature, and many persons build up some rather anthropomorphic views in regard to carnivorous animals. Hence, a lion is often pictured as a "bad" animal, and a sheep is evaluated as a "good" one. Such people seem actually to think that a

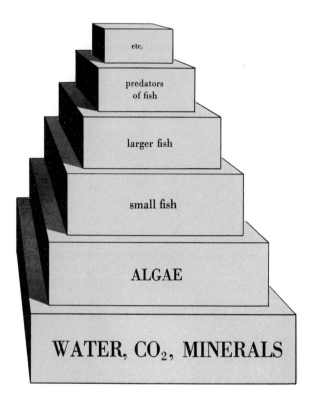

165 A generalized pyramid of numbers representative of a small pond.

carnivore is capable of making value judgements, and "ought" not to kill and devour other animals since this is cruel and wicked. What they fail to see is that an animal which is adapted through heredity for a carnivorous existence cannot be expected to shake off these structural and functional limitations and start eating grass. Their behavior, at least in respect to the acquisition of food, is quite determined. Furthermore, predation is not as bizarre a phenomenon as some people might think. In the first place, many plants and small animal forms, which apparently lack any sort of consciousness, are involved. They are no worse off for having been eaten than a rock is for having been broken. As for higher animals, there is no reason to believe that they are capable of the mental anguish with which human beings regard death. Although this certainly does not justify an inhumane attitude toward necessary animal death, it does indicate that human values cannot be extended fully to other animals. At any rate, predation is a part of nature and should be accepted philosophically.

Aside from such considerations as these, predation is very important in the over-all **balance of nature.** We have observed that reproductive potential in organisms runs far ahead of available food and space; were it not for predators, animals and plants would overproduce, and certain forms would become extremely numerous. Such an imbalance is often seen when normal population ratios of nature are upset in some way. For example, the coyote of the western United States is generally regarded as a very harmful predator because it sometimes eats valuable livestock animals. When it is extensively hunted by man so that numbers of individuals are greatly reduced in a given area, the result is usually one that is ecologically worse, even for man, than was the former situation. With the decline of the coyote population, smaller animals, upon which they would normally prey, increase in number until they become more detrimental than coyotes. The natural prey of coyotes is the rabbit, whose reproductive potential is proverbial. Within a short time after the disappearance of coyotes in a given area, rabbits generally increase to such an extent that they consume pasture grass and other plants that support livestock. By this means, the rancher may be choosing the worse of two evils by eradicating coyotes.

Sometimes organisms of different species become rather intimately associated together in their environmental adaptations, and these relationships are of special interest to the ecologist. One such relationship is that of **mutualism,** wherein two associated organisms belonging to different species both derive benefit from living together. We have observed that a lichen is composed of an alga and a fungus, both of which are adapted to live under conditions where neither could exist separately. The alga is able to furnish photosynthetic materials to the fungus, while the fungus provides a suitable environment for the alga by supporting its cells and by holding water which it can use. We also mentioned the association of cellulose-digesting protozoa with termites, an arrangement that enables these insects to subsist on wood. At the same time, the protozoa are provided with a place to live, and they also receive essential materials such as water and inorganic salts from their mutualistic partners. Another type of relationship is that of **commensalism** in which two members of different species are so associated that one derives benefit while the other is neither harmed nor helped. It is common, for example, to find barnacles (which are arthropods) attached to the shells of mollusks or to other arthropods, and some even attach to the skin of whales. By virtue of this arrangement, a given barnacle may take in bits of food that drift away from the other organism when it eats, and in terms of species distribution, it may be carried to points it could not possibly reach otherwise. At the same time, it does no harm to its partner organism. A third important special relationship between members of different species is that of **parasitism** in which one member (the parasite) derives benefit at the expense of the other (the host). Man, for example, plays host to a number of parasites such as tapeworms and various bacteria. In their nutritive requirements or in the production of metabolic wastes, they may cause serious damage to organs or tissues of the host. Such parasites as these, that live within the body of the host, are known as **endoparasites.** Others, called **ectoparasites,** exist upon the bodies of animals or plants. Lice, ticks, and leeches are representative ectoparasites.

Summary

In their interrelations with each other and with their environments, organisms exhibit a great many adaptations which make it possible for them to survive, as species, the tremendous competition that exists in nature. The principles governing these interrelations are very complex, and we have introduced only a few of them here. Ecologists have contributed much to our understanding of the world of life through the formulation of these principles, and the field of ecology continues to be a highly important and vigorous branch of biology.

THE ORIGIN OF ADAPTATIONS: EVOLUTION

So far in this book, we have devoted attention almost entirely to biological principles that are demonstrable at the present time in nature. The adaptations discussed in this chapter and in previous ones obviously fulfill certain roles in maintaining species, and there is no real basis for argument as to their ecological significance. Clearly, a fish could not live in water without gills or some equally efficient adaptation for extracting oxygen from the water, nor could a desert plant survive in its environment unless it exhibited water-conserving structures. Sooner or later, however, if organisms are really to be understood, the question of origins must be asked and answered.

A Definition of Issues

Fundamentally, there are two possible explanations for the origin of adaptations: **special creation** and **organic evolution.** According to the concept of special creation, a supernatural force or personality fashioned and designed the great variety of plants and animals, along with the adaptations peculiar to each species. Hence, there is postulated the existence of a Creator who served at some time as a cosmic engineer, carefully working out structural and functional needs of organisms as they would need them in their chosen environments.

As late as the middle of the nineteenth century, most biologists were special creationists. In the main, they were content to explore the descriptive side of biology and to accept the authority of established religions as to origins. This accounts for the fact that taxonomic systems were wholly artificial since the idea of actual genetic kinship was largely unthought of. Linnaeus himself, for example, was entirely creationistic in his biological philosophy. Actually, creationism is a convenient way of ignoring the whole problem since it avoids biological explanations rather than providing any.

The concept of organic evolution is one of *change.* Essentially, it holds that present-day organisms are the descendants of ancestors that were, at some stage of time, more simple in organization. Although this is all that the term evolution means in biology, certain implications accompany the concept. Since life had to start *somewhere,* it is generally supposed by evolutionists that either once or many times, organization of chemicals occurred in some way so as to result in a quantity of matter that was alive. From this point on, species developed through change and the inheritance of change until the present time. Let us notice that the concept of evolution does not rule out the idea of God, nor is it *completely* irreconcilable with the concept of special creation. One might believe very strongly (and some biologists do) that the primary organization of protoplasm or at least the formulation of physical law governing the process was a supernatural event. It might even be held that a small number of species were divinely created, and that these gave rise to others, an idea which would still represent acceptance of an evolutionary process in explanation of the origin of species and their various adaptations.

However, most evolutionists believe that life originated in some fashion within the primeval seas, and that present-day forms are the results of these humble beginnings. This is not entirely a matter of speculation. For reasons that depend upon evidences from physics and geology, it is believed that great quantities of water, methane, and ammonia existed on earth some two billions of years ago. Atmospheric conditions were such, apparently, that electrical discharges in the form of lightning occurred with great frequency. Within recent years, experiments have been devised that attempt to reproduce these environmental circumstances under laboratory conditions. If water, methane, and ammonia are placed in a closed container and subjected to electrical currents for several days, analysis of the original mixture reveals the presence of several organic compounds that are normally associated only with life! This experiment has been repeated successfully many times, and it provides good evidence that compounds essential to the organization of protoplasm developed by natural means. Chance reactions between such compounds, occurring over tremendous periods of time, may well have produced nucleoprotein molecules capable of self-duplication. In the midst of a nutritious sea of organic compounds, life quite possibly had its beginnings when these nucleoproteins "learned" to accumulate proteins around them. The first living organisms, therefore, may have been somewhat similar to modern viruses (Fig. 14). Through mutation (see page 305) and the inheritance of change, they eventually gave rise to more complex descendants.

In consideration of this concept, two important principles should be kept clearly in mind. The first is that time, measured in terms of hundreds of millions of years, was available. Now this does not mean that time alone can account for any phenomenon; unless combinations or reactions are possible, it matters little whether a century or a billion years are available. However, it has been shown how organic molecules were possibly formed under the conditions that existed, and we know that organic molecules can react with each other and with inorganic molecules. Probably, it was simply a matter of time until the "right" combinations occurred for a relatively simple organism to exhibit the ability to make more of itself from the surrounding medium. The second principle of importance to our discussion is that the primeval environment was something of a rich soup of nutritives, affording unlimited opportunity for exploitation by developing and changing organisms. Hence, the development of changing forms was greatly encouraged by the environment because there was undoubtedly a place in nature for every sort of new organism.

It is reasonable to assume that up to this point organisms were heterotrophic, simply absorbing nutrients from the environment. Eventually, however, this situation must have changed when the early organic compounds began to disappear. Gradually, the victory of survival went to the autotrophs, which had developed synthetic ability, and to the phagotrophs, which consumed other types of organisms as well as each other. Some heterotrophs were able to survive by switching from "natural" nutrients to those provided by these two classes of new organisms, and they were the ancestors of modern heterotrophs. From this point on, it was a matter of further evolution to the present day.

It might be objected that this concept of the origin and early development of life is pure speculation. In consideration of this objection, it should be pointed out that the scientist dislikes the term "speculation," and prefers to think of his projected explanations as theories or, at the very least, hypotheses. If a given theory affords the best explanation possible in terms of the evidence, no matter how fragmentary this evidence may be, then the scientist feels obliged to use it as a working tool. Of course, we have no direct evidence that the account given above is strictly and historically correct, but let us remember the nature of scientific theory. **A good theory is one that accounts for more data than any alternate theory.** In this case, most biologists feel that the **theory of origins** outlined above is the most satisfactory explanation available on the basis of present evidence, even though there is some difference of opinion regarding the details.

Regardless of how they account for origins, virtually all biologists of the present day accept evolution as an explanation of the variety of living forms and their various adaptations to particular environments. This is because certain phenomena encountered in nature are meaningful and explicable *only* if the concept of evolution is accepted. In other words, it is impossible to reconcile the data of comparative morphology and physiology, cytogenetics, and geology with strict creationism, unless one completely abandons and ignores the methods of science. Although we have already considered some of these data in preceding chapters, let us examine certain aspects of those fields that have a special bearing upon evolution.

Some Principles That Support the Evolutionary Concept

As we have intimated, evolution is not a mere speculation that has been devised in order to avoid the alternative of special creationism. It is true that our knowledge is far from complete as to how and in just what directions the process occurred during various periods of time, but that it did occur is no longer a matter of doubt in the light of present-day information. For purposes of discussion, our knowledge regarding evolution may be classified according to these two subjects: resemblances among present-day organisms, and geological evidences of evolution.

RESEMBLANCES AMONG PRESENT-DAY ORGANISMS

Morphological resemblances. There are certain **morphological** resemblances among organisms that indicate close or distant genetic kinship. Some of these are very important taxonomically and have been known to biologists for some time. The study of **comparative anatomy** has revealed many striking examples of similarity. For example, the several systems of the vertebrates, including nervous, skeletal, muscular, excretory, and circulatory systems, show a basic similarity with a gradual increase in structural complexity as one proceeds from the agnathans to the mammals. We called attention to the comparative anatomy of nervous systems in this group previously (Fig. 154), and similar comparisons could be shown for those systems listed and for others. In fact, the study

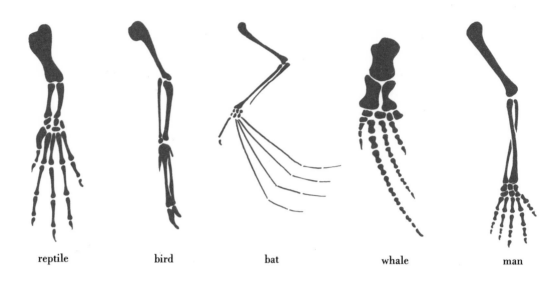

reptile   bird   bat   whale   man

166 A comparison of the forelimbs of various vertebrate animals. Note the general pattern of structure that exists among these homologous organs.

of phylogenetically homologous[1] organs, illustrated for one portion of the vertebrate skeleton in Fig. 166, is very revealing. Upon examination of embryos, it is found that such organs arise in precisely the same manner, indicating that certain gene groups must be shared in common among these animals.

Embryological characteristics are extremely valuable in relating animals in still other ways. The development of a notochord by all chordates, for example, indicates actual genetic kinship among them. Perhaps even more significant is the observation that many organisms develop **vestigial** structures that may disappear during the process of development, or they may persist. All vertebrate embryos, for instance, develop pharyngeal pouches, but these give rise to gills only in the fishes and amphibians. In the reptiles, birds, and mammals, they either disappear or become modified to form other structures. In man, such vestigial structures as the vermiform appendix, the shortened series of tail bones

[1] Homologous organs are those having a similar embryonic origin. Anatomists generally recognize three types of homology, as follows. **Phylogenetic** homology is that existing between different species. The arm of man and the wing of a bird, for example, are phylogenetically homologous. **Sexual** homology is that existing between sexes of the same species; the testes of a man and the ovaries of a woman are sexually homologous organs. **Serial** homology is that existing between organs of the same individual that occupy different levels of the body, such as the arm and leg of man.

(coccyx) and certain non-functional muscles indicate a degeneration of these parts from ancestral groups in which they were useful. Only if such morphological resemblances as these are interpreted according to an evolutionary concept do they become meaningful since creationism is at a loss to explain the significance of such similarities.

Physiological resemblances. There are **physiological** resemblances that are also of significance to our discussion. For example, certain parasites attack only organisms that bear a close resemblance to each other, and this indicates a similarity in body chemistry. Races of wheat rust, for instance, attack other cereal grains such as barley, rye, and oats, all of which are much like wheat in their external morphology. Undoubtedly, these grains bear a closer evolutionary kinship to each other than to plants that are not attacked by the rust. Among the mammals, endocrine glands and their secretions are sufficiently similar that hormones from one animal may be used to treat deficiency diseases in another. For years, before insulin was synthesized in the laboratory, this hormone was extracted from pancreatic tissue of the sheep and used to alleviate the sufferings of diabetic humans. Apparently, some identical genes exist in the human and other mammals which control the formation and function of the endocrine portion of the pancreas.

Among the most significant of all physiological resemblances (and differences) are those indicated by **comparative serological tests,** that is, the comparison of body fluids according to their respective chemical natures. In vertebrate animals, for example, the introduction of any protein into the blood stream of an animal in which that protein is not found causes a reaction to occur. The foreign protein in this case is called an **antigen,** and it elicits the production of counteracting substances, called **antibodies,** by the affected animal. This phenomenon of antigen-antibody reaction has very important implications for the production of animal diseases, since infectious microorganisms may possess or produce proteins that are antigenic to a host. Many diseases of the human, for example, may be prevented by artificially causing the production of antibodies through vaccination, thus effecting immunization against a given disease. This is made possible through the use of disease organisms that have been killed or modified so that they stimulate production of antibodies without producing the actual disease. For purposes of our present discussion, however, we are interested in antigen-antibody reactions as a tool for determining degrees of genetic kinship.

Serological testing is based on the principle that antibodies against the body fluids of a given animal react more strongly with the body fluids of animals closely related to it, and less strongly, in general proportion to morphological dissimilarity, with the fluids of distantly related ones. In practice, a test is conducted as follows. Let us suppose that we inject some blood from a dog into a rabbit. The rabbit gradually develops antibodies which will **precipitate** the foreign proteins out of solution should there be a second inoculation; these antibodies build up in the fluid portion (serum) of the rabbit's blood stream. If some of the blood from this rabbit is taken and the serum is separated from the other components of the blood, it can be used as an antiserum, and further reactions can be brought about in test tubes. Upon mixing some of this antiserum (developed in the rabbit) with the sera of other members of the order Carnivora, to which dogs belong, it is found that a gradation of responses occurs. A stronger reaction, shown by a greater degree of precipitation, is seen when the serum of a wolf is mixed with the antiserum than when that of a cat is used, and it is still less severe (or nonexistent) in animals that bear little morphological resemblance to dogs, such as horses or monkeys (Fig. 167).

In general, serological tests have only verified what was already known from comparative morphology, but there is an extremely important principle here. According to the concept of evolution, we would predict that morphological and serological resemblances and differences should agree, and this has proved to be the case almost without exception in the hundreds of species that have been tested. Hence, as a working theory regarding the origin of species, evolution is quite satisfactory because it is reliable in prediction. Furthermore, serological testing has been invaluable to taxonomy since it has helped to establish natural relationships among animals, and a variation of it has even been developed for plants. Since genes control protein synthesis, it seems evident that dogs and wolves share more of the same genes than do dogs and cats, for example, since dogs and cats show a greater diversity in their body proteins. Only if it is assumed that these genes had a common origin in the genotype of some remote ancestor do comparative serological tests and their results become meaningful.

Cytogenetic resemblances. It will have occurred to the student by this time that degrees of resemblance among organisms depend upon similarities and differences in genotypes. Hence, the morphological and physiological relationships discussed are, in the final analysis, genetic ones. There are certain relationships among organisms, however, that are more fundamentally related to genetics or to cytology than these. For example, the fruit fly *Drosophila* has been extensively studied cytogenetically, and the several species within the genus exhibit some interesting similarities. Some species can be induced to interbreed, with varying degrees of success as to survival and fertility of offspring. Other species will not interbreed under any conditions, even though they may be virtually indistinguishable to the eye. It is significant that when chromosomes from various species of the genus are stained and observed, they resemble

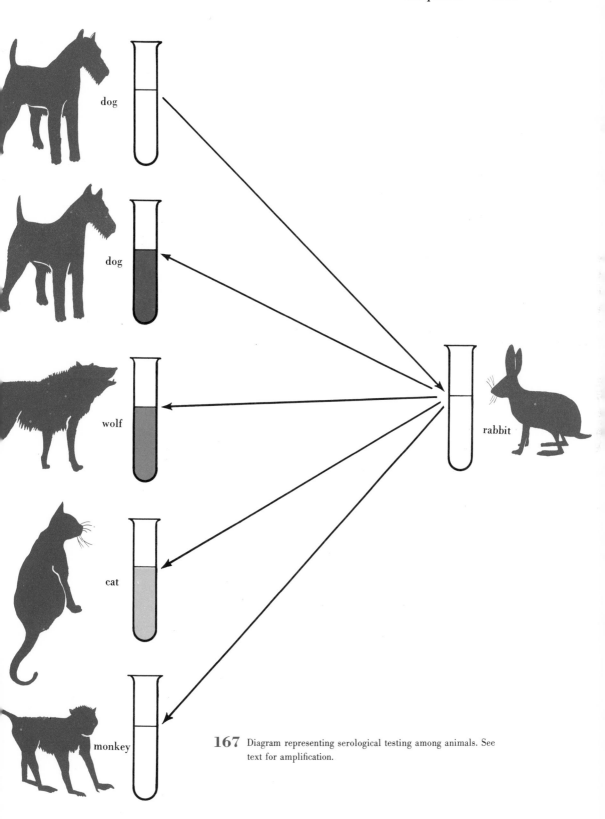

167 Diagram representing serological testing among animals. See text for amplification.

each other very closely; interbreeding species generally show more similarity in this respect than do non-interbreeding ones. It so happens that the chromosomes of these insects can be studied very profitably in regard to the presence of certain visible regions. Interbreeding species are quite similar in the possession of "landmarks" on their chromosomes, whereas those of non-interbreeding species differ markedly. Other cytological and genetic resemblances or differences have been studied closely, and the evidence is overwhelming that these several species share a common ancestry.

On the basis of cytogenetic knowledge, species have actually been "synthesized," which is proof that the concept of evolution, or change in nature, is a valid scientific principle. For example, in 1932 a Swedish geneticist, Arne Müntzing, reported his research in species synthesis using the hemp nettle, *Galeopsis*. He observed that one species, *G. tetrahit*, exhibited sixteen pairs of chromosomes, and that other species possessed eight pairs. Müntzing chose two of these eight-pair species, *G. pubescens* and *G. speciosa*, both of which resemble *G. tetrahit* very closely, and undertook to interbreed them. His efforts were successful, and the resulting offspring were morphologically indistinguishable from the *G. tetrahit* of nature. Thus, he reasoned that *G. tetrahit* had arisen in nature from a cross between the other two species, and that in egg fertilization, **polyploidy** had occurred.[2] In order to test this hypothesis, he crossed his new species with the natural *G. tetrahit*, and found them to be interfertile. Not only was this the case, but their seeds germinated to produce normal *G. tetrahit* plants. That *G. tetrahit* could be called a true species, not a variety, was shown in that neither the naturally occurring type nor the synthetic one could be made to interbreed with either *G. pubescens* or *G. speciosa*. In this fashion, Müntzing actually showed that evolution occurs, and he successfully demonstrated one of the mechanisms by which it comes about.

As is the case with morphological and physiological resemblances among organisms of different species, cytogenetic ones provide very good evidence of close or distant relationships. Unless evolution did occur, such resemblances or differences are entirely without meaning.

[2] The phenomenon of polyploidy occurs in plants, rarely in animals, whenever there is a multiplication of whole chromosome "sets." The most common method in nature seems to be that gametes from two plants that are members of different but closely related species fuse successfully, with each haploid "set" of chromosomes subsequently undergoing duplication. Polyploidy is fairly readily induced in many cultivated plants by the use of certain techniques, and it seems to occur often in nature. It is a very useful phenomenon, frequently resulting in varieties or species of cultivated plants which are more productive than ordinary diploid ones. All commercially valuable varieties of wheat, for example, are polyploids.

(a)

(b)

168 Fossil animals. a, an insect. b, a fish. These fossils are probably about 50,000,000 years old. (Courtesy General Biological Supply House, Inc.)

GEOLOGICAL EVIDENCES OF EVOLUTION. Geology, which is the study of the earth and its history, provides a great many clues to the process of evolution. In fact, of all the natural phenomena which indicate that such a process has occurred, those which are geological in nature are perhaps the most convincing of all. We shall call attention to some of the most important of these phenomena.

The fossil record. When organisms die, their bodies decompose under most conditions within a relatively short space of time, and no trace of them remains. There are some exceptions to this rule, however. They may be preserved entirely or in part by some means, or **imprints** of the organism may be preserved. Such **fossils** (Fig. 168) are the materials of that joint field of biology and geology known as **paleontology,** and in spite of the principle that relatively few plants and animals leave any sort of fossil record, sufficient kinds and numbers have been found and studied to lend considerable support to the evolutionary concept.

In the past, many living forms have died under such conditions that their bodies became covered with various sediments. Where the exclusion of oxygen was sufficiently complete as to prevent decay, a given organism would be entombed and fossilized. As layer after layer of deposited material covered the organism, with other organisms being fossilized in each succeeding layer, a fairly accurate record of living forms belonging to the region, over time, was established. By digging down through successive strata of deposits in a great many different areas, paleontologists have been able to gain a fair impression of the fossil record.

As might be expected, there is a general trend toward structural simplicity of fossil organisms as one proceeds from the surface of a deposit to greater depths. Among animal fossils, for example, only invertebrates appear in the lowest and most ancient strata. These are followed by primitive fish-like vertebrates, then by true fishes, and eventually by amphibians and reptiles. Birds and mammals are the last to appear, and in the youngest strata, fossilized representatives of these two groups resemble present-day forms more than do the earlier ones. Similarly, fossilized plants show a definite pattern in the correlation of complexity and order of appearance. In spite of the incompleteness of the fossil record, since some organisms did not lend themselves readily to fossilization, enough has been discovered to establish general evolutionary trends.

The estimation of time. How, it might be asked, can geologists establish time scales whereby it may be known that various fossil organisms lived during certain ages? This is a very important question mostly because no one location on earth has been found to contain strata representing all geological periods, and comparisons must be made in order that a true picture can be gained. Of the several factors that are indicative of geological time, the following are outstanding. At least, they should serve to satisfy the student that geologists have not merely guessed at the matter.

One class of rocks, the **sedimentary** rocks, are formed by the accumulation of eroded materials and various sediments that settle out. On the basis of time measurements, present rates of sedimentary rock formation are known rather accurately. If it is assumed that rates of sedimentation have always been about the same, then some estimation of ages of sedimentary rock deposits (which often contain fossils) may be made. Unfortunately for the accuracy of this method, it is not certain that these rates have always been the same. In a comparative way, however, by establishing relationships between strata of different areas, this method of dating is quite valuable. Consequently, it provides a rough indication of just how long ago a given fossil became entombed. By this means, it has been possible to determine with some accuracy the age of any given stratum of sedimentary rock and to relate it to a comparable stratum. At the very least, *relative* ages of fossil organisms may be established.

Early in the present century, a more accurate method of dating materials was developed. This is called the **uranium-lead method,** and it depends upon the principle that uranium, which is a radioactive element,[3] disintegrates at a constant rate to form lead and helium. It is

---

[3] A radioactive element is one whose atoms are unstable, disintegrating at a certain rate to form stable elements of less complex atomic structure.

known that through such spontaneous decomposition a given deposit of uranium loses half its weight in 4,500,000,000 years. This loss is accounted for by the presence of a certain quantity of lead. Since the rate of lead formation under these circumstances is thus known, the age of a rock can be determined rather accurately by comparing the weights of uranium and lead which are present in the rock. Fortunately for the accuracy of this method, a newly-crystallized rock contains only uranium, no lead from previous disintegration, and the time that the rock was originally formed may thus be determined. Now let us suppose that a fossil organism is present in the rock, or in one of a comparable stratum. This means that it was trapped within the rock at the same time as the uranium, and its age is thus determinable.

Unfortunately, uranium is relatively rare, and those rocks we would like most to date seldom contain it. However, the uranium-lead method has proved to be highly valuable, particularly in telling us something of the age of the earth and of the probable time that life has existed on it. Furthermore, methods of dating have been developed that depend upon other radioactive elements than uranium. One of the most useful of these is the **radiocarbon method.** It depends upon the principle that of the carbon utilized by organisms, a small but constant proportion is radioactive. A given quantity of radioactive carbon loses half its weight in about 5,760 years. This means that a material such as bone, leather, or wood, which at one time formed a part of a living organism, can be analyzed for the amount of radioactive carbon present. This may be compared with the amount present in a *fresh* piece of similar material, and the age of the test piece can be determined by computation. This method is highly accurate, since tests involving materials of known age, such as manuscripts written on animal skins, show that estimated age agrees very closely with known age.

The accuracy of the radiocarbon method is limited, unfortunately, to materials that are no more than about 40,000 years old. Nevertheless, it has proved to be quite valuable in dating fossils of recent periods of time, and doubtless its applicability to paleontological problems will eventually be increased. Thus far, it has been extremely valuable in solving a number of archeological problems in regard to the ages of certain civilizations and in determining the ages of recently fossilized organisms.

On the basis of all methods of estimating geological time, there is no doubt that evolution has occurred over a period of many millions of years. In fact, paleontologists are fairly certain of the periods of time that various organisms first appeared on earth and when some of them vanished. Table II summarizes estimates that are now generally accepted as being reasonably accurate ones.

TABLE II. GEOLOGIC TIME, THE EARTH, AND THE RISE OF LIVING FORMS.

Era	Period	Time*	Environmental Conditions	Biotic Development
Cenozoic	Quaternary	1	Successive ice ages; after last one (25,000 years ago) climate warmer.	Man and other placental mammals dominate scene; many plants and animals become extinct.
	Tertiary	60	Rise of Alps and Himalayas; climate growing colder.	Man evolved; mammals become dominant animals. Forests become widespread.
Mesozoic	Cretaceous	130	Rise of Rockies and Andes; inland swamps common.	Dinosaurs flourish and become extinct; gymnosperms decline.
	Jurassic	155	Continents high and small, much of present area submerged under sea.	Rise of marsupial mammals; rise of angiosperms from gymnosperms.
	Triassic	185	Great desert areas prevail.	Rise of dinosaurs, birds, and egg-laying mammals. Gymnosperms dominant plants.
Paleozoic	Permian	210	Rise of mountains; glaciers and deserts become common.	Rise of mammal-like reptiles; decline of dominant fern-like plants.
	Carboniferous	265	Climate warm and humid, becoming cooler; coal deposits formed.	Rise of reptiles; fern-like plants and gymnosperms form great forests.
	Devonian	320	Inland seas grow smaller; glaciers and deserts form.	Rise of amphibians; first vascular plants. Fishes widespread.
	Silurian	360	Rise of large land areas with great inland seas; continental seas large.	Rise of insects, fish species become very numerous; algae are dominant plants.
	Ordovician	440	Land extensively submerged; climate very warm over entire earth.	Rise of fishes; many species of invertebrates widespread. Rise of land plants.
	Cambrian	520	Lands very low, climate mild.	Rise of primitive vertebrates and protochordates; algae widespread.
Pre-Cambrian†		1000	Extremely violent conditions, involving volcanos, glaciers, and unstable atmospheric conditions.	Rise of algae, fungi and modern invertebrates. No fossil record. It is assumed that first living forms developed less than 2 billion years ago.
		2000		

* Estimated time in millions of years, measuring from beginning of the period or era to the present.

† The term "Pre-Cambrian" is not used by geologists to represent an era; it simply denotes time that existed previous to the Cambrian Period. Although the universe is probably some five billion years old or more, Pre-Cambrian time is usually considered that which began about two billion years ago.

Mechanisms of Evolution

Probably, there have been evolutionists ever since man first began to contemplate nature, but it was not until the nineteenth century that very much serious observation and experimentation in this direction was carried out. One of the first biologists to develop any sort of theory in regard to the origin of adaptations was Jean Baptiste Lamarck (1744–1829). In 1809, this French biologist published a theory of evolution based on the use and disuse of parts. It was supposed by him that the continual use of a body structure on the part of an organism would strengthen and perhaps enlarge the structure and that this modification would then be inherited. This would explain the length of a rabbit's ears, that of the neck of a giraffe, or the long talons of an eagle. Known today as the theory of **inheritance of acquired characteristics,** Lamarck's theory is unacceptable to modern biologists. However, it must be remembered that it was almost a century after Lamarck that genes and their role in inheritance were known, and it is worthy of note that any biologist would recognize the principle of evolution and attempt an explanation of the forces responsible for it. Although his was an inadequate explanation, Lamarck did much to focus the attention of other biologists upon the problem.

THE LIMITING FORCE—NATURAL SELECTION. It remained for Charles Darwin (1809–1882), an English biologist, to shape his observations and researches of some twenty years into a reasonable and acceptable theory of evolution. In 1859, he published *The Origin of Species,* a book which doubtless had a greater impact upon biological thought than any single writing prior to it. In fact, it created such a public sensation that many fields other than biology became profoundly influenced by it.[4] Essentially, Darwin's book advanced the concept of **natural selection** as an explanation of how evolution has occurred (or, to express it another way, how adaptations have arisen). In explanation of natural selection as a force in evolution, Darwin called attention to the following:

(1) *Overproduction.* The reproductive potential of organisms runs far ahead of available food and space.

(2) *Variation.* Within a reproducing population, offspring show numerous differences.

(3) *Competition.* Because there are more individuals than an environment can support, there is a struggle for existence.

---

[4] Some of the influences which Darwin's theory of evolution had upon other fields are discussed in Chapter 10.

(4) *Survival of the fittest.* The variations within species provide some individuals with advantages which enable them to live longer and produce more offspring than some others.

(5) *Inheritance of superior traits.* The advantages which the surviving individuals enjoy are passed on to their offspring.

In the main, these five points, or principles, are obviously valid when taken separately. In fact, it is difficult to question their operation together. That natural selection is a force in nature could not be intelligently denied by Darwin's contemporaries, and most biologists were soon won to his point of view. Whether or not they agreed with Darwin in every detail, most informed people of the late nineteenth century were convinced that evolution had occurred. This was largely because a vast amount of evidence was accumulating from such fields as paleontology and comparative morphology that made creationism, the other alternative, seem ineffectual as an explanation of living forms and their various adaptations.

Although Darwin's work was a step in the right direction, his theory that natural selection is sufficient to explain evolution contains some rather serious difficulties. One of these is that Darwin was unable to distinguish between **acquired** traits and **inheritable** ones. After all, Mendelian genetics did not come into its own until some four decades after *The Origin of Species* was published, and Darwin had no real basis upon which to make proper distinctions. His own theory of inheritance, which he knew to be inadequate, was actually a modification of Lamarck's. More serious than this, however, is the principle that natural selection is by its very nature a **limiting** force, not an **initiating** one. For example, let us suppose that one bird of a given species happens to be born with extra large wings. Assuming that within the limits of its particular environment this gives the bird an advantage in escaping from its enemies, it will live to reproduce after many of its less adept kinsmen have been caught and eaten. Assuming further that the extra wing size is genetically controlled, any offspring inheriting the gene or genes involved will prove to be superior, and the trait will gradually become widespread in the species. Hence, natural selection becomes, in this case, a force in evolution. Nevertheless, how did the trait appear in the first place? Certainly, the bird did not analyze the situation and decide to grow larger wings in order that it might be more successful. Even man, with his superior intellect, cannot "will" a genetic change. It is at this point that natural selection fails to explain evolution. In other words, natural selection controls the direction of evolution once a change occurs in a species, *but it cannot initiate changes.*

THE INITIATING FORCE—MUTATION. Since Darwin's time, the phenomenon of **mutation** has been discovered and studied extensively. A mutation is a change in a gene, and although genes are highly stable, reliably duplicating themselves with fine exactness, every now and then a mutation does occur. This may be due to some fault of genic reproduction; for example, the "wrong" nucleotide may somehow be substituted for the original one somewhere in the gene. Another explanation for mutation is that a chance "hit" on some portion of the gene by a high-energy radiation particle may cause a chemical change. Experimentally, mutation rates may be increased many fold by the use of such radiations. At any rate, genes are not completely stable, and when a gene mutates, its new form is as faithfully duplicated in cell division as was the old one.

If a mutation occurs in non-reproductive cells of an organism, there is neither genetic nor evolutionary significance to the event. Any resulting changes spread no farther than such cells as may be produced from this cell, and effects are thus localized. In other words, the mutation, whether potentially advantageous or detrimental to the organism, is of necessity lost to the species when its bearer dies. However, if a mutation occurs in a reproductive cell which becomes involved in the formation of a new individual, there is a chance that it may produce significant effects in the species. It so happens that most mutations are harmful ones; a mutant gene may change the smooth balance of factors concerned with development so radically, for example, that the bearer does not even survive until birth. In other instances, mutant genes may be responsible for structural or functional abnormalities.[5] It should not be difficult to see why most mutations are harmful; after all, the thousands of genes that contribute to the genetic make-up of a complex organism are of necessity highly coordinated. Over long periods of time, the species of which it is a member has adjusted to its environment and is obviously successful to some degree, or it would be extinct. The chances are considerably greater that a chance mutation will upset this fine adjustment rather than make it finer. To draw an analogy, it is conceivable that one might improve the efficiency of a highly organized machine by throwing a heavy wrench into ts gears, but the chances are much greater that such action will only ucceed in tearing up the machine.

[5] Of course, if the "new" gene were recessive to its normal allele, as most mutant genes are, it would be carried in the heterozygous condition and would not appear until a combination of two such genes occurred. Because there is a good chance that any given human gamete may carry a harmful recessive mutation, laws forbidding the marriage of two persons who are closely kin are genetically sound since this sort of mating provides an opportunity for two recessives originating in a common ancestor by mutation to come together in the homozygous condition.

Nevertheless, an advantageous mutation does appear sometimes in a species, and when this occurs, there is a chance that it may become a part of the stable genotype through the process of natural selection. Thus, over long periods of time, species may change for the better *in terms of ecological success* through the accumulation of few to many advantageous mutations.

ISOLATION MECHANISMS. The appearance of new species in nature seems to depend largely upon the development of **sub-species.** Let us suppose, for example, that a new mutation or a series of mutations appear within a population.[6] Assuming that these mutations were to become established in the population, this still would not alter the entire species in its total distribution. It would merely tend to separate this one population from others through genetic isolation (inability of one population to interbreed successfully with another population). Given enough time and with complete isolation, this population might become sufficiently different to be called a new species.

The original isolation might have been a purely geographical one. For example, populations may become separated by water or land barriers and thus are obliged to go their separate evolutionary ways. Chance mutations then effect such restrictions that if the populations are again thrown together, mating will not occur. Or, even if it does, differences in genic and chromosomal arrangements preclude interfertility. We have already called attention to the fact that several degrees of such genetic isolation have occurred in the genus *Drosophila*. It should be noted that genetic isolation resulting in the rise of a sub-species (partial genetic isolation) and then a species (complete genetic isolation) may take a tremendously long time. It has been estimated that, on the average, establishment of a new species in nature by this route takes something like one million years. Accustomed as we are to thinking in terms of much shorter periods of time, it is small wonder that many people fail to grasp or to appreciate the process of evolution. ·

Perhaps we are in position now to formulate a better definition of the species on the basis of genetical and evolutionary concepts than was supplied tentatively in Chapter 4. At least among sexually reproducing organisms, we can say that **a species is a group of similar organisms which are actually or potentially capable of successful interbreeding with the production of fertile offspring.** However, it must be remembered that it is rather difficult to determine the exact point at which a population becomes a sub-species, or just when a sub-species becomes a species. For this reason, students of speciation and evolution

[6] A population is a group of individuals belonging to the same species which occupy some definite environmental area.

constantly face a great many problems both in their studies of natural groupings and in their agreement on definitions at all levels.

The Course of Evolution

On the basis of available evidence from paleontology, evolution has proceeded very much according to the pathways diagrammed in Fig. 168. Unfortunately, the fossil record does not extend as far back as a billion years, and even in rocks that can be identified as being almost this old, recognizable fossils are rather scarce. Organic materials found in older rocks, however, indicate that life originated considerably more than a billion years ago. Beginning with rocks that are almost a billion years old, enough fossils have been uncovered to enable paleontologists to establish a general pattern. Figure 169 indicates probable origins and relationships of only major plant and animal groups; for further details regarding any particular group, the student is urged to consult a textbook of paleontology or evolution.

It should be pointed out that many animal and plant groups have arisen and have later become extinct. No attempt is made in Fig. 169 to indicate these groups, but many are well known to paleontologists. One of the best-known examples of extinction is the case of the dinosaurs, a group of giant reptiles that flourished during the Mesozoic era. Apparently, they were unable to meet the general environmental and biotic changes that occurred during this time, and they ultimately perished. Undoubtedly, this pattern of the rise and fall of species (and more inclusive taxonomic categories) has played an important role in the process of evolution.

The pattern of evolution, then, should be visualized as a branching tree whose separations into more and more diverse groups have continued over tremendous periods of time to the present day. According to this concept, no present-day species necessarily ascended (or descended) from any other present-day species, but groups of organisms that are closely related structurally and functionally share a common ancestry. In the final analysis, of course, all organisms of the present day share a common ancestry through the primeval life which apparently originated some two billion years ago or less.

Summary

The world of life as we know it today is the result of a long process of evolution. A great many present-day species have endured for long periods of time without appreciable change, whereas others are relatively new.

Attention has been called repeatedly in this book to the principle

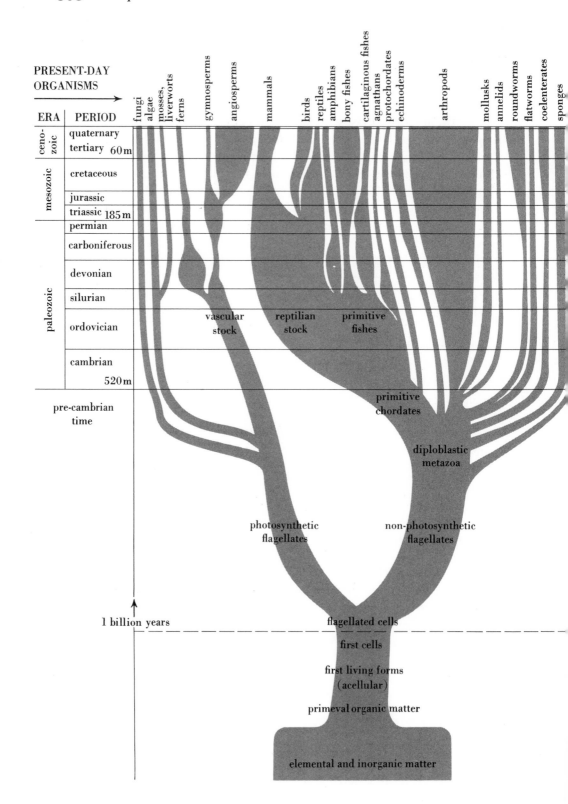

169 The course of evolution, indicating approximate time a group of modern organisms arose and something of relative numbers of extant species. Because pre-Cambrian fossils are rare, that portion of this diagram is built largely upon inference.

that certain biological mechanisms are shared either by all organisms or by large groups. For example, the ATP-ADP energy system, mitosis, meiosis, and photosynthesis apparently are such successful adaptations that, once having appeared, they became firmly established as a way of life. In the light of the evolutionary concept, it is most significant that organisms share so many fundamental processes in common. Since all living processes are controlled by genes, in the final analysis, this indicates that there are some which are shared, perhaps in identical DNA structure, by all living forms.

CONCLUSION

The most important single aspect of adaptation as a characteristic of living forms is that it is a *process,* and it is one that occurs over time. The mechanism of adaptation is evolution, and the chief mechanisms of evolution are mutation (the initiating force) and natural selection (the limiting force). Separate *adaptations,* then, have resulted from the entire process, and any given species has accumulated numbers of these through heredity. Slowly but surely, therefore, the accumulation of genes which control the development and function of these adaptations has made any given species what it is today.

It has been pointed out that metabolism, growth, reproduction, and responsiveness are characteristics of protoplasmic systems as such. Adaptation, in contrast, is not a characteristic that can be readily demonstrated in the laboratory, although such work as that of Müntzing on *Galeopsis* (called **species synthesis**) does constitute a demonstration of evolution. One must visualize the process of adaptation as an inherently long-range characteristic the results of which, but not many of the specific operations of which, can be seen. Thus, we know that organisms have adapted through evolution, but we did not see them adapt. Nevertheless, it is possible to trace the adaptations of populations through careful statistical studies, and we are not entirely in the dark as to the workings of the process. Of much more value to us in this respect, of course, are the evidences of evolution (such as the fossil record) which were presented earlier in this chapter.

Let us make one final observation in regard to adaptation. In the over-all analysis, the characteristics of metabolism, growth, reproduction, and responsiveness are adaptive since the mechanisms involved within a given organism accumulated through evolution. For example, we have chosen in this book to discuss mechanisms of heredity within the framework of reproduction. Actually, it is an important part of adaptation, since the segregation of genes in meiosis and their recombination in fertilization determine to a great extent the role that an individual will play in its environment. Again, the same might be said for mechanisms of responsiveness, growth, or metabolism. It is the whole organism and the species to which it belongs that must survive and reproduce in its environment, and it is only within limits set for teaching purposes that we are justified in viewing the world of life from the standpoint of five characteristics. Books, not organisms, are separated into chapters. The phenomenon called life is dependent for its maintenance and perpetuation upon the coordination of all protoplasmic and organismal mechanisms, and it is only through this concept that we can view the world of life meaningfully.

Having given some attention to each of the five characteristics of living forms that were presented early in this book, and with the observation that these characteristics are highly coordinated in the organism, we bring to a close the purely informational aspect of our subject. How does this body of knowledge (which has been presented only in survey within this brief text) relate to all knowledge, and what is its significance to man as a species? We shall seek some of the answers to these questions in the next, and final, chapter.

QUESTIONS

Multiple Choice

1. A wolf pack constitutes (a) a society, (b) an aggregation, (c) a population, (d) two of these, (e) all of these.

2. Which of the following most adequately defines organic evolution? (a) Life may arise from previously non-living material; (b) Life may not arise from previously non-living material; (c) Present-day organisms are the descendants of simpler ancestors; (d) Man descended from the apes; (e) life originated in the primeval seas some two billion years ago.

3. The initiating force of evolution is (a) adaptation, (b) natural selection, (c) mutation, (d) competition, (e) extinction.

4. Commercial nurserymen sometimes induce plants to bloom out of season. In doing this, they utilize the principle of (a) photoperiodicity, (b) phototropism, (c) physiological adaptation, (d) geotropism, (e) temperature regulation.

5. Barnacles sometimes attach to the skin of whales, by virtue of which they derive benefit without harming the whales. This is an example of (a) mutualism, (b) commensalism, (c) parasitism, (d) adaptability, (e) competition.

6. In which of the relationships above does the tapeworm relate itself to man and other higher animals?

7. Whenever a multiplication of whole chromosome "sets" occurs in an organism, which of the following is said to have occurred? (a) adaptation, (b) adaptability, (c) evolution, (d) polyploidy, (e) parthenogenesis.

8. Uranium disintegrates at a known rate to form helium and (a) hydrogen, (b) carbon, (c) radium, (d) zinc, (e) lead.

9. Which of the elements above is involved in a method of dating whose reliability is limited to materials that are no more than about 40,000 years old?

10. Which of the following men is associated with the theory of the inheritance of acquired characteristics? (a) Darwin, (b) Lamarck, (c) Müntzing, (d) Mendel, (e) Linnaeus.

11. Most mutant genes are (a) harmful to the bearer, (b) beneficial to the bearer, (c) neither harmful nor beneficial to the bearer, (d) about equally distributed in terms of harm or benefit.

12. Evidence indicates that life originated in which of the following eras? (a) Paleozoic, (b) Mesozoic, (c) Cenozoic, (d) none of these.

13. Which of the following evolved first? (a) fishes, (b) amphibians (c) reptiles, (d) birds, (e) mammals.

14. Nitrogen becomes available to crop plants in the form of (a) urea, (b) ammonia, (c) nitrites, (d) nitrates, (e) amino acids.

15. Carbon becomes available to crop plants in the form of (a) monosaccharides, (b) amino acids, (c) elemental carbon, (d) carbonates, (e) carbon dioxide.

16. The law of the minimum holds that (a) when life originated, organic molecules were at a minimum in nature; (b) only a minimum number of potential offspring in a species can survive; (c) only a small percentage of the original energy is found at the top of a pyramid of numbers; (d) unless all its requirements are met, an organism cannot survive and flourish; (e) most mutations are harmful to their bearer.

17. In an aqueous environment, microscopic plants and animals are collectively known as (a) parasites, (b) commensals, (c) carnivores, (d) herbivores, (e) plankton.

18. Which of the above refers to animals whose diet consists of plants?

19. Darwin's theory of inheritance was (a) essentially the same as the modern interpretation, (b) essentially the same as Mendel's interpretation, (c) a modification of Lamarck's theory, (d) the strongest part of his argument, (e) based on mutation as an initiating force in evolution.

20. In terms of the theory of origins, the first organisms must have been (a) autotrophs, (b) phagotrophs, (c) heterotrophs, (d) parasites, (e) carnivores.

True-false

1. Of all animals, only birds and mammals are able to maintain constant body temperatures.

2. Competition is seen only between members of different species; members of the same species never compete.

3. In a food chain, the longer the chain, the more there is to show for energy stored by the producers in the chain.

4. With a very few exceptions, predators are all animals.

5. Lice, ticks, and leeches are representative endoparasites.

6. Most biologists were creationistic in their philosophy until as late as the middle of the nineteenth century.

7. The concept of evolution is completely irreconcilable with the concept of God.

8. The wing of a bird and the forelimb of a cat are phylogenetically homologous organs.

9. The hemp nettle, *Galeopsis*, was used in an experiment, cited in this chapter, to exemplify physiological resemblances as a proof of evolution.

10. As one proceeds from the surface of a fossil deposit to greater depths, there is a general trend toward structural simplicity of organisms.

11. Darwin based his theory of evolution on one force: mutation.

12. According to modern interpretation, the giraffe has a long neck because its ancestors, seeing the advantages to such a structure, began to grow accordingly.

13. A population is the sum total of all organisms occupying a given environment.

14. The five major premises of Darwin's theory are not questioned by present-day biologists as being valid.

15. Virtually all modern biologists are evolutionists.

16. In the final analysis, the characteristics of metabolism, growth, reproduction, and responsiveness are included in the characteristic of adaptation.

17. All vertebrates possess gills at some stage of development.

18. Laws forbidding the marriage of two people who are closely kin have no real genetic basis.

19. If a rabbit is immunized against the serum of a dog, the serum of the rabbit then reacts more strongly with that of a cat than with that of a wolf.

20. Apparently, Darwin failed to appreciate the principle that natural selection is a limiting, not an initiating force in nature.

Questions for Consideration and Discussion

1. Advance some possible reasons why the fossil record is no more complete than it is.

2. What is a comparative serological test? How is it valuable to the evolutionist? To the taxonomist?

3. What are the three major environmental factors with which the ecologist is concerned? Give an example of adaptation to each from both the plant and animal kingdoms.

4. In what sense is adaptation a *process?* In what sense may adaptation be the *result* of a process?

5. Give an example of the following relationships: mutualism, commensalism, parasitism.

6. Why is natural selection inadequate as a complete explanation of evolution? Does natural selection play any part at all in evolution?

7. What experiments have been performed that partially clarify the manner by which life may have originated?

8. How may predation actually be beneficial to man under certain circumstances?

9. Arrange the following in the order they apparently evolved: amphibians, fishes, echinoderms, sponges, birds, reptiles, angiosperms, gymnosperms, mosses, fungi.

10. To what extent do you believe that evolution and creationism can be reconciled?

REFERENCES

DODSON, E. O., *Evolution: Process and Product.* New York: Reinhold Publishing Corporation, 1960. An orderly presentation of the basic principles of evolution.

HUXLEY, J. S. *Evolution: The Modern Synthesis.* New York: Harper & Brothers Publishers, 1943. A classic in evolutionary thought.

ODUM, E. P. *Fundamentals of Ecology*, 2nd ed. Philadelphia: W. B. Saunders Company. 1959. Additional reading in this textbook of general ecology will help the student in regard to this field.

SIMPSON, G. G., *The Major Features of Evolution.* New York: Columbia University Press. 1953. An outstanding book on the subject.

STOKES, W. L. *Essentials of Earth History.* Englewood Cliffs, N.J.: Prentice-Hall, Inc. 1960. The student who wishes to know more about paleontology will find this to be an excellent reference.

WALLACE, BRUCE and **A. M. SRB.** *Adaptation.* Englewood Cliffs, N.J.: Prentice-Hall, Inc. 1961. This book, one of the FOUNDATIONS OF MODERN BIOLOGY series, is recommended in its entirety for this chapter.

In addition to the books above, the following articles from *Scientific American* are recommended.

DEEVEY, E. S. "Radiocarbon Dating," Volume 186 (February, 1952), p. 24. The general principles of radiocarbon dating are explained.

GLAESSNER, M. F. "Precambrian Animals," Volume 204 (March, 1961), p. 72. This article, which tells of the discovery of fossils over half a billion years old, is of value at this point in regard to paleontology and its methods.

WALD, GEORGE. "The Origin of Life," Volume 191 (August, 1954), p. 44. An account of the processes which may have given rise to life on earth.

WENT, F. W. "The Ecology of Desert Plants," Volume 192 (April, 1955), p. 68. An interesting interpretation of adaptation and the struggle for existence in the desert.

CHAPTER 10

Biology, Evolution and Human Affairs

At one time in the history of civilization, a learned man made little attempt to become an intellectual specialist; he merely served his society as a **philosopher** and was interested in all knowledge. Although the modern philosopher still serves in something of the same capacity, attempting to coordinate the several intellectual areas into a meaningful whole, most present-day scholars feel obliged to concentrate on one particular field such as biology, sociology, or mathematics.

In one sense, this specialization is unfortunate because it deprives the specialist of a broad view which might help him to communicate more easily with other specialists. Furthermore, his own field frequently suffers from sheer isolation. Since human knowledge is now so vast, such a system of specialization is inevitable, but no intellectual person should cut himself off from fields other than his own. Furthermore, it is particularly important that the student, in seeking a broad or generalized education, attempt to relate his several studies to each other. Regardless of how much he may specialize later, his undergraduate education should be directed toward an understanding of his world as a whole and not toward isolated aspects of it.

This final chapter, then, represents an effort to relate the subject matter that has been presented thus far to at least some other areas of learning. At the same time, it should be of value to examine certain philosophical implications of biology.

BIOLOGY AND EVOLUTION

Biology has always been an important science from the practical standpoint, serving as it does such applied fields as agriculture and medicine. Furthermore, man himself is an organism, and the principles and laws that he formulates in regard to other organisms usually have an important bearing on his own welfare. Psychology and medical research have utilized this principle very effectively through the experimental approach based on the reactions of laboratory animals to conditions set by the researcher.

Although these practical contributions of biology to the welfare of mankind are highly important, it is in an altogether different realm that biology has made its greatest impact upon society—the realm of ideas. An idea or a great conceptual scheme in any field that catches the imagination and proves to be productive of other ideas or technological developments is always of far-reaching importance, and all too seldom are such conceptual schemes formulated. Thus far in biology, there has been one outstanding idea (among less engaging but perhaps equally important ideas) that has had a profound influence upon human thought, and this is the concept of evolution. It is to this subject that we shall now turn our attention.

Evolution and Man

It was mentioned in the preceding chapter that Darwin initiated something of an intellectual revolution in 1859 by publishing *The Origin of Species.* Historians are aware that a number of factors were responsible for the general public reaction to this book, and many of these could be discussed at this point very profitably. However, two reasons for this reaction seem outstanding. First of all, the concept of evolution, which was not widely accepted by lay persons at that time, stood out in direct opposition to the literal interpretation of the Genesis account of creation which was almost universally accepted in those countries that were predominantly Christian in their religion. We shall defer a discussion of this factor until later. The second factor, and one that was more fully emphasized in a later book by Darwin, *The Descent of Man,* was that evolution reached by implication and by direct evidence to man himself, reducing his biological nature to the level of other higher animals.

It is quite understandable that in Darwin's day, and especially in mid-nineteenth century England, this latter idea would provoke a widespread revolt. Even today, one occasionally encounters a person who refuses to accept the animal nature of man. Yet, it is inevitable that, once having accepted the general principle of evolution, one is obliged to extend it to man also. It is not within the scope of this brief text to review the considerable evidence of man's evolution, but it should be mentioned that all the evidence discussed in the preceding chapter points to man's close genetic kinship to (but not necessarily descent from) other existing primates. Although this was a disturbing thought to most people of Darwin's time, and it is a topic that can still arouse heated discussion in many circles, the evolution of man is generally accepted by people who are informed and who have examined the evidences without prejudice.

Evolution and Religion

In view of the fact that any religion must ultimately evaluate man, his dignity, and his place in nature, it is not difficult to understand why evolution became a matter of concern to religion as soon as Darwin made it a matter of concern to science. It immediately became necessary for religion to debate within its own ranks whether the link which evolution declared to exist between man and other organisms was degrading, uplifting, or neither. At the first, opinion among religious leaders generally was that evolution deprived man of his uniqueness and reduced him to a mere animal. Around this point centered some of the most heated debates ever witnessed by the intellectual world. In fact, during the latter portion of the nineteenth century, the rift between biology and religion became so great that in most civilized countries an attitude of "science or religion, God or evolution" prevailed. This rift has not entirely healed in the minds of a great many people, and to them, even the word "science" may be associated with complete rejection of religion.

Although many leaders of religious thought during this time were characterized by the position stated above, some adopted the view that it was not degrading at all, but actually uplifting, to realize that man held actual genetic kinship with other organisms. According to this interpretation, man should feel that his emergence as a uniquely gifted species from the biological shackles of past ages was a matter of which to be proud rather than ashamed. In an attempt to reconcile evolution and religion, many proponents of this view adopted the philosophy of **theistic evolution;** that is, they saw evolution as a divinely guided process. The point with them was no longer "God *or* evolution," but "God *through* evolution."[1]

It was mentioned earlier that the immediate cause of conflict between evolution and religion centered around the Genesis account of creation.[2] According to the traditional and literal interpretation of this account, God first created the inanimate earth and then proceeded to create living forms successively; preparation of the earth for these forms and their creation occupied a period of six days. Also traditional with this viewpoint, although not stated in the actual account, was the interpretation that living forms were immutable (not subject to genetic changes that would cause the production of other species from them).

Obviously, a literal interpretation of the Genesis account is at direct odds with evolution. For those persons who accept the Bible as an inspired or God-given volume of writings, and yet who do not choose to blind themselves to the evidences, data, and methods of science, this poses something of a problem. Although the extremes of evolution and creationism appear to many people to be completely irreconcilable, others have found a satisfactory middle ground. If one accepts the Genesis account as a rather figurative and completely non-scientific narrative, according to this position, it becomes meaningful and highly accurate. It is pointed out that the Hebrew word for "day" was also used to correspond to long ages or indefinite periods of time. Thus, the figurative interpretation of *Genesis* is made to complement, not contradict, evolution.[3]

Today, the controversy between evolution and religion has largely subsided for the simple reason that, as philosopher John Dewey says, people do not really solve the great problems; they get over them. By one way or another, two viewpoints which appeared at one time to be impossible of reconciliation no longer seem so far apart to serious students of both science and religion. For this reason, many excellent scientists (and many thorough-going evolutionists) have not found it inconsistent with the methods of science to accept metaphysical ideas or religious

[1] For an excellent presentation of the case for theistic evolution from an outstanding figure of the nineteenth century, see Henry Drummond, *The Ascent of Man*. New York: James Pott and Co., 1894. More recently, a number of books have been written setting forth the philosophy of *finalism*, according to which evolution moves in response to goals predetermined by God. One of the most widely circulated of these is Lecomte du Noüy, *Human Destiny*. New York: Longmans, Greene and Co., 1947.

[2] See *Genesis* 1.

[3] This viewpoint is widely held among present-day Jewish and Christian theologians and scientists. For a representative and well-stated attempt to reconcile evolution and the Genesis account, see Edward McCrady, "Religious Perspectives of College Teaching in Biology," in *Religious Perspectives of College Teaching*. New York: The Ronald Press, 1952.

values. Those who have probed into the matter have either found an answer or else the question, as Dewey says, no longer seems so important. At the very least, one may be led to believe in a God who was responsible for the initial creation of matter, of energy, or of physical and chemical law. The possibility for such belief is stated by a present-day biologist as follows.

> A theory of evolution that postulates that life arose by natural processes from non-living precursors and achieved its present diversity, including man, through the natural selection of rare favorable rearrangements in the genetic material is on first thought abhorrent to many. It is a mechanistic view and it appears to conflict with the teachings of many religions. How, then, can it be accepted by science?
>
> It is true that the thesis here defended does conflict with the Bible as literally interpreted. In fact, any acceptance of organic evolution leads logically to such a conflict. One must accept all of evolution or none. And the evidence for organic evolution is overwhelmingly convincing.
>
> The direct conflict is avoided by many through the acceptance of a non-literal interpretation of religious gospel. Once this possibility is accepted, it can be argued that belief in evolution, including the spontaneous origin of life from non-living antecedents, need in no way conflict with religion.
>
> The argument can be put in the following way: Suppose one believes in a higher intelligence responsible for the creation and direction of the universe—a belief that is a matter of faith, for present science can neither prove nor disprove it. It is clear that such a supreme being did not create present man, for we have direct evidence of our immediate ancestors. One can then argue that what was created was rather ancestors capable of giving rise to us. How remote were they? Were they primitive men of a million years ago? Or were they perhaps preman ancestors? Once embarking on this line of thought there is no logical place to stop. One is led easily but firmly to the conclusion that the creation of a universe of elementary physical particles endowed with properties that made inevitable the evolution of elements and molecules and life when the conditions were proper is just as remarkable and just as deserving of awe and reverence as is the direct creation of man.
>
> Like the universe and like life, religions are not immutable. The ancestral forms of many of them conflict with modern science as do some of those that now exist. But the conflict is not necessary. And if man is to achieve the loftiest goals made possible by his biological and cultural evolutionary potentials, he must see to it that in the future religions and science evolve together in harmony.[4]

Evolution and Society

It seems evident that Darwin, who certainly was no social revolutionist, never intended that his theory should extend beyond the

---

[4] G. W. Beadle, *The Physical and Chemical Basis of Inheritance*, The University of Oregon Press, Eugene, Oregon, 1957, by permission of the Oregon State Board of Education.

scientific realm. The society into which he cast the concept of evolution by natural selection was, however, of such a nature that it was inevitable that all areas of thought should become affected by it. We have seen how this was true in religion. Not long after the initial clash between evolution and religion, it became intellectually popular to interpret every field in the light of natural selection. A number of books appeared in the latter part of the nineteenth century on the subjects of sociology, psychology, ethics, and political science with natural selection as their main theme. Indeed, it was a rare field of endeavor that escaped an evolutionary interpretation during this period. As one biological historian expresses it, "The generation to which *The Origin of Species* was delivered followed Darwin blindly." [5]

A concept as intimately concerned with human life as that proposed by Darwin could not fail to exert very profound influences, not all of which were good, upon practical affairs. To men on both sides of the question, the logical consequences of the theory seemed to undermine the authority of moral values. It became evident, in the decades following Darwin, that this was not without its effects. That phase of natural selection which Darwin chose to term "struggle for existence" was particularly emphasized. It appealed very strongly to the apologists for war who saw a way for the strong to justify by "natural law" the conquest of the weak. In Germany, where a strong feeling of racial supremacy had already been carefully nurtured, the Darwinian concept of struggle for existence and survival of the fittest was received with particularly strong enthusiasm. During the latter part of the nineteenth century, her political philosophy became saturated with the doctrine of the right of the strong nation to deprive the weak of human rights. By 1914, this feeling had reached these proportions:

> Wherever we look in Nature we find that war is a fundamental law of development. This great verity, which has been recognized in past ages, has been convincingly demonstrated in modern times by Charles Darwin. . . . The struggle for existence is ruled by biological laws.[6]

Unfortunately, it was to take more than one great war to eradicate transplanted and misinterpreted Darwinism from the minds of political theorists:

---

[5] Charles Singer, *A History of Biology*. New York: Abelard-Schuman Ltd., copyright 1959.

[6] Friedrich Bernhardi, *Britain As Germany's Vassal* (translated). New York: George H. Doran Co., 1914.

We are all aware that in the future mankind will have to deal with problems, to cope with which some most noble race will have to be summoned as the master nation, supported by the forces of the whole globe.[7]

Not only in terms of actual war, but in economic affairs, the "struggle and survival" concept became popular. Karl Marx, the German economist who was contemporary with Darwin, found it easy to think of Darwin's species as being analogous to the "struggling" classes of economic society. Hence, it was only a step to the justification of ruthless business and economic practices which were based, as in the case of the waging of war, on "natural law."

In short, Darwin's theory of evolution was lifted from the field of biology during the nineteenth century and was applied to virtually every area of human thought. It certainly was not Darwin's intention that this should happen because all he tried to say, basically, in *The Origin of Species* was that species become extinct if they cannot survive. However, he was made to say a great deal more than this:

> Darwin had tried, once or twice, to show his metaphors for what they were, but few read him. They read his expounders instead who dramatized the "story of evolution" by stressing the business of chase, capture and death. It was always a tiger and a gazelle, and a gazelle with slightly longer legs . . . To accept the absolute value of survival, the common mind wanted it to represent a "genuine" value. It would have been horrified to learn that "fittest" only means "those who survive," and that the sickly coddled child of wealth who lives and procreates is fitter than the robust laborer who dies of overwork and bad food.[8]

Even in biology, we have had to revise our thinking about natural selection. Let us be careful to remember that Darwin conceived of it as an initiating force in evolution, whereas we know today that it is not. In other words, the concepts of "struggle for existence" and "survival of the fittest" not only are unjustifiable in social relations; they are inadequate in biology as an explanation of evolution. Darwin himself used these expressions only in a metaphorical sense; today, we use the term "competition" to replace the phrase "struggle for existence," and the fittest, as Barzun says, are simply those that survive. It seems never to have occurred to most people of Darwin's time that plants may struggle (compete) for light or moisture; they labored under a literal misunder-

---

[7] Adolph Hitler, *Mein Kampf* (translated). New York: The Houghton-Mifflin Co., 1933.

[8] Jacques Barzun, *Darwin, Marx and Wagner: Critique of a Heritage*. Boston: Little, Brown and Co., and Atlantic Monthly Press, 1941. Reprinted by permission.

standing of his expressions. In fact, a second look at natural selection in terms of the animal kingdom alone revealed to biologists of a later generation that the concepts of "struggle" and "survival" had been somewhat overemphasized:

> It is a misfortune to suppose that Natural Selection implies a keen struggle and survival through brute force, for in many species, cooperation, altruism of certain sorts and self-sacrifice are elements of the utmost importance in racial success.[9]

> The fact is that the struggle for existence need not be competitive at all ... The world is not only the abode of the strong; it is also the home of the loving.[10]

The historical lesson of society's experience with natural selection should not be lost on modern man. It is dangerous to draw analogies too freely between fields, especially when the basic premise is only a theory in the field from which it is transplanted. Darwin's theory of evolution, based on natural selection as an initiating force, was inadequate even in biology. How much more inappropriate it proved to be as a social theory is now obvious.

Evolution and Biological Philosophy

Today, we take for granted the "common sense" approach of the scientific method and the validity of cause-and-effect reasoning. For centuries before Darwin's time, however, this was not the case. Biologists were divided over two philosophies of living processes, which we now call **vitalism** and **mechanism.**

Vitalism is the philosophy of life that views life processes as depending for their efficiency upon forces that exist in addition to physical and chemical ones. Mechanism, in contrast, views life processes as depending exclusively upon physical and chemical principles. For example, suppose a question were to arise over why the pancreas of a higher animal body secretes pancreatic juice at exactly the right time in the digestive process. Assuming that neither knows the answer (which we learned in Chapter 8), the vitalist might answer, "It secretes its product because it is supposed to." The mechanist, however, would probably say, "I don't know, but I believe that there is an answer which can be understood in terms of physics and chemistry."

[9] H. H. Newman, *The Gist of Evolution*. New York: The Macmillan Co., 1926.

[10] J. B. S. Haldane, *The Causes of Evolution*. New York: Longmans, Green and Co., 1932.

Now which of these answers is the more satisfactory? Actually, neither of them is adequate, although the vitalist may feel that he has solved the problem by ignoring it. Notice that his answer implies that the pancreas possesses built-in intelligence or that it has been set in operation directly by supernatural force. Notice also that his answer is a dead end; it will never lead him any closer to solving the problem. Although the mechanist is obliged to confess ignorance in this case, **his is the answer that leads to an hypothesis and hence to investigation of the problem.**

There was a time when the vast majority of biologists were vitalists. They believed in spontaneous generation and in the magical operation of living processes. To them, physiological investigations in particular were heretical and a waste of time. It is small wonder, then, that biology did not emerge very far from the purely descriptive stage until Darwin's theory had been thoroughly digested by philosophers and biologists. Why did it take Darwin to start a trend toward the mechanistic philosophy held by virtually all biologists today? Actually, it was neither Darwin, nor even his theory, that seems to have been the stimulus; it was the whole concept of evolution as a process in the world of life. Once it was accepted that the variety of living forms could be accounted for by mechanistic processes, the door was open for the extension of mechanism to other phenomena of living matter. Without doubt, the concept of evolution as opposed to special creation solved the greatest of all possible problems for the mechanist. Once having embraced mechanism for the origin of species, it was easy to accept it for other life processes, *as a working principle.*

Actually, this seems to have been the cause of the great appeal of Darwin's theory. *The Origin of Species* itself was not a great scientific contribution:

> Despite its great value and stimulating character and despite the conviction that it carried, its arguments are frequently fallacious. It often confuses two distinct themes. On the one hand there is the question whether living forms have, or have not, an evolutionary origin. On the other hand is the suggestion that Natural Selection is the main factor in Evolution. These themes can and should be discussed independently. In the *Origin* they are inextricably confused.[11]

Darwin happened to come up with what historian Barzun calls the "right wrong" answer to the vitalism-mechanism controversy. Evolution was not so much accepted by nineteenth century biologists, then, because Darwin proved it, *but because he pointed the way out of vitalism.*

A great many people, including some biologists, seek to avoid

---

[11] Charles Singer, *op. cit.*

the philosophy of mechanism because it would seem to imply a denial of God. Actually, as was stated for the concept of evolution in the preceding chapter, it does nothing of the sort. It does, however, imply that the power of God operates through natural law. Nevertheless, there are many biologists and other scientists who are thoroughly mechanistic in their approach to research but who maintain a belief in a highly personal God.

The concept of evolution has altered biological philosophy in still other ways and has opened pathways to knowledge that could never have been attained otherwise. To say the least, it has stimulated a tremendous amount of thought and has caused man to re-examine such issues as determinism and free will, matter and spirit, and to seek seriously a philosophy of life that is at the same time satisfying and consistent with the methods of science.

THE FUTURE OF BIOLOGY

Of necessity, we have been concerned entirely in this book with the past and present of biology. What of the future? One of the rewards of living in a civilization whose events move rapidly is the excitement that comes from anticipating major changes within fields of knowledge. If the past is any indication, we may expect a great many new developments in biology within even a few years. Some of the most interesting possibilities are discussed below.

The Theoretical and the Practical

It will be recalled that the biologist is somewhat dissatisfied with his present definition of "life." In many respects, he is almost obliged to regard this phenomenon vitalistically, and yet he knows that only a mechanistic approach to the problem will yield further knowledge. We may expect to learn a great deal more about the nature of life within the next few years, and with such theoretical knowledge will come the understanding and conquest of such abnormal manifestations of life processes as cancer and feeble-mindedness in man. These are exciting challenges to the biologist who is interested in "pure" research, and it is conceivable that within a relatively brief period of time we shall discover a principle or principles of life as profound in their influence as evolution was to nineteenth century biology or as the Einstein equation has been to twentieth century physics.

Another exciting prospect which may be within our grasp is the possibility of discovering life elsewhere than on earth. From what we know of our own planet and the conditions that apparently gave rise to life upon it, there is no reason why life may not also have originated on one of the thousands of planets whose environmental conditions seem to parallel those of our own in its evolution. What will we find to be the forms of such organisms? Once we have first-hand evidence for the existence of other life than that we know, we shall open a new chapter in the history of biology.

In the meantime, there are more practical problems to be dealt with. Given a little more understanding of marine ecology, we shall solve many of the food problems of the world. Our greatly improved agricultural methods have already gone far toward this goal. One day, we shall learn to mimic nature in the large-scale production of carbohydrates through the combination of carbon dioxide with water, and this will contribute greatly to the solution of the problem. There are unconquered diseases of the human that will be completely brought under control through continued research, and many of the knotty problems of psychology and philosophy that await biological explanations will be made clearer. These are but a few of the practical triumphs of biology that most of us can expect to see within our lifetimes.

The Future of Man

There is not much reason to suppose that man, who stands out as the dominant species on earth, will make a great deal more physical progress. Most students of human evolution feel that although man is not physically perfect, he is sufficiently specialized biologically that there can be very little real change according to the usual concepts of evolution. For all practical purposes, at least to those who are concerned with the immediate well-being of man, his biological progress has virtually come to an end.

Although there is little hope that man will undergo mutation and natural selection at a rate sufficient to change him significantly for the better, at least within the near future, there is a distinct possibility that he can create conditions that will definitely degrade him. The most direct outstanding danger at the present time exists in radiation hazards. With the increase of ionizing radiations in the environment, man is running more and more risk of acquiring serious genetic damage. As we have observed, ionizing radiations step up natural mutation rates in proportion to the strength of dosage, and such mutations are entirely random. Since most mutations are harmful ones, and because the majority are recessive, a single nuclear war of even short duration might well do far more damage to the human species in the long run than merely killing a few thousand or million people. For generations following, the induced mutations in sensitive germinal tissue would keep cropping out. Unless we take strict measures to control the disposal of certain radioactive wastes from industry and commerce, and unless we take greater precautions in regard to the needless exposure of human beings to X rays, we may be in for serious trouble. This is not to suggest that nuclear reactors and X-ray machines do not have a definite place in our society; both have more than proved their usefulness in terms of human welfare. Nevertheless, exposure of human tissues, and especially germinal tissues, to radiation is a very serious matter and one that has caused many biologists to become thoroughly alarmed. Here again, we see that what might appear to be a political or social problem is actually a biological one, basically. A more indirect but perhaps equally serious danger to civilization as we know it lies in the modern population "explosion" that the world is experiencing. Like other biological problems that we have discussed, this one is accompanied by economic, political, and ethical overtones. Furthermore, as is the case with all such inter-disciplinary problems, we are going to have to make some difficult decisions; in this case, they will have to be made in regard to birth control and the wiser use of the earth's available space. Because these are problems that must be dealt with in one way or another, the present-day citizen owes it to his society to become well informed in respect to them.

However, to return to the matter of man's evolution, there are those biologists who suggest that just as man's physical evolution may have come to a virtual end, he is on the threshold of new heights in an entirely different realm—the evolution of the spirit. Whether one conceives of the spirit of man as a matter of personality or as a divine investment, this is an intriguing possibility. All are agreed that mankind could be less "animal" and more "spiritual" in nature, but until relatively recent years, it had occurred to few biologists that they had any stake in the area; traditionally, it has been the concern of philosophy and religion, in the main.

Without doubt, there are principles to be found in biology that help some persons to arrive at a more satisfying philosophy of life than if they had not studied the subject. Certainly, a large number of books have been written on the subjects of spiritual evolution and human destiny, many of them authored by outstanding biologists. Probably most biologists feel, however, that these are matters that must ultimately become the concern of religion, not biology. Although religion and biology have much to offer each other, they still must travel two separate roads toward their respective truths. It is the task of biology to observe, to experiment, to learn more about natural phenomena; it is the task of religion to relate man to ultimate reality. Whether man has a divine or a purely human destiny is not a matter for biology, as a field, to decide. This is a far cry, of course, from saying that biology is opposed to religion.

It is simply that the biologist, as such, is bound to the scientific method, and religion is not scientific. It deals, of necessity, with matters that are not subject to experimental analysis.

However, what of man's future in his world community? Here, he has a destiny to fulfill, and he must fulfill it if he is to survive. The next few decades must see moral and ethical values catch up with technological and scientific knowledge. Here again, religion and philosophy must take the lead, but on this point biology can be of help. Perhaps the one thing that all biologists have in common, no matter how diverse their special interests, is their concern for life. Unable to agree on an exact definition for the phenomenon, they nevertheless esteem it highly enough that they all devote their energies to some aspect of it. The biologist is in a unique position, therefore, to appreciate the need for any measures that will ensure world peace and that will prevent the needless loss of human life. That there is a direct connection between a desire for the preservation of life and respect for it as a biological phenomenon is illustrated by the following statement from a contemporary cytologist:

> The more we delve into these problems, the more life remains mysterious. All that we can do is to contribute by our work to the solution of the biological riddles. But, what we must also do, is to admire, respect, and love life; we must protect it, and not destroy it. We, biologists, must work more than anybody else for peace among men.[12]

Most biologists, regardless of how much they might disagree on philosophy, religion, or even biology, are in wholehearted agreement with this sentiment.

QUESTIONS

1. Is the term "Darwinism" synonymous with the term "evolution?" Explain.

2. Explain the difference between vitalism and mechanism.

3. To what extent did nineteenth century ideas of evolution apparently contribute to the causes of the world wars of recent generations?

4. Can one be a mechanist and still believe in God? What is your personal feeling in this matter?

5. Why was Darwin's theory of evolution so widely accepted in spite of its apparent weaknesses?

---

[12] Jean Brachet, *Biochemical Cytology*. New York: Academic Press, 1957.

6. Name some possible triumphs of biology that may be expected in the near future.

7. Do you believe that a living organism will ever be synthesized or created from non-living material? Assuming that this is accomplished at some time, what, if any, influence will this have on the argument for or against God?

8. Why are ionizing radiations dangerous to man in the long-range sense?

9. By what means is evolution reconciled by some people with the Genesis account of creation?

10. To what extent do you think that biologists are justified, as biologists, in advancing ideas regarding the evolution of man's spirit?

REFERENCES

BATES, MARSTON. *Man In Nature.* Englewood Cliffs, N.J.: Prentice-Hall, Inc., 1961. One of the FOUNDATIONS OF MODERN BIOLOGY series, this book is concerned with man's evolution and his present status in relation to his biotic environment.

BECK, L. W. *Philosophic Inquiry.* Englewood Cliffs, N.J.: Prentice-Hall, Inc., 1952. This introductory textbook of philosophy is recommended for those who wish to pursue the subject further. Chapters 3 through 6 are particularly appropriate.

IRVINE, WILLIAM. *Apes, Angels and Victorians.* New York: McGraw-Hill Book Co. Inc., 1955. A very interesting book that deals with the social climate that surrounded Darwin and his contemporaries.

KEMENY, JOHN. *A Philosopher Looks At Science.* New York: D. Van Nostrand Company, Inc., 1959. Chapter 12 of this book is particularly recommended as collateral reading in the philosophy of science.

SINNOTT, E. W. *The Biology of the Spirit.* New York: The Viking Press, 1955. An outstanding botanist presents the case for biological finalism, or the philosophy of "goals" in regard both to organismal differentiation and the human spirit.

WALLACE, BRUCE and **TH. DOBZHANSKY.** *Radiations, Genes and Man.* New York: Henry Holt and Company, 1959. A discussion of radiation hazards written in such a manner that most of it will be understandable to the student who is familiar with the principles of biology that are set forth in the present text.

WHITEHEAD, A. N. *Science and the Modern World.* New York: The Macmillan Company, 1925. One of this century's outstanding philosophers writes of science, society, religion, and God. This book is definitely above the elementary level, but for the student who likes to be challenged in his reading, it will prove very stimulating.

In addition to the books above, the following articles from *Scientific American* are recommended.

BEADLE, G. W. "Ionizing Radiation and the Citizen," Volume 201 (September, 1959), p. 219. A stimulating discussion of radiation, its hazards, and its potential as a tool for the betterment of mankind.

DOBZHANSKY, TH. "The Present Evolution of Man," Volume 203 (September, 1960), p. 206. An outstanding geneticist discusses man's evolution and the part that he plays in it.

EISELEY, L. C. "Is Man Alone In Space?" Volume 189 (July, 1953), p. 80. An interesting speculation on the subject of the article.

MULLER, H. J. "Radiation and Human Mutation," Volume 193 (November, 1955), p. 58. A distinguished geneticist warns against the careless handling of radiation.

PUCK, THEODORE. "Radiation and the Human Cell," Volume 202 (April, 1960), p. 142. A good discussion of the mode of action of ionizing radiations and the extent to which human cells may be affected by them.

Glossary

The following system in indicating pronunciation is used by permission. From Webster's New International Dictionary, Second Edition, copyright 1959 by G. & C. Merriam Co., Publishers of the Merriam-Webster Dictionaries.

active transport: the movement of materials through cell membranes accompanied by the expenditure of energy, as contrasted to simple diffusion, where no energy is expended.

adaptation (ăd'ăp·tā'shŭn): (1) the development of structural and functional features in a sequence of organisms, over time, which enable them to survive and reproduce within the limits of a particular environment; (2) any structural or functional characteristic of an organism that contributes to its over-all adjustment to its environment.

adenosine diphosphate (a·děn'ō·sēn dī·fŏs'fāte), abbreviated ADP: a compound featuring two phosphate groups, the bond between which is a "high energy" bond. Important in cellular energy transfers. See Fig. 80 of text for structural formula.

adenosine triphosphate (a·děn'ō·sēn trī·fŏs'fāte), abbreviated ATP: a compound featuring three phosphate groups carrying two "high energy" bonds. With ADP it forms an energy transfer cycle in protoplasm. See Fig. 80 of text for structural formula.

ADP: see adenosine diphosphate.

ATP: see adenosine triphosphate.

aerobe (ā′ẽr·ōb): an organism which utilizes gaseous oxygen as an ultimate hydrogen acceptor in respiration.

aggregation (ăg′rẽ·gā′shŭn): a group of animals belonging to the same species which band together temporarily for cooperative activity.

Agnatha (ăg′nà·thà): the least advanced class of vertebrates in terms of structural complexity which is made up of the jawless fishes.

algae (ăl′jē): a group of plants whose members are photosynthetic and relatively simple in structure.

allele (ă·lēl′): any one of contrasting genes that may occupy a given point, or locus, on a chromosome. For example, each member of the gene pair *Aa* is an allele as it relates to the other member.

amino acid (à·mē′nō ăs′ĭd): a type of molecule characterized by an ($-$NH$_2$) group and a (COOH) group, several of which may become linked through dehydration to form a protein molecule.

Amphibia (ăm·fĭb′ĭ·à): the class of vertebrate animals whose members are intermediate between the fishes and the land vertebrates in their characteristics.

amylase (ăm′ĭ·lās): an enzyme which is capable of decomposing polysaccharides into less complex carbohydrates.

anabolism (à·năb′ō·lĭz′m): the phase of metabolism that is constructive, or energy-consuming.

anaerobe (ăn·ā′ẽr·ōb): an organism which does not utilize gaseous oxygen in its metabolism.

anaphase (ăn′à·fāz): the stage or phase of mitosis during which daughter chromosomes move toward opposite poles.

anatomy (à·năt′ō·mĭ): (1) a field of biology whose interest is the study of structure as determined by dissection; (2) the gross structure of an organism or one of its parts.

angiosperm (ăn′jĭ·ō·spûrm′): a name applied to any flowering plant.

Annelida (ă·nĕl′ĭ·dà): the phylum which includes those worms whose bodies are composed of similar segments.

anthropomorphism (ăn′thrŏ·pŏ·môr′fĭz′m): a philosophy or means of interpretation according to which the actions of any given organism or the conditions of existence of an object are presumed to arise from an intelligence similar to that of man.

antibody (ăn′tĭ·bŏd′ĭ): a substance produced within the body of an organism that is capable of uniting with a specific antigen, thereby rendering the antigen inactive.

antigen (ăn′tĭ·jĕn): a substance, usually of a protein nature, that elicits a chemical response from an organism into which it is introduced.

aqueous (ā′kwê·ŭs): watery or pertaining to water.

archenteron (är·kĕn′tēr·ŏn): the enclosed cavity of an embryo at the gastrula stage, the intermediate boundary of which is endoderm.

artery (är′tēr·ĭ): any blood vessel carrying blood away from the heart.

Arthropoda (är·thrŏp′ŏ·dà): the phylum which includes those invertebrates exhibiting paired, jointed appendages.

autosome (ô′tŏ·sōm): any chromosome other than a sex-determining chromosome.

autotroph (ô′tŏ·trŏf′): an organism capable of synthesizing organic compounds from inorganic materials, utilizing carbon dioxide as its sole source of carbon.

auxin (ôk′sĭn): a plant hormone, or substance produced in one area of a plant that may influence another area, particularly in regard to growth.

Aves (ā′vēz): the class of vertebrate animals whose members are feathered bipeds, most of which are capable of flight.

bacteria (băk·tēr′ĭ·à): a group of fungi that are typically unicellular whose nuclear materials are somewhat atypical in their organization.

binomial nomenclature (bī·nō′mĭ·ăl nō′měn·klā′tūr): a system of naming that employs two names. In biological classification, these are the generic and specific names.

biogenesis (bī′ŏ·jĕn′ê·sĭs): the principle that organisms arise only from previously existing organisms.

blastula (blăs′tū·là): an early stage in the development of an animal, during which the cells are typically arranged in a single layer around a cavity, thus forming a hollow ball.

botany (bŏt′à·nĭ): that branch of biology which is concerned with plants.

bud (bŭd): a portion of an organism that is capable of growth to form another, independent organism, or in the case of higher plants, a new plant organ.

Calorie (kăl′ŏ·rĭ): a unit of heat used in physiology and defined as the amount of heat required to raise the temperature of one kilogram of water one degree centigrade.

cambium (kăm′bĭ·ŭm): meristematic or embryonic tissue located elsewhere in the plant than at the tips of plant organs, whose divisional activities result in secondary growth of the plant.

capillary (kăp′ĭ·lĕr′ĭ): a small, thin-walled vessel within which body fluids are conducted.

carbohydrate (kär′bṓ·hī′drāt): a type of organic compound composed of carbon, hydrogen, and oxygen in the general ratio CH_2O.

carnivorous (kär·nĭv′ṓ·rŭs): a term applied to those animals whose natural food is the flesh of other animals.

catabolism (kȧ·tăb′ṓ·lĭz′m): the phase of metabolism that is destructive, or energy-releasing.

centriole (sĕn′trĭ·ōl): a small body or granule from which astral rays and spindle fibers radiate during cell division of most animals and certain of the lower plants.

centromere (sĕn′trṓ·mēr): the point, or region, on a chromosome at which a spindle fiber is attached during nuclear division.

centrosome (sĕn′trṓ·sōm): a small, clear body typically located just outside the nuclear membrane in animal cells and containing the centriole(s).

cephalization (sĕf′ȧ·lĭ·zā′shŭn): the tendency toward an accumulation of nervous and sensory structures at the anterior end of an animal.

cerebrum (sĕr′ē·brŭm): a portion of the vertebrate brain, largely concerned with such "higher" mental functions as learning, imagination and memory.

chemoautotroph (kĕm′ṓ·ô′tṓ·trŏf′): an organism whose energy for carbohydrate synthesis is derived from reactions involving inorganic compounds or certain elements.

chitin (kī′tĭn): a tissue of which the exoskeletons of arthropods are chiefly composed.

chlorophyll (klō′rṓ·fĭl): a green plant pigment which functions in the capture of light energy during photosynthesis.

chloroplast (klō′rṓ·plăst): a type of plastid that contains chlorophyll.

Chondrichthyes (kŏn·drĭk′thĭ·ēz): a class of vertebrates that includes the fishes whose skeletons are composed entirely of cartilage, notably, the sharks, skates, and rays.

Chordata (kôr·dā′tȧ): the phylum which includes all animals possessing a notochord, dorsal nerve cord, and pharyngeal pouches at some stage of development.

chromatid (krō′mȧ·tĭd): one half of a prophasic or metaphasic chromosome.

chromatin (krō′mȧ·tĭn): the material (chiefly DNA protein) found in chromosomes, so called because of its affinity for certain stains with which it combines to form colored complexes (*chroma*, color).

chromosome (krō′mȏ·sōm): a structural and functional unit of chromatin within the nucleus of the cell.

chylomicron (kī′lȏ·mī′krŏn): a small aggregate of fat molecules produced in the digestive process of higher animals by the combined action of fatty acids and bile salts on fats.

chymotrypsin (kī′mȏ·trĭp′sĭn): a protein-specific enzyme found in pancreatic juice.

cilium (sĭl′ĭ·ŭm): a microscopic, hair-like structure found in large numbers on the surfaces of certain types of cells; some microorganisms employ cilia for a locomotor function, and in higher animals, ciliated epithelial cells line the surfaces of certain tubules or ducts, as in the respiratory tract of man.

Coelenterata (sê·lĕn′tẽr·ā′tȧ): the phylum of animals whose members possess a body wall of two cell layers within which is a digestive cavity with one opening to the outside.

coelome (sē′lōm): a body cavity of an animal, the lining of which is a peritoneum derived from mesoderm.

co-enzyme (kō·ĕn′zīm): a substance, either organic or inorganic, that makes it possible for an enzyme to function in a particular reaction.

collenchyma (kŏ·lĕng′kĭ·mȧ): a simple type of plant tissue found chiefly in young plant organs, whose cells characteristically possess walls thickened by cellulose deposits.

commensalism (kŏ·mĕn′sȧl·ĭz′m): a relationship between two organisms of different species wherein one receives benefit while the other is neither harmed nor helped.

conifer (kō′nĭ·fẽr): a gymnospermous plant bearing a structure called a cone, upon whose scales seeds are produced.

copulation (kŏp′û·lā′shŭn): the physical union of two animals in the function of gamete transfer.

cortex (kôr′tĕks): a region of the plant stem or root that lies between the epidermis and stele; also, the outer portion of an animal organ.

cotyledon (kŏt′ĭ·lē′dŭn): the primary, or first, leaf of a seed plant formed in the embryo.

cyclosis (sī·klō′sĭs): the movement of protoplasm within the cell.

cytochrome (sī'tô·krōm): one of the types of hydrogen carriers in respiration; a series of cytochromes transfer hydrogen from flavoprotein to gaseous oxygen.

cytokinesis (sī'tô·kĭ·nē'sĭs): that phase of cell division by means of which the cytoplasm is separated into daughter cells.

cytology (sī·tŏl'ô·jĭ): a field of biology concerned with the study of cells.

cytoplasm (sī'tô·plăz'm): that portion of the protoplasm of a cell exclusive of the nucleus.

deciduous (dê·sĭd'û·ŭs): a term describing the falling off at maturity of some structure or structures, as in the case of trees which shed their leaves at the end of a growing season.

defecation (dĕf'ê·kā'shŭn): the elimination of digestive residues by an animal.

dehydration (dē'hī·drā'shŭn): chemically, a type of reaction in which water is formed by the removal of hydrogen and oxygen from a substrate or substrates.

deoxyribonucleic acid (dē·ŏk'sĭ·rī'bō·nû·klē'ĭk ăs'ĭd), abbreviated DNA: a substance whose molecules are composed of deoxyribonucleotides, which are themselves composed of deoxyribose (a five-carbon sugar), a base, and a phosphate group.

determinism (dê·tûr'mĭn·ĭz'm): the philosophy, or viewpoint, according to which man's actions are dictated by forces that are fundamentally biological ones, as opposed to the philosophy of freedom of the will.

diastase (dī'a·stās): a starch-digesting enzyme.

dicotyledon (dī·kŏt'ĭ·lē'dŭn): a flowering plant whose embryos exhibit two cotyledons, or primary leaves, within the seed.

differentiation (dĭf'ēr·ĕn'shĭ·ā'shŭn): the alteration of a cell or structure from a generalized state to a more specialized or mature one.

diffusion (dĭ·fū'zhŭn): the process by which ions, molecules, or other particles move about in their medium.

digestion (dĭ·jĕs'chŭn): the process by which non-diffusible food molecules are broken down to such a state that they will diffuse through cell membranes.

dioecious (dī·ē'shŭs): a term describing any species whose members are definitely either male or female.

diploblastic (dĭp'lô·blăs'tĭk): a term applied to an animal or to a species of animals whose adult body structures are derived from two germ layers, the ectoderm and endoderm.

diploid (dĭp′loid): a term describing a cell or an organism whose chromosomes exist in pairs, that is, there is a double "set" of chromosomes.

DNA: see deoxyribonucleic acid.

duodenum (dū′ô·dē′nŭm): the portion of the small intestine of vertebrates that attaches to the stomach.

Echinodermata (ê·kĭ′nô·dûr′ma·tȧ): the phylum which includes those animals whose skin contains large numbers of imbedded calcareous spines.

ecology (ê·kŏl′ô·jĭ): a field of biology whose interest is the relationship of organisms to each other and to their environments.

ectoderm (ĕk′tô·dûrm): the outermost germ layer of an embryonic animal.

ectoparasite (ĕk′tô·pằr′ȧ·sīt): a parasite that attaches to the external surface of a host.

element (ĕl′êmĕnt): a substance composed of similar atoms.

embryology (ĕm′brĭ·ŏl′ô·jĭ): a field of biology whose interest is the development of organisms from relatively simple to relatively complex stages.

endocrine (ĕn′dôkrĭn): a term applied to any animal organ of secretion whose product is delivered directly to the blood stream or body fluids rather than being released into a special duct or tube of conveyance.

endoderm (ĕn′dô·dûrm): the innermost germ layer of an embryonic animal.

endoparasite (ĕn′dô·pằr′a·sīt): a parasite that lives within the body of a host.

endoskeleton (ĕn′dô·skĕl′ê·tŭn): a supporting structure located within an animal body.

endosperm (ĕn′dô·spûrm): the portion of a seed that surrounds the embryo serving as a storage tissue.

energy (ĕn′ĕr·jĭ): the capacity to do work.

enterocoelic pouch (ĕn′tĕr·ô·sē′lĭk): a primordial coelome, formed in echinoderms and chordates (of the phyla considered in this book) when several somites, or segments, develop as outpushings from the endoderm (see Fig. 103). These separate cavities later fuse to form the common coelome.

enzyme (ĕn′zīm): an organic catalyst of protein nature which is capable of accelerating the rate of some particular chemical reaction.

epidermis (ĕp′ĭ·dûr′mĭs): the outermost cell layer or layers of an organism.

epithelium (ĕp′ĭ·thē′lĭ·ŭm): a tissue type of multicellular animals whose chief function is protection.

esophagus (ê·sŏf′a·gŭs): the portion of the gastro-intestinal tract in vertebrates that leads from the pharynx to the stomach.

evolution (ĕv′ô·lū′shŭn): (1) the concept that present-day species developed through change from simpler forms of life; (2) the process by which change occurs in the world of life, so that new species ultimately appear that differ more or less from ancestral stocks.

excretion (ĕks·krē′shŭn): the elimination of metabolic wastes by an animal.

exoskeleton (ĕk′sô·skĕl′ê·tŭn): a supporting structure located without an animal body.

fat: a type of organic compound the molecules of which are typically composed, in the simplest forms, of one glycerol and three fatty acid fractions.

fatalism (fā′tăl·ĭz′m): the philosophy or view according to which all events are fixed or determined in terms of a predestined cosmic pattern, and that human efforts cannot alter them.

fatty acid (făt′ĭ ăs′ĭd): one product of fat digestion. See Fig. 11 for structural formula.

fermentation (fûr′mĕn·tā′shŭn): the anaerobic catabolism of non-nitrogenous compounds resulting in the formation of lactic acid or ethyl alcohol.

fetus (fē′tŭs): the prenatal stage of a mammal extending roughly from the time that the individual begins to resemble fully developed members of its species to birth. In the human, this stage extends from about the third month of development through about a ninth month.

fiber (fī′bēr): (1) an elongated, sclerenchymatous plant cell whose function is that of support; (2) an elongate cell of an animal body, a protoplasmic extension of a cell, or a non-living filament produced by a cell but located outside it.

finalism (fī′năl·ĭz′m): the philosophy or viewpoint that development, whether in an organism or in regard to evolution, is purposeful and goal-seeking; also called *teleology*.

flaccid (flăk′sĭd): a term describing the condition of a cell or tissue whose internal (turgor) pressure is less than normal.

flagellum (fla·jĕl′ŭm): a microscopic, whip-like structure that serves as a locomotor organelle for any cell possessing one or more of them.

flavoprotein (flā′vō·prō′tē·ĭn): a derivative of the vitamin riboflavin that transports hydrogen from certain nucleotides to the cytochrome series in respiration.

freedom: philosophically, the view that man's actions are not determined solely by forces that are physical and chemical in nature but that he has the independent power to make choices.

fucoxanthin (fū′kō·zăn′thĭn): a brown pigment characteristic of certain algae, notably the brown algae.

fungi (fŭn′jī): a group of plants whose most outstanding characteristic is their lack of chlorophyll coupled with a relative structural simplicity.

gamete (găm′ēt): a cell that is specialized for sexual union with another cell.

gametophyte (ga·mē′tō·fīt): (1) any gamete-producing plant; (2) that phase of an alternating plant life cycle in which there is the production of gametes.

gastrula (găs′trōō·la): a stage of embryonic animal development in which there are two or three primary germ layers that typically form a hollow sac with one opening.

gene (jēn): a functional unit of a chromosome that is capable of influencing the development of some trait or process in an individual.

genetics (jē·nĕt′ĭks): that field of biology whose interest is the phenomenon of heredity in organisms.

genotype (jĕn′ō·tīp): the symbolic expression assigned to an organism to represent its genetic constitution for any trait or traits under consideration.

geotropism (jē·ŏt′rō·pĭz'm): the response of a plant organ to gravity.

germ layer: any one of three possible "sheets" of cells formed in an early animal embryo, namely, the ectoderm, endoderm, or mesoderm.

gland (glănd): a cell, tissue, or organ that is specialized for secretion.

glucose (glōō′kōs): a monosaccharide sugar of the formula $C_6H_{12}O_6$; it is the most common form by which carbohydrates are transported in plant and animal bodies.

glycerol (glĭs′ĕr·ōl): one product of fat digestion. See Fig. 11 of text for structural formula.

glycogen (glī′kō·jĕn): a polysaccharide made up of about twelve to eighteen molecules of glucose that serves as a storage carbohydrate in animal tissues.

glycogenesis (glī'kŏ·jĕn'ē·sĭs): the process whereby glycogen is synthesized from monosaccharide sugars in certain animal organs, notably the liver.

glycogenolysis (glī'kŏ·jĕn·ŏ'lĭ·sĭs): the process whereby glycogen is broken down to glucose.

glycolysis (glī·kŏl'ĭ·sĭs): the anaerobic catabolism of non-nitrogenous compounds resulting in the formation of pyruvic acid.

Golgi matter (gôl'jē): a cellular constituent that has been identified with the function of secretion.

gymnosperm (jĭm'nŏ·spûrm): one of a group of non-flowering seed plants whose seeds are borne upon scales.

haploid (hăp'loid): a term describing a cell or an organism whose chromosomes are not paired; that is, there is only one "set" of chromosomes.

hemoglobin (hē'mŏ·glō'bĭn): a red pigment of blood; in vertebrate animals, it is carried in red blood cells (erythrocytes).

herbaceous (hûr·bā'shŭs): a term applied to a plant that does not develop a woody body.

herbivorous (hûr·bĭv'ŏ·rŭs): a term applied to an animal whose diet consists entirely of plants.

hermaphrodite (hûr·măf'rŏ·dīt): an individual that is functionally both a male and a female.

heterotrophic (hĕt'ĕr·ŏ·trŏf'ĭk): a term describing an organism whose carbon source is organic compounds that are obtained by diffusion or active transport from the environment.

heterozygous (hĕt'ĕr·ŏ·zī'gŭs): a term describing a genotype that consists of alleles, as in the expression *Aa*.

histology (hĭs·tŏl'ŏ·jĭ): a field of biology whose interest is the study of tissue structure, that is, microscopic anatomy.

homology (hŏ·mŏl'ŏ·jĭ): the relationship existing between two structures having a similar embryonic origin.

homozygous (hō'mŏ·zī'gŭs): a term describing a genotype that consists of identical genes, as in the expressions *AA* and *aa*.

hormone (hôr'mōn): a chemical substance produced in one part of a plant or animal body that is transported in the body fluids to another part of the body where it exerts a specific effect.

hybrid (hī'brĭd): an organism whose parents were genetically different for any trait or traits under consideration.

hydrolysis (hī·drŏl′i·sĭs): chemically, a type of reaction in which water is added to a substance in the decomposition of that substance.

hypertonic (hī′pĕr·tŏn′ĭk) a term applied to any solution whose concentration of diffusible water molecules is less than that of a solution from which it is separated by a differentially permeable membrane.

hypothesis (hī·pŏth′ê·sĭs): a tentative explanation for a natural phenomenon.

hypotonic (hī′pô·tŏn′ĭk): a term applied to any solution whose concentration of diffusible water molecules is greater than that of a solution from which it is separated by a differentially permeable membrane.

ileum (ĭl′ê·ŭm): the portion of the small intestine of vertebrates that connects with the large intestine.

inorganic (ĭn·ôr·găn′ĭk): a term applied to compounds the molecules of which do not contain carbon, except that carbonates are classified as inorganic compounds.

instinct (ĭn′stĭngkt): an act of behavior on the part of an animal that is wholly or almost entirely determined by unconditioned reflexes.

insulin (ĭn′sû·lĭn): a hormone of vertebrate animals produced by patches of tissue in the pancreas known as the islets of Langerhans; it is essential to the conversion of glucose to storage materials.

interphase (ĭn′tĕr·fāz): a term that is applied to a nucleus during the time that it is not involved in divisional processes.

ion (ī′ŏn): an atom or radical that bears an electrical charge.

isomer (ī′sô·mẽr): a molecule that is identical with some other molecule with which it is being compared in atomic proportions, but that is different from it in structure.

isotonic (ī′sô·tŏn′ĭk): a term applied to any solution whose concentration of diffusible water molecules is equal to that of a solution from which it is separated by a differentially permeable membrane.

isotope (ī′sô·tōp): an atom that differs in mass from other types of atoms making up an element due to a dissimilarity in number of neutrons within the nucleus.

jejunum (jê·jōō′nŭm): the portion of the mammalian small intestine that lies between the duodenum and the ileum.

larva (lär′và): an immature animal of a species characterized by some type of metamorphosis, or change in form, from this stage to the adult.

leucocyte (lū′kô·sīt): a "white" blood cell of vertebrates.

lichen (lī′kĕn): a plant composed of an algal species and a fungal species that live in a mutualistic type of association.

lignin (lĭg′nĭn): a material found in the walls of tracheids, vessels, and fibers that lends great strength to them.

linkage (lĭngk′ĭj): a term used in genetics to describe the presence of two or more genes on the same chromosome.

lipase (lī′pās): any enzyme capable of splitting fat molecules to fatty acids and glycerol.

liverwort (lĭv′ẽr·wûrt′): a green plant characterized by an alternation of generation in which the gametophyte is the dominant phase; the liverworts are very similar to mosses, but differ from them in a number of ways.

lymph (lĭmf): fluid located within lymphatic vessels, originating as tissue fluid which in turn filters out of the blood capillaries.

maltose (môl′tōs): a disaccharide sugar of the formula $C_{12}H_{22}O_{11}$, which breaks down by hydrolysis to two glucose molecules.

Mammalia (mă·mā′lĭ·a): the class of vertebrate animals that generally exhibit hair as an external body covering, and whose young are nourished by milk.

marsupial (mär·sū′pĭ·ál): any mammalian species, of which the kangaroo and opossum are representative, whose female individuals exhibit a pouch in which the offspring, born in a very immature state, are nourished until they reach further maturity.

mechanism (mĕk′á·nĭz′m): that philosophy according to which life processes and phenomena are entirely dependent upon physical and chemical principles.

meiosis (mī·ō′sĭs): a type of nuclear division in which the chromosome number is reduced one half.

menopause (mĕn′ō·pôz): the stage in the human female at which menstruation and ovulation cease.

menstruation (mĕn′strŏŏ·a′shŭn): the process by which the lining of the uterus (in the human and certain other primates) is periodically broken down and discharged, with bleeding, through the vagina.

meristem (mĕr′ĭ·stĕm): a type of simple plant tissue characterized by the ability to undergo division.

mesoderm (mĕs′ô·dûrm): a germ layer formed in the embryos of triploblastic animals between the ectoderm and endoderm.

metabolism (mĕ·tăb′ô·lĭz′m): the chemical activity occurring within cells.

metamorphosis (mĕt′*a*·môr′fô·sĭs): a change in body form of an organism as in the transformation of a larva into an adult.

metaphase (mĕt′*a*·fāz): the phase of mitosis in which chromosomes become oriented on the spindle in such a way that chromatids may subsequently separate and move toward opposite poles.

metazoa (mĕt′*a*·zō·ȧ): the multicellular animals.

microsome (mī′krô·sōm): a cytoplasmic organelle containing RNA, visible only by means of the electron microscope, which serves as a site of protein synthesis.

mitochondrion (mī′tô·kŏn′drĭ·ŏn): a cytoplasmic organelle which serves as the site of cellular respiration.

mitosis (mī·tô′sĭs): the process of nuclear division during cellular reproduction.

molecule (mŏl′ê·kūl): a unit of matter consisting of two or more atoms joined together in covalent union.

Mollusca (mŏ·lŭs′kȧ): the phylum of animals including those forms that exhibit a structure called the foot and whose relatively soft bodies are usually enclosed within a shell.

monocotyledon (mŏn′ô·kŏt′*i*·lē′dŭn): a plant whose embryo exhibits one primary, or seed leaf.

monoecious (mŏ·nē′shŭs): a term applied to any species in which individuals are functionally both male and female.

monosaccharide (mŏn′ô·săk′*a*·rīd): a sugar of relatively simple molecular structure, usually exhibiting either five or six carbon atoms per molecule.

monotreme (mŏn′ô·trēm): one of a very small group of primitive, oviparous mammals, such as the platypus.

morphology (môr·fŏl′ô·jĭ): a broad field of biology whose interest is the study of structure.

mutation (mū·tā′shŭn): a change in a gene.

mutualism (mū′t̪ū·ăl·ĭz′m): a relationship between two organisms of different species in which both derive benefit.

mycelium (mī·sē′lĭ·ŭm): a term used in regard to fungi to describe any mass or body of growth consisting of filaments.

natural selection: that process in nature by means of which those individuals or species capable of adapting to their environments compete successfully for survival.

nematocyst (nĕm′*a*·tô·sĭst′): a structure characteristic of coelenterates that discharges a stinging thread when stimulated.

Nematoda (nĕm′*a*·tōd′*a*): a phylum of pseudocoelomate worms whose bodies are cylindrical and unsegmented.

neuron (nū′rŏn): a nerve cell.

notochord (nō′tô·kôrd): a dorsal, elastic rod derived from mesoderm, characteristic of all chordate embryos.

nucleic acid (nū·klē′ĭk ăs′ĭd): a compound whose molecules are very complex, consisting of a chain of nucleotides. See ribonucleic acid and deoxyribonucleic acid.

nucleolus (nū·klē′ô·lŭs): a body found within the cell nucleus composed in large part of RNA.

nucleoplasm (nū′klē·ô·plăz′m): the fluid matrix enclosed by the nuclear membrane in which the chromosomes and nucleoli reside.

nucleoprotein (nū′klē·ô·prō′tē·ĭn): a complex type of compound whose molecules consist of a nucleic acid, either RNA or DNA, combined with a protein.

nucleotide (nū′klē·ô·tīd): a molecule composed of a five-carbon sugar (either ribose or deoxyribose), a base, and a phosphate group.

nucleus (nū′klē·ŭs): (1) the central part of an atom; (2) a cellular inclusion whose contents are incompletely separated from the cytoplasm by a nuclear membrane.

omnivorous (ŏm·nĭv′ô·rŭs): a term describing an animal whose diet consists of both plant and animal materials.

ontogeny (ŏn·tŏj′ê·nĭ): the process of development on the part of an organism.

operculum (ô·pûr′kŭ·lŭm): the gill covering in bony fishes.

organ (ôr′găn): a group of tissues that are associated together in the performance of a particular function.

organic (ôr·găn′ĭk): a term describing those compounds the molecules of which contain carbon, except for the class of compounds called carbonates.

organism (ôr′găn·ĭz′m): an individual living entity or being.

osmosis (ŏs·mō′sĭs): the movement of water molecules from a region of greater concentration to a region of lower concentration through a differentially permeable membrane.

Osteichthyes (ŏs′tê·ĭk′thĭ·ēz): the class of vertebrate animals which includes those fishes whose skeletons are composed largely of bone.

ovary (ō′v*a*·rĭ): (1) a reproductive organ, or gonad, of the female animal, in which eggs are produced; (2) the structure of a flower in which the ovules are produced.

oviparous (ō vĭp′*a* · rŭs): a term applied to an animal or a species of animals in which relatively large eggs that characteristically develop outside the body are produced.

ovulation (ō′vû · lā′shŭn): the release of an egg or eggs from the ovary.

paleontology (pā′lê · ŏn · tŏl′ō · jĭ): that field of biology and geology whose interest is the study of fossil organisms.

parasitism (păr′*a* · sīt · ĭz′m): a relationship between two organisms in which one benefits at the expense of the other.

parenchyma (p*a* · rĕng′kĭ · m*a*): a type of simple plant tissue the cells of which are typically thin-walled and relatively isodiametric.

parthenogenesis (pär′thê · nō · jĕn′ê · sĭs): the development of an egg without benefit of fertilization.

pathogen (păth′ō · jĕn): a disease-causing organism.

pepsin (pĕp′sĭn): a protein-specific enzyme produced in the stomachs of vertebrate animals.

peptidase (pĕp′tĭ · dās): any enzyme capable of hydrolyzing a peptide (short protein fraction) into smaller protein chains or amino acids.

perennial (pēr · ĕn′ĭ · *a*l): a plant or plant species characterized by a year to year existence.

peritoneum (pĕr′ĭ · tō · nē′ŭm): a thin, membranous covering of the body cavity and internal organs in coelomate animals.

permeability (pûr′mê · *a* · bĭl′*ĭ* · tĭ): the state of a membrane whose properties are such that certain substances may penetrate it.

PGA: see phosphoglyceric acid.

PGAL: see phosphoglyceraldehyde.

phagotrophic (făg′ · ō · trŏf′ĭk): a term applied to those animals whose food is obtained through eating or taking entire food particles into the body.

phenomenon (fê · nŏm′ê · nŏn): any object, process, or characteristic that becomes known through the senses.

phenotype (fē′nō · tīp): the hereditary expression of a particular genotype.

philosophy (fĭ · lŏs′ō · fĭ): that field of study whose interest is the comprehensive, or over-all, view of life and the universe with an attempt to discover meaning.

phloem (flō′ĕm): a complex plant tissue whose chief function is the transport of soluble foods.

phosphoglyceraldehyde (fŏs'fō·glĭs'ẽr·ăl dê·hīd), abbreviated PGAL: a compound that is important in photosynthesis and glycolysis as an intermediate product.

phosphoglyceric acid (fŏs'fō·glĭ·sẽr'ĭk ăs'ĭd), abbreviated PGA: a compound that serves both as an intermediate and an end product in photosynthesis and as an intermediate in glycolysis.

photoautotroph (fō'tō·ô'tō·trŏf'): an autotroph in which light energy is used for the synthesis of organic molecules.

photolysis (fō·tŏl'ĭ·sĭs): the splitting of water to hydrogen and oxygen, using light as an energy source.

photoperiodicity (fō'tō·pẽr'ĭ·ô·dĭs'ĭ·tĭ): a response by an organism to light in regard to some regulated process, such as the time of flowering in certain plants.

photosynthesis (fō'tō·sĭn'thê·sĭs): a process whereby carbon dioxide and water are combined in the presence of light and chlorophyll to produce carbohydrates and oxygen.

phototaxis (fō'tō·tăk'sĭs): the response of a motile organism to light.

phototropism (fō·tŏt'rō·pĭz'm): the response of a non-motile organism to light, especially in terms of growth.

phycocyanin (fī'kō·sī'á·nĭn): a blue pigment found in certain algae, notably the blue-green algae.

phycoerythrin (fī'kō·ê·rĭth'rĭn): a red pigment found in certain algae, notably the blue-green and the red algae.

phylogeny (fī'·lŏj'ê·nĭ): the ancestral or evolutionary history of an organism.

physiology (fĭz'ĭ·ŏl'ô·jĭ): a broad field of biology whose interest is function in the world of life.

pistil (pĭs'tĭl): the portion of a flower that is ovule-bearing.

placenta (plá·sĕn'tá): a temporary organ formed between the mother and embryo in all but a few mammals by means of which materials are exchanged; in addition, it is an important endocrine organ during pregnancy.

planarian (plá·nâr'ĭ·án): any free-living flatworm.

plankton (plăngk'tŏn): a term applied to the mass of organisms within a given body of water that are carried about more or less passively; most organisms that are regarded as plankton are microscopic in size.

plasmolysis (plăz·mŏl'ĭ·sĭs): the loss of turgidity by a cell.

plastid (plăs′tĭd): a cytoplasmic inclusion that is frequently pigmented; the most common type is the chloroplast, which is green by virtue of its chlorophyll.

Platyhelminthes (plăt′ĭ·hĕl·mĭn′thēz): a phylum of animals whose bodies are flattened dorso-ventrally, commonly called the flatworms.

polarization (pō′lĕr·ĭ·zā′shŭn): the separation of electrical charges or ions that bear electrical charges into positive and negative groups on either side of a differentially permeable membrane, as in the fiber of a nerve cell.

polyploidy (pŏl′ĭ·ploi′dĭ): a condition in which the chromosomal complement of a cell or organism is composed of more than two "sets" of chromosomes.

polysaccharide (pŏl′ĭ·săk′a·rīd): any carbohydrate, of which starch and glycogen are representative, that is composed of monosaccharide units.

Porifera (pō·rĭf′ĕr·à): a phylum of animals whose members·are called sponges which are colonies of cells that share a common skeletal structure.

predation (prē·dā′shŭn): a mode of existence that involves feeding on other organisms.

prophase (prō′fāz′): the phase of mitosis in which chromosomes become definite and visible.

protein (prō′tē·ĭn): a type of organic compound whose molecules consist of chains of amino acids.

protochordate (prō′tŏ·kôr′dāt): any chordate whose adult stages are not marked by the presence of a vertebral column.

protoplasm (prō′tŏ·plăz′m): matter that is alive.

protoplast (prō′tŏ·plăst): a unit of protoplasm, exclusive of a cell wall or any other non-living covering.

Protozoa (prō′tŏ·zō′à): a phylum of animals that includes all unicellular forms.

pseudocoelome (sū′dō·sē′lōm): a cavity lying between the digestive tube and body wall in roundworms and certain other animals which is not lined by a peritoneum of mesodermal origin.

pseudocopulation (sū′dō·kŏp′û·lā′shŭn): "false" copulation, as in frogs, during which the male does not introduce sperm into the body of the female.

pseudohermaphrodite (sū′dō·hûr·măf′rō·dīt): a "false" hermaphrodite, that is, a member of a dioecious animal species that exhibits characteristics of both sexes.

puberty (pū'bĕr·tĭ): the onset or beginning of sexual maturity on the part of an animal.

pupa (pū'på): the stage in the life cycle of completely metamorphic insects that is usually marked by outward inactivity accompanied by internal transformation to the adult form.

pyruvic acid (pī·rōō'vĭk ăs'ĭd): a compound that serves as the end product of glycolysis and as an intermediate product for certain substances as they enter the respiratory sequence.

RDP: see ribulose diphosphate.

reflex arc (rē'flĕks ärk): the pathway described by a nervous impulse in its passage from a receptor to an effector.

regeneration (rē·jĕn'ĕr·ā'shŭn): the development of an entire organism from a part or the re-growth of a lost or injured portion of an organism.

Reptilia (rĕp·tĭl'ĭ·å): a class of vertebrates that includes those forms such as snakes, turtles, and alligators; reptiles are "cold-blooded" and exhibit scales and claws as a group.

respiration (rĕs'pĭ·rā'shŭn): the aerobic phase of catabolism, in which energy is released to the cell, accompanied by the utilization of oxygen.

rhizome (rī'zōm): a stem that characteristically grows beneath the surface of the soil.

ribulose diphosphate (rī'bū·lōs dī·fŏs'fāte), abbreviated RDP: a compound that serves as an intermediate in photosynthesis.

ribonucleic acid (rī'bō·nū·klē'ĭk ăs'ĭd), abbreviated RNA: a substance whose molecules are composed of ribonucleotides, which are themselves composed of ribose (a five-carbon sugar), a base, and a phosphate group.

RNA: see ribonucleic acid.

sagittal (săj'ĭ·tål): a plane or section that separates a bilaterally symmetrical animal into right and left portions.

saprozoic (săp'rô·zō'ĭk): a term describing an animal, such as the tapeworm, that absorbs its food from its surroundings.

sclerenchyma (sklê·rĕng'kĭ·må): a simple type of plant tissue whose cells possess walls that are greatly thickened with lignin; a strengthening and supporting tissue.

secretion (sê·krē'shŭn): the movement of some substance in quantity from inside a cell to its immediate environment, usually accompanied by the expenditure of energy.

seta (sē′t*a*): a stiff, bristle-like structure of locomotion found typically in number on the annelid body.

society (sō·sī′ĕ·tĭ): a group of animals belonging to the same species that live together in a relationship that features division of labor and diversification of effort, the result of which is a closely knit mode of existence for the individuals involved.

species (spē′shĭz): a taxonomic group that includes organisms whose over-all similarity is sufficiently great that they are considered to be a single "kind." Among sexually reproducing organisms, it is generally regarded that members of a single species must be capable of inter-breeding freely with the production of fertile offspring. "Species" serves both as a singular and a plural.

spore (spōr): a single cell of an organism that is capable of develop-ing asexually into a new individual.

sporophyte (spō′rō·fīt): (1) any spore producing plant; (2) that phase of an alternating plant life cycle in which there is the produc-tion of spores.

stamen (stā′mĕn): a structure of the flower that bears a sporangium (anther) in which pollen is produced.

starch (stärch): a polysaccharide made up of a large number of glu-cose molecules that serves as a storage carbohydrate in plant tissues.

stimulus (stĭm′ū·lŭs): an energy change in the vicinity of a receptor that is sufficient to produce a response.

stoma (stō′·m*a*): an opening formed in the surface of a leaf whenever a pair of guard cells separate by reason of their turgidity.

substrate (sŭb·strāt′): in an enzymatic reaction, the substance that is acted upon.

synapse (sĭ·năps′): the region or point of contact between two inter-connecting nerve fibers.

synapsis (sĭ·năp′sĭs): the union of homologous chromosomes during meiosis.

synthesis (sĭn′thê·sĭs): the formation of a compound from two or more substances that are simpler in structure.

taxis (tăk′sĭs): the over-all movement of a motile organism in re-sponse to a stimulus.

taxonomy (tăks·ŏn′ô·mĭ): that field of biology whose interest is the classification of organisms.

telophase (tĕl′ô·fāz): the stage or phase of mitosis during which chromosomes lose their apparent individuality, nucleoli reappear and nuclear membranes are formed around daughter nuclei.

testis (tĕs′tĭs): a reproductive organ, or gonad, of the male animal in which sperm are produced.

tetrad (tĕt′răd): (1) a name used to describe the four products of sporic meiosis when they remain together just before their separation into individual spores; (2) a name used to describe the four chromatids of a synapsing pair of homologous chromosomes during meiosis.

theism (thē′ĭz′m): belief in God, especially in the sense of a supreme or divine personality who plays an active role in the affairs of the universe.

theory (thēô·rĭ): a conceptual scheme whose validity has been sufficiently confirmed by observation and experimentation that it is reliable in predictability.

tissue (tĭsh′ū): a group of cells that are structurally and embryologically similar which are associated together in the performance of a particular function.

tracheid (trā′kê·ĭd): one type of conducting element found in xylem.

triploblastic (trĭp·lô·blăs′tĭk): a term applied to an animal or to a species of animals whose adult body structures are derived from three germ layers, the ectoderm, endoderm, and mesoderm.

tropism (trō′pĭz′m): the over-all movement of a non-motile organism in response to a stimulus.

trypsin (trĭp′sĭn): a protein-specific enzyme produced in the pancreas.

turgid (tûr′jĭd): a term applied to a cell whose internal pressure is greater than that of its immediate environment.

urea (û·rē′a): a compound that is formed principally in the liver from ammonia and carbon dioxide.

uterus (ū′tĕr·ŭs): a portion of the female reproductive system in mammals where offspring develop. The term is also used to describe an enlarged portion of the female reproductive system of certain oviparous animals in which eggs may be contained for a time.

vacuole (văk′ū·ōl): any space within the cytoplasm of a cell that is filled with a watery fluid and separated from the cytoplasm proper by a differentially permeable membrane.

vascular bundle (văs′kû·lêr): any bundle of conducting elements (xylem and phloem) that may be located within a plant organ, particularly in herbaceous plants and the younger portions of woody plants.

vertebrate (vûr′tê·brāt): any chordate animal whose notochord is either partially or entirely replaced by a vertebral column, namely, the fishes, amphibians, reptiles, birds, and mammals.

vestigial (vĕs·tĭj′ĭ·ăl): a term applied to a structure that is not fully functional or completely developed, but which was functional either at an earlier developmental stage or at a previous period in evolution.

villus (vĭl′ŭs): a microscopic, finger-like projection of the lining of the small intestine in the vertebrate body, by virtue of which the secretory and absorptive surface of that organ is increased tremendously.

virus (vī′rŭs): a unit, or entity, of submicroscopic proportions composed of nucleoprotein and protein, capable of self-duplication within any cell which it may parasitize, but which is not protoplasmic.

vitalism (vī′tăl·ĭz′m): that philosophy according to which life processes and phenomena are the result of forces that exist in addition to those that are physical and chemical in nature.

vitamin (vī′tȧ·mĭn): an organic substance that functions within a cell in a regulatory capacity, being especially important in reactions involving enzymes, or in serving as a precursor for co-enzymes.

viviparous (vī·vĭp′ȧ·rŭs): a term applied to an animal or a species of animals whose offspring undergo development within the mother's body and are born in a more or less well-developed state.

xylem (zī′lĕm): a complex plant tissue whose chief function is the transport of water and minerals upward in the plant.

zoology (zô·ŏl′ô·jĭ): that branch of biology which is concerned with animals.

zygote (zī′gōt): a cell resulting from gametic union; a fertilized egg.

Index